art

2107 N. Howard St.

Phila. Penna 19122

121 ͔

T $5.95   № 46600

IF   TEACHING   FRACTIONS, P. 143

UNDERSTANDING
ARITHMETIC

UNDERSTANDING ARITHMETIC

Robert L. Swain

Revised by Eugene D. Nichols
THE FLORIDA STATE UNIVERSITY

HOLT, RINEHART and WINSTON, INC.
New York   Chicago   San Francisco   Toronto   London

IN MEMORIAM

Robert L. Swain
1913-1962

PREFACE

This revised edition of the late Robert L. Swain's *Understanding Arithmetic* deals, as did the original edition of this remarkable book, with those aspects of contemporary mathematics that are relevant to teaching in the elementary school. It may be used in college mathematics courses, in methods courses for students preparing to teach in the elementary school, and in in-service courses and training programs for elementary school teachers.

The far-reaching changes that have taken place both in mathematics and in the teaching of mathematics during the past several years have necessitated a substantial revision of Dr. Swain's book. Perhaps, in part, the teaching of elementary school mathematics has changed so much and so quickly because of Dr. Swain's work and because of the considerable impact of the first edition of *Understanding Arithmetic*. In modifying the book to fill the needs of the present, every attempt has been made to maintain the tone, the maturity of thought, the thoroughness, and even the style of the original.

The present author is immeasurably indebted to the original author, whose untimely death precluded his preparing the revision himself. He is indebted also to the many college instructors, students, and elementary school teachers who have studied from the original edition and have adopted for their own use many of the ideas that it contains.

Several primary features of the revised edition of *Understanding Arithmetic* deserve special mention.

1. The contents and spirit of the edition are consistent with the most recent recommendations of national committees and groups concerned with the teaching of mathematics in the elementary school.

2. The book provides the necessary background for the teaching of *all* mathematics in the elementary school because it treats sets, numeration systems, number systems and operations (both the conceptual and computational aspects), nonmetric geometry, metric geometry, and coordinate geometry.

3. The book is recommended for a sequence of two one-semester courses, with the first seven chapters to constitute the first course and the remaining seven chapters the second course. Of course, the instructor may choose not to follow the chapters in sequence; this, in some instances, may be quite appropriate.

4. The treatment of all topics, those dealing with number aspects of mathematics and those of geometric nature, is mathematically sound; thus, the book is designed to serve as a preparation for the teaching of the up-to-date mathematics programs written for the elementary school. The book should also be of help to those teachers who, for the first time, are teaching from some modern mathematics textbook.

5. The aim of the book is to improve the reader's understanding of mathematics by leading him to observe the unfolding structure of mathematics, reinforcing that structure with examples of applications of mathematics to various areas. Thus, the concern is with the comprehension of the subject in its broad aspects.

6. Occasional excursions into the historical and cultural aspects of mathematics enhance the view of mathematics as a living subject as well as add to the reader's motivation.

7. Up-to-date bibliographical references at the end of each chapter point to sources dealing with the subject matter of that chapter. The instructor may choose, in accordance with his own judgment, to assign additional readings from these sources.

8. Ample problems, both easy and difficult, serve as further practice and to test comprehension of the ideas presented in various sections of the book.

The authors spared no effort to make this book teachable and exciting. It is hoped that you will find it so.

Eugene D. Nichols

Tallahassee, Florida
March 1965

CONTENTS

1

NUMBERS
AND
NUMERALS

1. PRIMITIVE NUMBER SCHEMES

Word and Number—these twin creations blaze the trail of human progress. To the degree that man has mastered their use, to this degree he controls the world about him.

Where the extent of man's mastery over nature is slim, his number system reflects his ineptitude:

1.	Neecha	(1)
2.	Boolla	(2)
3.	Boolla Neecha	(2 + 1)
4.	Boolla Boolla	(2 + 2)

A primitive chant? The sequence furnishes a fine accompaniment to the boom-boom drone of the tom-tom. Yet it is actually the complete *counting system* of a native Australian tribe (*Bourke, Darling River*). It provides two basic number names from which other number names are compounded and is accordingly termed a "base-two" or *binary* system.

The material culture of the Australian aborigines is among the most backward to be found in the world today. It is surely a simple way of life for which the number scheme described above may prove adequate. Posing to ourselves the questions "How big? How far? How many? How much?" a hundred times a day, we can scarcely imagine what it would be like to face the world around us with mental tools so crude and blunt.

Certain Greenland Eskimos use a more elaborate system:

1. Atauseq
2. Machdlug
3. Pinasut

4. Sisamat	
5. Tadlimat	
6. Achfineq-atauseq	(other hand 1)
7. Achfineq-machdlug	(other hand 2)
8. Achfineq-pinasut	(other hand 3)
9. Achfineq-sisamat	(other hand 4)
10. Qulit	
11. Achqaneq-atauseq	(first foot 1)
12. Achqaneq-machdlug	(first foot 2)
13. Achqaneq-pinasut	(first foot 3)
14. Achqaneq-sisamat	(first foot 4)
15. Achfechsaneq	
16. Achfechsaneq-atauseq	(other foot 1)
17. Achfechsaneq-machdlug	(other foot 2)
18. Achfechsaneq-pinasut	(other foot 3)
19. Achfechsaneq-sisamat	(other foot 4)
20. Inuk navdlucho	(a man ended)

This is a "quinary-vigesimal" system. The counting proceeds by groups of five up to twenty, then goes on by twenties.

A striking feature of the system—and there are others like it—is its literal incorporation of the idea of counting on the fingers and toes. When a child counts on his fingers, he is perpetuating an association between the human hand and number notions that is a basic element in cultural history. It is surely this association that has given us our *tens*, or *decimal*, system of counting. There is no natural advantage in counting by tens. We might just as well have learned to count by sixes, say, or eights, or twelves. Yet the major numeration systems of history have all been on a scale of ten or of a multiple of ten, such as 20, 40, or 60. If we had twelve fingers, would we not count by twelves?

In the meantime, let us regard our counting by tens as evidence that the concepts and structures of mathematics are of *human* origin, and that they evolve and change as do all other works of man.

2. OUR NUMERATION SYSTEM

In this chapter we shall survey some numeration systems of earlier times, and shall contrast them with our own. It will be helpful to review the significant features of our own system before delving into the past.

We form our number symbols, or **numerals,** out of the ten *basic numerals*, also called *digits:* 0, 1, 2, 3, 4, 5, 6, 7, 8, 9. Consider the numeral 237.

This is commonly read "two hundred thirty-seven." The digits occupy positions with the following place values:

HUNDREDS	TENS	UNITS
(100)	*(10)*	*(1)*
2	3	7

The digit 7 contributes 7×1, or 7 units, to the value of the numeral. The digit 3 contributes 3×10, or 3 tens. The digit 2 contributes 2×100, or 2 hundreds. Thus

$$237 = 2 \times 100 + 3 \times 10 + 7 \times 1$$
$$= \quad 200 \quad + \quad 30 \quad + \quad 7 \; .$$

The value of any numeral is the *sum* of the values that the digits contribute by virtue of their *position* in the numeral. Our numeration system is based upon the concept of **place value.**

From right to left, each place has a value ten times that of the place to the right. Hence the place values are the successive powers of ten, listed in Table 1-1. We count not just by tens, but by **powers of ten.** The expansion of 365,309 by powers of ten would be shown as:

$$365{,}309 = 3 \times 10^5 + 6 \times 10^4 + 5 \times 10^3 + 3 \times 10^2 + 0 \times 10^1 + 9 \times 10^0.$$

Table 1-1

PLACE NAME	PLACE VALUE	POWER OF TEN
Units	1	10^0
Tens	10	10^1
Hundreds	100	10^2
Thousands	1,000	10^3
Ten thousands	10,000	10^4
Hundred thousands	100,000	10^5
Millions	1,000,000	10^6

The zero power of ten needs a closer examination. Consider the pattern

$$10^4 = 10{,}000; \quad 10^3 = 1{,}000; \quad 10^2 = 100; \quad 10^1 = 10; \quad 10^0 = ?$$

What should 10^0 be equal to, to fit into the pattern? Since we divide each number by 10 as we proceed to the right, $10^0 = 10/10 = 1$.

You and I have an accurate intuitive sense of the magnitude of the number 237, acquired over years of experience. A Roman citizen of the early A.D.'s, displaced into modern times, would lack this sense that we take for granted.

But the Roman would readily grasp our scheme of coinage. He could come to grips with the place value feature of our numeration system by watching a counting operation in which pennies, dimes, and dollars are used as tokens to keep track of the count.

Imagine that a long line of people file through a gateway. As each person passes, we lay a penny on our counting table. Lacking a place value scheme, we would end the counting with just a large pile of pennies on the table. Instead, as the tenth penny goes down, we scoop up the group and put down a dime in exchange. The next ten pennies are replaced by a second dime. This goes on until the tenth dime is put down, whereupon we clear the table and put down a dollar bill. When the counting is done, there lie on the table

2 dollar bills, 3 dimes, 7 pennies;

then we have counted to the number denoted by our numeral 237.

The function of any numeration system is to provide a systematic and efficient way of *naming* the numbers that are used in counting. In addition to word names like thirty-seven, the system provides special symbolic expressions, like 37. These number names are called **numerals.** They are what we write or say when we refer to numbers. A numeral *names* a number. Hence a numeral is a symbol, whereas a number is a mathematical entity. [An object, say a stone, is quite unlike the *word* "stone" by which we denote it for the purpose of communication.]

This important distinction between number and numeral sometimes escapes notice, because the word "number" is widely used to refer to either concept. In this book we shall make the distinction whenever it seems wise to do so. At present our attention is chiefly upon numerals.

3. THE ABACUS

In our offices and in our laboratories the electrons spin our number wheels—and our engineers slide their numbers on a stick. Thus we depute the burden of our arithmetic to the unprotesting machine.

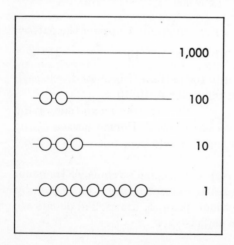

	1,000
	100
	10
	1

Fig. 1-1 **Line Abacus**
The number 237 is represented.

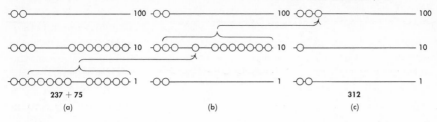

Fig. 1-2   Adding, on a Line Abacus, 237 + 75 = 312

In (a), 237 is represented on the left, 75 on the right portion of the abacus. The ten counters on the units (1) line beneath the "brace" (⌣) are taken off the abacus, and a single counter is placed on the tens (10) line, as the arrow indicates (b). A similar exchange of one hundred (100) for ten tens gives the final result (c).

Our forebears were no less ingenious. From earliest times calculation has been aided by devices of one sort or another, most often by some form of **abacus.**

Etymological skirmishes have been waged over the origin of the word "abacus." According to one version, it evolved through the Greek word *abax* (slab) from a Semitic word meaning "dust." This would make an abacus a "dustboard," or table covered with dust or sand, on which one could mark with a stylus and erase by smoothing with the fingers. Such a form of abacus was indeed among those used by the Greeks, Romans, and Hindus.

The most popular historical form was the *line abacus*. To draw a model, rule several equally spaced lines on a sheet of paper and give them the successive values 1, 10, 100, 1,000, . . . , as in Figure 1-1. Numbers may be represented by laying counters (pennies, buttons, etc.) on the rods. The number 237 is shown in the figure. The rule for using this abacus is that ten counters on a line are equivalent to a single counter on the next, higher valued line.

To count on the line abacus, successively lay counters on the units (1) line until ten are down. Then "exchange" by scooping these up and laying a single counter on the tens (10) line. Continue to lay counters on the tens line until ten are down, then exchange again. When ten counters are assembled on the tens line, they are exchanged for one counter on the hundreds line. And so on.

To *add* two numbers on the line abacus, represent them both separately, then treat the combination as the representation of a single number, simplifying by exchanges. Figure 1-2 indicates the procedure, applied to 237 + 75 = 312.

To *subtract* on the line abacus, it may be necessary to exchange in reverse. Figure 1-3 shows how this may be done in the case of the difference 312 − 75.

Modern abaci are of the rod-and-bead variety. A simple form is shown

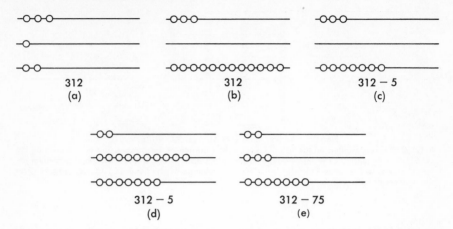

312
(a)

312
(b)

312 − 5
(c)

312 − 5
(d)

312 − 75
(e)

Fig. 1-3   Subtracting, on a Line Abacus, 312 − 75 = 237
The first step is to put 312 on the abacus, as shown in (a). In a reverse exchange, one counter is taken off the tens line, and ten counters are laid on the units line (b). Now 5 can be taken away (c), leaving 70 to go, that is, 7 on the tens line yet to be taken off. Again a reverse exchange is performed. A hundreds counter is removed and ten are placed on the tens line (d); 7 of them are taken off, and the work is ended (e).

in Figure 1-4, a rectangular wooden frame bearing several rods strung with ten sliding beads per rod. Numbers may be represented by sliding the appropriate beads to registering position at the right.

The rule for operating this abacus is similar to that for the line abacus above. Ten beads on a rod may be slid back, and one bead on the next higher valued rod slid to the right. Suppose that 75 is to be added to the 237. Begin to add the 5, counting 1, 2, 3 and sliding over a units bead at each count. At the count of 3 all units beads are at the right. Exchange by drawing them back and moving a tens bead over. Then finish the count,

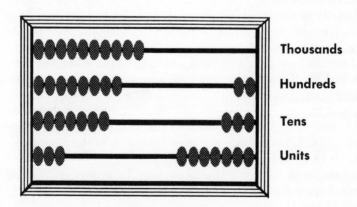

Thousands

Hundreds

Tens

Units

Fig. 1-4   Rod Abacus
The number 237 is shown.

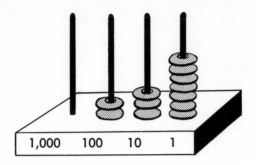

Fig. 1-5 A form of Abacus
The number 237 is shown.

4, 5, ending with 2 units beads in registering position. Move to the tens rod and repeat the procedure, this time counting to 7.

A more efficient way of operating the rod abacus is as follows: With 237 on the abacus, we propose to add 75, as before. First, 5 is to be added to the 7 already on the abacus in the units row. It is noted that there are not 5 beads left to be moved to registering position. But to add 5 is the same as to *take away 5 and add 10* (5 = 10 − 5). Move 5 units beads back and move 1 tens bead over to the right. What shows on the abacus is now 242, and 70 is yet to be added. To add 7 is the same as to take away 3 and add 10 (7 = 10 − 3). Therefore, move 3 tens beads back and move 1 hundreds bead over to the right.

An interesting form of abacus can be made by inserting several vertical rods or heavy wires into a flat base, as in Figure 1-5. Loose rings may be dropped onto or taken off the rods. This device is useful for displaying structures of numeration systems, as well as for computing.

In connection with both numerical work and with the discussion of arithmetic principles, we shall from time to time use abacus illustrations or direct the student to employ an abacus. The student should keep some pennies, checkers, poker chips, tiddlywinks, or other counters handy for line-abacus practice. He may purchase a rod abacus at a toy store, but will do better to make his own. Schoolrooms have abaci of various forms—from hand models to large demonstration types with vertical rods and spring-inset colored beads that stay put wherever they are slid.

Problem Set 1

1. How could the Australian tribe have continued to count five and six?
2. Write word names for the following:

   (a) 563
   (b) 369,289
   (c) 27,908
   (d) 2,105,363

3. Give the place value of each basic numeral (digit):

   (a) 37,207   (b) 5,653,024

4. Expand by powers of ten:

   (a) 359   (b) 27,507   (c) 2,308,270

5. Starting with $2^4 = 16$, $2^3 = 8$, $2^2 = 4$, and so on, show that $2^0 = 1$.
6. Show that

   (a) $5^0 = 1$ (b) $25^0 = 1$

7. Show that $17^0 = 365^0$.
8. To what number does the word "quinary" refer?
9. To what number does the word "vigesimal" refer?
10. How many basic numerals or digits does the decimal numeration system have?
11. For each sentence below, tell whether it is a sentence about *numbers* or *numerals*.

    (a) 25 is greater than 18.
    (b) 5 is larger than 8.
    (c) 367 consists of three basic numerals.
    (d) The sum of 3 and 18 is 21.
    (e) When 6 is dropped in 376, 37 is left.
    (f) 99 is made up of two 9's.
    (g) .0000675 is longer than .23.
    (h) The product of 7 and 3 is 21.

12. Describe how you would perform the following operations on an abacus:

    (a) $267 + 38$ (b) $125 - 36$

13. You know that $10^0 = 1$, $10^1 = 10$, and $10^2 = 100$. How many zeros would there be in each of the following if shown as 1 followed by zeros?

    (a) 10^5 (b) 10^{12} (c) 10^{100}

14. You know that $635 = 6 \times 100 + 3 \times 10 + 5 \times 1$. Show in similar form each of the following:

    (a) 3652   (b) 27,509   (c) 307,500

4. EGYPTIAN NUMERALS

Unlike our contemporary nomadic Australian natives, the ancient Egyptians possessed a material (and a religious) culture of some complexity. The pyramids stand as monuments to their engineering ability. Traders as well as builders and surveyors, they needed accurate means to represent and handle large numbers.

As early as 3000 B.C., the Egyptians had developed an effective numeration system. Stone was then their writing medium. We can today inspect
their numerals in *hieroglyphic* or picture-symbol form, carved on the
walls of their tombs. For the powers of ten from one to one million, the
hieroglyphs look like those in Table 1-2, the forms being simplified and
the appended interpretations uncertain.

Table 1-2

EGYPTIAN HIEROGLYPHIC NUMERALS						
1	10	100	1,000	10,000	100,000	1,000,000
Stroke	Arch	Coiled Rope	Lotus Flower	Pointed Finger	Tadpole	Astonished Man

Just as we group several coins and bills, the Egyptians could put
together several symbols whose values added up to a given number. They
represented our number 23,529 as:

Sometimes they carved the symbols in descending order of value, as
above (from left to right), and sometimes in ascending order. However,
they could have scattered them about in as disorderly a way as they
pleased without affecting the value of the numeral. Each of the following,
for example, names the same number (10,210):

There is no hint here of such notions as those of digits and position value.

Adding by the use of Egyptian numerals is easy. The separate hieroglyphic symbols appearing in the given numbers may be grouped together. The result may be simplified wherever possible—for example, by
replacing 13 strokes by 3 strokes and an arch. *Subtracting* is easy too, but
multiplying and dividing offer some difficulties. The Egyptian multiplication method will be mentioned in Chapter 6.

The Egyptians made clever use of fractional numerals and were able to use some simple algebra as early as the time of the "Middle Kingdom," from 2000 to 1800 B.C. A "handbook" of their methods is preserved in the British Museum: the celebrated *Rhind papyrus*, compiled by the scribe Ahmes, about 1650 B.C., from earlier sources. This and other Egyptian mathematical texts are primarily concerned with such practical applications of mathematics as might ordinarily be encountered by surveyors, builders, traders, and administrative officials—areas, volumes, quantities of money, and materials.

It is painful to follow through the work schemes used by the Egyptians in solving simple problems. Handling fractional numerals was a task for an expert. One looks in vain for *general methods*, always our principal concern today. Egyptian geometry, for example, was largely a collection of area and volume formulas, some right and some wrong. With their attention focused too narrowly on what seemed practical, the Egyptians failed to see the need for developing any basic *theory*. They were empiricists.

When they began to write on papyrus in place of stone, the Egyptians abandoned the colorful but cumbersome hieroglyphs in favor of a script form called *hieratic* ("priestly"). There was also a form called *demotic* ("popular"). Much computation and problem work seem to have been carried out in script form. The Egyptians may also have used abaci made by ruling lines on stone or by tracing grooves in sand.

5. BABYLONIAN AND GREEK NUMERALS

Before 3000 B.C., the Sumerians in southern Mesopotamia wrote by pressing the ends of cylindrical rods into clay tablets. Their numeral characters were like little moons and half-moons. Later, the end of the rod was sharpened to prism form, and this stylus was used to produce two types of *cuneiform* ("wedgy") characters, a "single-tailed" and a "two-tailed" form (Fig. 1-6). By the time of the first Babylonian dynasty (Hammurabi, ca. 1800 B.C.), into which the Sumerians were absorbed, an extensive body of mathematical knowledge and an effective positional numeration system had been developed.

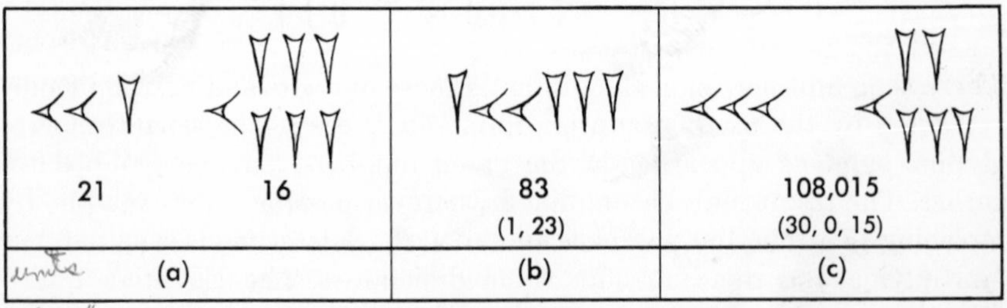

Fig. 1-6 Examples of Babylonian Numerals

The single-tailed character, written vertically, stood for the unit 1; the two-tailed character, written horizontally, stood for 10. Figure 1-6a depicts two numerals constructed from the symbols. Up to 60, the numerals were constructed in this straightforward way. Now a surprise: The Babylonian was a sexagesimal system, based on 60, so that the numerals 1, 2, 3, . . . , 59 were just the *digits* of the system. (Hence our seconds and minutes units for time and angle, based on 60.) Babylonian numerals were successions of such digits, even as are our own numerals. Thus in Figure 1-6b, the digit 1 is followed by the digit 23, so that the value is

$$1 \times 60 \ + \ 23 = 83.$$

The Babylonian scheme was much like ours in structure, except for two important features. First, the Babylonians lacked a symbol for *zero*. When a place value was missing, as in Figure 1-6c, they originally just made a wider separation between characters. Later they put in a special character, but as a separatrix rather than as a numeral for zero, as indicated by the fact that it was never written at the *end* of the numeral. Second, they lacked a decimal point concept. The value of their numerals had to be told from the context of the discussion. We labeled the numeral in Figure 1-6b with the value $83 = 1 \times 60 + 23$. But we might just as logically have taken it to mean

$$4,980 = 1 \times 60^2 \ + \ 23 \times 60,$$

or to mean

$$1\frac{23}{60} = 1 \ + \ 23 \times \frac{1}{60}.$$

With their superior numeration system and an effective arithmetic based upon it, the Babylonians made excellent progress, pretty much covering that part of mathematics taught in our schools through the ninth grade. It was evidently they who discovered the form of the famous Pythagorean theorem—the square relation between the measures of the legs and the hypotenuse of the right triangle. In this and in other ways they revealed knowledge of some general methods. But as with the Egyptians, their turn of mind was more practical than theoretical. So it was left to the Greeks to invent the concept of *proof* and to develop mathematical *theory*.

But the Greeks, intellectual giants though they were, failed to appreciate the virtues of the Babylonian arithmetic. In the time of the first known Greek mathematician Thales (about 600 B.C.), the Greeks used letter symbols for numerals in much the same way as the Romans were to do several centuries later. Structurally, this early Greek scheme was like the Egyptian, but with extra symbols for 5, 50, etc., inserted between those for the powers of ten, giving more compact expressions. (See Table 1-3.) These "five-multiples" were constructed by hanging each power-often symbol from a gibbet. At least it looks that way to us—but the gibbet, or "gallows," is actually but an old form of the capital "pi," Π. (*Note to the student:* Do not memorize the Greek numeral values unless you are

Table 1-3

GREEK NUMERALS (Old Form)				
1	10	100	1,000	10,000
I	△	H	X	M
5	50	500	5,000	50,000
⌐	⌐△	⌐H	⌐X	⌐M

specifically instructed to do so. There is a risk that you will confuse the symbols for 1,000 and 10,000 with our present X and M, which as Roman numerals have different values.)

Like the Egyptian, the Greek scheme is based on an additive principle. A number is represented by the minimum group of symbols whose values add to the number:

$$X X \ulcorner H H H H \ulcorner \triangle \triangle \ulcorner I I = 2,977$$

2000 + 500   + 400   + 50 + 20 + 5 + 2

Perhaps a hundred years later, the Greeks developed a second numeration scheme, patterned after the Egyptian hieratic and demotic forms. Values were assigned to all the letters of their alphabet, and special devices were employed for naming very large numbers and fractional numbers. The Hebrews employed a similar alphabetical numeration system. These alphabetical schemes will be referred to in Chapter 10, when certain mystical ideas that have been associated with numbers are discussed. The two systems of the Greeks, the literal and the alphabetical, continued in use concurrently.

The student who wishes to explore more deeply the mathematics of antiquity is referred to the historical works listed in the bibliography at the end of this chapter.

Most of our knowledge of Babylonian mathematics has been acquired within the last 25 years, as a result of extensive research carried out by

Neugebauer and a few others. Thousands upon thousands of clay tablets have been unearthed since the mid-1800's. A typical tablet may be about $\frac{3}{4}$ in. thick and bear 20 to 30 lines of characters on a 3-in. by 4-in. face. *History of Mathematics* by Smith and *Science Awakening* by Neugebauer contain photographs of these tablets.

The impact of mathematics and of mathematical thought upon our society is described in a nontechnical, yet masterly, way in Kline's *Mathematics in Western Culture.*

Problem Set 2

1. Name each number using Egyptian hieroglyphs:

   (a) 3   (b) 26   (c) 307   (d) 23,640
   (e) 30   (f) 274   (g) 1,040   (h) 508,006
   (i) 300   (j) 620   (k) 3,002   (l) 2,672,873

2. How many symbols are needed to name 620,987 in hieroglyphs?
3. Name, using hieroglyphs, then add:

   (a) 23 + 42   (c) 174 + 258
   (b) 28 + 46   (d) 582 + 733

4. Name, using hieroglyphs, then subtract:

   (a) 46 − 34   (b) 384 − 321
   (c) 23 − 9   (d) 1,023 − 768

5. Why is it that we need 0 to write 306, whereas the Egyptians did not?
6. Make a sketch of an abacus that you would suggest for use with the Egyptian system.
7. The Egyptian hieroglyphic numeration system is based upon an additive principle. Explain this statement.
8. Make a sketch of an abacus that you would suggest for use with the Babylonian system.
9. Neugebauer suggested the following notation to fit the sexagesimal base: Write 1 through 59 in parentheses, separating the powers of 60 by commas. Thus, the value of (1,42,20) is $1 \times 60^2 + 42 \times 60 + 20 = 6,140$. Expand similarly and compute the value of each of the following:

   (a) (1,1)   (f) (1,1,59)
   (b) (1,1,1)   (g) (59,59,0)
   (c) (1,1,1,1)   (h) (2,3,4)
   (d) (1,59)   (i) (10,10,0)
   (e) (59,59)   (j) (50,0,59)

10. Give each of the following numbers using Neugebauer's notation:

    (a) 61   (d) 216,575
    (b) 121   (e) 300,120
    (c) 3,720   (f) 450,000

11. If a semicolon is used as a "sexagesimal point," then (5;20) may be taken
to mean

$$5 \times 1 \quad + \quad 20 \times \tfrac{1}{60} = 5\tfrac{1}{3}.$$

What is the value of each of the following?

(a) (0;30)

(b) (4;3,30)

(c) (2,50;12)

(d) (10,10;4,20)

6. ROMAN NUMERALS

Roman numerals are still in use. They are inscribed on public buildings,
on memorial tablets, and on cornerstones. Ornamental clock faces display
them. In books they designate chapter numbers, or prefatory page
numbers.

Since the Romans used large numbers infrequently, their symbols for
1,000 and higher numbers remained unstandardized. A common form for
1,000 was CⅠↃ; the D symbol for 500 may have evolved from the half
of this form (ⅠↃ). The M symbol for 1,000 was seldom used in combination with lower numerals. Not until medieval times did the M attain wide
use. A bar symbol placed over a numeral to indicate multiplication by
1,000 also appeared in the Middle Ages ($\overline{I} = 1,000$; $\overline{X} = 10,000$;
$\overline{C} = 100,000$; $\overline{\overline{I}} = 1,000,000$).

There is an extensive literature on the Roman notation: what forms
were used by the Romans; how they were used; where they came from;
how they were modified in medieval times and after the Renaissance; etc.
The mathematician takes a dim view of the Romans, because their total
contribution to mathematics and the sciences was nearly negligible. But
Roman numerals lingered long in history, and their structure has interesting features that we shall wish to examine here.

As now used the Roman numerals are shown in Table 1-4. Numerals
are written according to the additive principle, just as with Egyptian
hieroglyphs, the basic numeral symbols being strung out in descending
order of values. For example,

$$\mathrm{M\,D\,C\,C\,C\,C\,L\,V\,I\,I\,I\,I} = 1959.$$

It is easy to add and to subtract numbers given by Roman numerals.
It is unnecessary to refer to the list of values cited in Table 1-4. Instead,
use the following *addition table* for handfuls (5) and pairs (2):

$$
\begin{array}{ll}
\mathrm{I\,I\,I\,I\,I = V} & \mathrm{V\,V = X} \\
\mathrm{X\,X\,X\,X\,X = L} & \mathrm{L\,L = C} \\
\mathrm{C\,C\,C\,C = D} & \mathrm{D\,D = M}
\end{array}
$$

To add two numbers, group the basic numerals together, then simplify according to Table 1-4.

Table 1-4

MODERN ROMAN NUMERALS			
1	10	100	1,000
I	X	C	M
5	50	500	
V	L	D	

Example 1 Add: MDCCCLXII + CXXXXIIII.

$$
\begin{aligned}
\text{MDCCCLXII} + \text{CXXXXIIII} &= \text{MDCCCCLXXXXXIIIIII} \\
&= \text{MDCCCCLLVI} \\
&= \text{MDCCCCCVI} \\
&= \text{MDDVI} \\
&= \text{MMVI}.
\end{aligned}
$$

Subtraction can be a direct "take-away" procedure, except that some numerals may need to be replaced by lower value numerals to make the taking away possible.

Example 2 Subtract: MDV − CCLXII.

$$
\begin{aligned}
\text{MDV} - \text{CCLXII} &= \text{MCCCCCIIIII} - \text{CCLXII} \\
&= \text{MCCCIII} - \text{LX} \\
&= \text{MCCLLIIII} - \text{LX} \\
&= \text{MCCLIII} - \text{X} \\
&= \text{MCCXXXXXIII} - \text{X} \\
&= \text{MCCXXXXIII}.
\end{aligned}
$$

It is somewhat shocking to reflect that Roman numerals were used in Europe as late as 1600 A.D. for many ordinary purposes of business: bookkeeping, banking, etc. One reason is that our modern Hindu-Arabic numerals did not become standardized in typographical form until after the invention of printing. Roman numerals were less subject to misreading and to forging.

The general populace, moreover, was poorly educated. You and I may regard addition by the use of Roman numerals as an awkward procedure. Yet it is far *simpler* and requires much less training to master than our own familiar process.

In modern times we employ a *subtractive* as well as an *additive* principle when using Roman numerals. Both the Babylonians and the Romans occasionally used the subtractive idea. Why did it not become popular? For one thing, only numerals in additive form can readily be put on an abacus or added and subtracted.

It has been said that the Romans may have avoided the use of IV for 4 because these are the initial letters of the name of the god IVPITER. The Babylonians, Hebrews, and others are known to have avoided certain numeral combinations for like reasons.

According to the subtractive principle, when a numeral symbol precedes one that it would ordinarily follow, its value is subtracted instead of added. In practice, only these combinations were used:

$$
\begin{array}{lll}
\text{IV} = \text{IIII} & \text{XL} = \text{XXXX} & \text{CD} = \text{CCCC} \\
\text{IX} = \text{VIIII} & \text{XC} = \text{LXXXX} & \text{CM} = \text{DCCCC}
\end{array}
$$

More extensive use of the principle can lead to confusion or ambiguity. Thus, should IVX mean 4 or 6? Take your choice.

To add or to subtract using Roman numerals that contain a subtractive combination, first rewrite them in purely additive form.

Example 1 Add: XCIV + CDXLIV

$$
\begin{aligned}
\text{XCIV} + \text{CDXLIV} &= \text{LXXXXIIII} + \text{CCCCXXXXIIII} \\
&= \text{CCCCLXXXXXXXXIIIIIIII} \\
&= \text{CCCCLLXXXVIII} \\
&= \text{CCCCCXXXVIII} \\
&= \text{DXXXVIII.}
\end{aligned}
$$

Example 2 Subtract: CMXLIX − XCIX.

$$
\begin{aligned}
\text{CMXLIX} - \text{XCIX} &= \text{DCCCCXXXXVIIII} - \text{LXXXXVIIII} \\
&= \text{DCCCC} - \text{L} \\
&= \text{DCCCLL} - \text{L} \\
&= \text{DCCCL.}
\end{aligned}
$$

Roman fractional numerals were not decimal but *duodecimal*, having multiples of 12 for their denominators. They will be referred to and elaborated upon in Chapter 2.

7. THE COUNTING TABLE

As mentioned before, the abacus has an ancient history. Herodotus wrote that the Egyptians "reckoned with pebbles." A Greek abacus consisting of a ruled marble slab is displayed in an Athens museum. That the use of pebbles for counters was common in Roman times is suggested by the etymology of our word "calculate," which derives from the Latin *calculare* and this in turn from *calculus*, which means "pebble."

In its most widespread use, the line abacus took the form of the medieval **counting table.** Merchants or accountants sat before this counting table or "counter" (whence our term *counter*, over which we trade in stores). Either the table itself or a cloth laid over it was ruled with lines valued according to the ascending powers of ten: I, X, C, M. The spaces between the lines were assigned the values V, L, D. The shopkeepers then "laid their sums" and reckoned "on the lines," using loose counters for the purpose. The well-known "Court of the Exchequer" of twelfth-century England took its name from the *exchequer* itself, which was simply a large counting table.

The student may construct his own counting table by ruling lines on a large sheet of paper and laying pennies for counters. The number 782 is shown "laid out" in Figure 1-7.

The rules for using the counting table are:

1. A handful of counters on a line may be replaced by a single counter on the space above.

2. A pair of counters in a space may be replaced by a single counter on the line above.

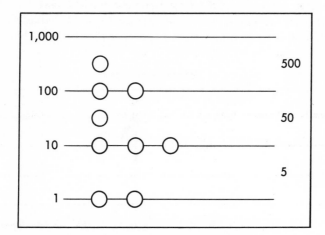

Fig. 1-7   The Counting Table (Schematic)
The number 782 is shown "laid out."

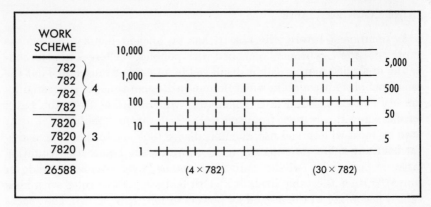

Fig. 1-8   34 × 782
Each vertical dash represents one counter.

Hence, if 53 is to be added to the 782 of the illustration, one "50" counter and three "1" counters are laid out, and then the resulting five "1's" may be replaced by a "5," and two "50's" by one "100." (This is the exchange process.) A few minutes of practice will lead one to become fairly adept at adding or subtracting on the counting table. With chalk in one hand and eraser in the other, the student may also carry out the work effectively at the blackboard, marking and erasing instead of putting down and picking up counters.

Multiplication and division are lengthier processes. Suppose that 782 is to be multiplied by 34. This means that 782 is to be multiplied by 4, then by 30, and the results summed. Multiplication by 4 is effected by laying out 782 four separate times (left portion of Fig. 1-8). Note now that multiplication by ten (7,820) may be accomplished just by laying the original 782 pattern of counters a *full line higher* on the table. So to multiply by 30, do this three times (right portion of Fig. 1-8). At this stage, the

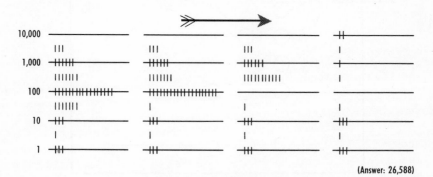

(Answer: 26,588)

Fig. 1-9   34 × 782 = 26,588
Some steps of simplification (initial array shown in Fig. 1-8).

counters on the table represent the desired product, 34 × 782, and
rest of the work consists in simplifying according to the "handful"
"pair" rules. Work from the bottom up, as shown in Figure 1-9.

The multiplication just illustrated is a kind of *repeated additio*
indicated in the work scheme set down at the left in Figure 1-8. Div
may be carried through in a similar way by *repeated subtraction*. T
techniques will be explained further in Chapter 6. The abacus
reposes beneath the counter in many of our Chinese laundry sho
operated much like the counting table; on it the deft fingers of the e
may compute more rapidly than may the swiftest of us with pen
paper.

The design of a Roman abacus of late origin is shown in Figure
Made of bronze, the abacus was grooved for the pebbles or cou

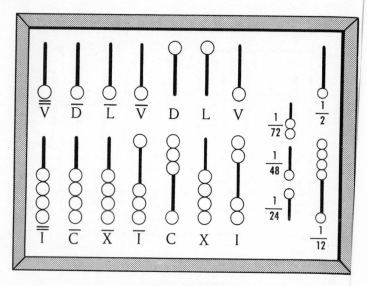

Fig. 1-10   Roman Abacus
Schematic diagram.

shown in the diagram as circles. The grooves or slots are labeled w
appropriate Roman numerals, except those for fractional numbers
are shown tagged with our own symbols to help the student who
to figure out how they were used. Counters at the lower ends of th
are in neutral or nonregistering position. The number shown
abacus is 1,852⅜.

In modern use, the abacus takes several forms. The *s'choty*, Figu
is specifically adapted to the monetary system of Russia, and is st
throughout that country. The Chinese *suan pan* (Fig. 1-12) a
Japanese *soroban* (Fig. 1-13) are more efficient computing devi

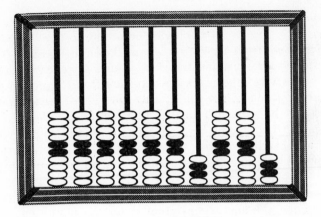

Fig. 1-11   Russian S'choty

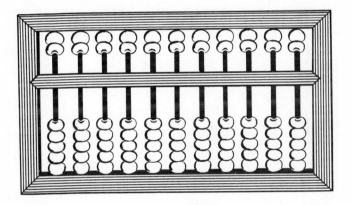

Fig. 1-12   Chinese Suan Pan

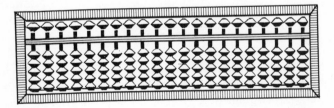

Fig. 1-13   Japanese Soroban

their lower rods the beads are worth 1, 10, 100, etc., and on the upper 5, 50, 500, etc. On the soroban, the distance toward the center crosspiece that the beads must be moved to register is less than finger width, so that an expert may operate the instrument just by stabbing with his finger tips.

Problem Set 3

1. Express each number in Roman numerals, without subtractive combinations:

(a) 7	(d) 48	(g) 372	(j) 1949
(b) 9	(e) 49	(h) 819	(k) 1956
(c) 16	(f) 53	(i) 970	(l) 1990

2. Proceed as in Problem 1, using subtractive combinations.
3. Add. Check by converting to our own numerals.

(a) XIII + IIII	(e) CCCVI + CLXXXXVII
(b) XVII + III	(f) MDXII + DCVIII
(c) LXXV + XXV	(g) MCCL + DCCL
(d) CLI + L	(h) DLVI + DLVI

4. Subtract. Check by converting to our own numerals.

(a) XVIII − XII	(e) C − X
(b) XV − III	(f) DC − CCLXII
(c) X − VII	(g) MCCVI − DCLXIII
(d) LXXV − XXXIII	(h) MMDX − CCXXXVI

5. Give an interpretation according to which IVX names 6. Give another interpretation according to which it names 4.
6. At least how many rods must an abacus of our variety have in order to show the following?

(a) 1,000	(b) 9,000	(c) 10,000	(d) 9,999,999

7. At least how many rods must an abacus of our variety have in order to show these sums?

(a) 23 + 39	(c) 967 + 24	(e) 23,655 + 9,000
(b) 23 + 84	(d) 967 + 56	(f) 90,000 + 10,000

8. Draw counting tables for computing with Roman numerals by ruling four lines on a sheet of paper, labeling them I, X, C, M, then labeling the spaces V, L, D. Show the following problems on these tables:

   (a) XIV + LIX　　　　　　(b) MDXCIV + CCCLXXVIII

9. Draw counting tables and show the following problems on these tables:

   (a) CDLVII − CCCXXIV　　　　(b) DMXLIII − CXXIX

10. Modernize the counting table of Problem 8 by replacing the Roman with the modern labels 1, 10, 100, 1,000 on the lines and 5, 50, 500 in the spaces. Represent the following numbers:

(a) 27	(b) 78	(c) 566	(d) 2,650

11. Add, on the counting table of Problem 10:

(a) 78 + 27	(b) 508 + 674	(c) 673 + 327

12. Subtract, on the counting table of Problem 9:

   (a) $46 - 23$ (b) $367 - 154$ (c) $1,000 - 666$

13. Write abacus work schemes for these problems:

$$Add$$
$$\left.\begin{matrix} 265 \\ 265 \end{matrix}\right\} 2$$

   (a) 32×68 (b) 234×308 *Answer* (c): $\left.\begin{matrix} 2650 \\ 2650 \\ 2650 \end{matrix}\right\} 3$
   (c) 32×265 (d) 208×417

$$\overline{8480}$$

14. Perform the following multiplications on the simple form of line abacus consisting of five lines labeled 1, 10, 100, 1,000, 10,000:

   (a) 30×42 (b) 32×265 (c) 208×417

8. HINDU-ARABIC NUMERALS

The central feature of our modern numeration system is the use of digits whose values are determined by their *position* in the sequence of digits that make up the numeral. This feature has enabled us to develop an efficient arithmetic.

This concept of place value is our heritage from the Babylonians and from the Hindus. The Hindus held the computational arts in high esteem. They were delighted by fanciful, poetically phrased problems involving large numbers. Such problems were fashionable in their court circles and played an important role in the education of their princes.

The Hindus developed the digits 1, 2, 3, 4, 5, 6, 7, 8, 9. They assigned a name to each power of ten, continuing far into the upper number realms, as they sought to number the very atoms in the world. We ourselves name the powers only to the third: ten, hundred, thousand. Thereafter we name the powers of a thousand: million, billion, trillion, etc. The number which we read as "Two billion, three hundred seventy-one million, five hundred thirty-two thousand, one hundred sixty-four" might have been read by a Brahman as:

   2 padmas, 3 vyarbudas, 7 kōtis, 1 prayuta, 5 laksas, 3 ayutas, 2 sahasra, 1 sàta, 6 dasan, 4

From such a rendition, it is a short step to omitting the place value names and just writing the ditits in succession, as we do: 2,371,532,164. But this step could not be taken until a symbol was provided to indicate a *vacancy*. Else "2 *sahasra*, 3" and "2 *sàta*, 3 *dasan*" (2,003 and 230) would both telescope into the same digital sequence 23, resulting in hopeless confusion.

The digit 0, which we presently use, was needed to take care of this situation. Sometime prior to 600 A.D., the symbol mysteriously showed up as a new tenth Hindu digit. The 0 is surely one of the great inventions of human history. Once historians gave sole credit to the Hindus for it. The tale was impressive. It is nicely set forth in *Number, The Language of Science,* by Tobias Dantzig. But now there is evidence that the invention took place by gradual growth instead of by sudden discovery.

As we noted earlier, the Babylonians left space where it was needed to separate digits. In the late Greek period, the usage was extended. Ptolemy, in about 150 A.D., employed the sexagesimal scheme in his astronomical calculations. He used a little circle *o* ("omicron"), initial letter of the Greek word *ουδεν*, meaning "nothing." He used this symbol at the end of a succession of digits, as well as between digits. It, therefore, seems likely that the Hindus borrowed both the idea and the symbol.

So we owe our present-day arithmetic to the achievements of at least three important cultural groups—Babylonian, Greek, and Hindu. If the Hindus were not the gifted mathematical innovators they were at one time held to be, at least it was they who completed the monumental task of framing our modern numeration system.

The "golden age" of Greek mathematics extended from about 400 to 200 B.C. Why did the brilliant mathematicians of those times fail to develop the zero idea and to devise a sound arithmetic? No easy answer can be given to this query. An important factor seems to have been that their interest in computation was theoretical rather than practical and that they conceived exact computation to be possible only in geometric rather than in numerical terms. The development of a sound arithmetic might well be supposed to have required a blend of practical and theoretical interests. "It takes all kinds of people to make a world"—from abstruse ivory-towerists to hard-headed down-to-earthers.

In the year 1050, the Hindu digits appeared as shown in Table 1-5. Our present digits evolved from these. So did some others that resemble ours very little, such as those of modern Sanskrit.

The Hindu arithmetic became known to the Arabs, themselves no mean mathematicians. Shortly before the year 1000, the Arabian mathematics, incorporating the Hindu, began to filter into Europe by way of Spain and other channels. Europe was then slowly awakening from her

Table 1-5

HINDU DIGITS (1050 A.D.)									
0	1	2	3	4	5	6	7	8	9
o	ﻉ	২	३	४	৯	६	৫	৮	৯

five-hundred-year cultural slumber (the Dark Ages). Several more centuries were to pass before the revival would be complete and European peoples ready to assume a leading role in secular activities—commerce, industry, the arts, the sciences, and mathematics.

By the thirteenth century, the intellectual awakening was fairly under way. Some respectable mathematics was done, an Italian named Fibonacci being outstanding for his work in that era. The true mathematical renaissance, however, came in the sixteenth century. The many excellent mathematicians of that period brought the subject to a stage at which the giants of the seventeenth century (Newton, Leibniz, Descartes, Pascal, Fermat, etc.) could take over, to lay the sturdy foundations of modern mathematics. The physical sciences ran their parallel course.

Over a 500-year period terminating in the sixteenth century, a bloodless battle royal had been waged between the "algorists" and the "abacists." The former championed the Hindu-Arabic arithmetic, the latter the abacus or counting-table form of computation. As we well know, the algorists' victory was complete. By the year 1600, arithmetic had substantially reached its present form.

In Chapters 5 and 6 we shall take up the development of the techniques of elementary arithmetic for adding, subtracting, multiplying, and dividing, as they evolved from their Hindu-Arabic origins.

9. MISCELLANEOUS FORMS

A variety of interesting and significant numeration systems were not mentioned in the preceding account; many of them belong to lines of evolutionary development separate from our own. In Yucatan, for example, the Mayas used a clever symbol scheme that was essentially *vigesimal*, that is, based on powers of twenty.

Oriental systems display interesting features[1] (See Fig. 1-14). A curious Chinese development was a "monogram" form of numeral derived from diagrams drawn to show the positions of *rods* laid out for computing purposes. The Chinese computing rods passed to Japan and Korea. The abacus (*suan pan*) displaced the rods in China in about the thirteenth century. The *sangi* board of Japan, on which the rods were laid out for computation, gave way to the abacus (*soroban*) not long after the end of the seventeenth century. The Koreans tossed away their number rods in favor of the superior abacus only about 1915.

In addition to numeration systems designed for computational purposes, there have been a host of curious schemes for simple counting and for recording numbers. The Peruvian *quipu* was a great sheaf of colored cords, the strands bearing small and large knots representing numbers by

[1] See Smith and Mikami, *A History of Japanese Mathematics* (Chicago: Open Court, 1914).

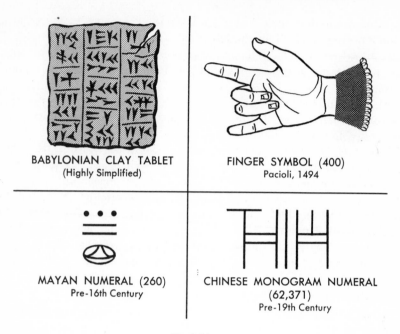

BABYLONIAN CLAY TABLET
(Highly Simplified)

FINGER SYMBOL (400)
Pacioli, 1494

MAYAN NUMERAL (260)
Pre-16th Century

CHINESE MONOGRAM NUMERAL
(62,371)
Pre-19th Century

Fig. 1-14

units and tens. These were used to record census results and other public data.

In England, tally sticks served as official accounting records from the twelfth century to the early part of the nineteenth. Notches were cut into the sticks according to a decimal code signifying sums from pence to £1000. Parliament at last abolished the system in 1826. Several years later the great accumulation was put to the torch. The dry old sticks made a fine hot fire—too hot for the stoves. The Parliament buildings went up in flames along with the tallies.[2]

10. FINGER RECKONING

Finger ways of representing numbers presumably preceded all others, though we have no definite historical reference to finger symbolism until the fifth century B.C., when it was mentioned by the Greek historian Herodotus.

A common way to begin counting on the fingers is to place the right forefinger upon the little finger of the open left hand. In most systems of finger reckoning the number *one* was indeed represented by a folding

[2] For photographs of Exchequer tallies, see page 9 of Oystein Ore, *Number Theory and Its History* (New York: McGraw-Hill Book Company, Inc., 1948). For an interesting account of the fire episode, of Tobias Dantzig, *Number, The Language of Science*, 4th ed., revised and augmented (New York: The Macmillan Company, 1956), p. 23.

inward of this left little finger. It became customary to represent the numbers from 1 to 99 on the left hand, the hundreds on the right. The Roman satirist Juvenal tells us, "Happy is he indeed who has postponed the hour of his death so long and finally numbers his years upon his right hand."

Finger symbolism flourished in pre-Renaissance Europe; it assisted barter between those of different tongues, served as a memory device, and aided in simple calculations.

Many of the more poorly educated peoples in Europe used finger reckoning until quite recent times, some even today, as an agreeable substitute for learning the full "times" tables. Select any two of the digits 6, 7, 8, 9, or take one of them twice. The product of the values of the two digits may be found as follows: Subtract 5 from the value of each selected digit. Hold up as many fingers on each hand as given by the two differences. The raised fingers count as *tens* toward the answer. Add to this the result of multiplying together the numbers of closed fingers on each hand.

Products like 7 × 3 can be found as follows:

$$7 \times 3 = 5 \times 3 \quad + \quad 2 \times 3.$$

Using this notion in conjunction with the finger method above, a poorly educated peasant could make out by learning the multiplication tables only up to 5 × 5.

The representation of the numbers on the fingers is perhaps the most primitive, yet the most intimate or personal way of all. This is of special interest to us, as we are in this text concerned with the *meaning* and *significance* of numbers rather than with their history as such. The capsule dose of numeral history provided in this chapter is intended primarily to aid the student to perceive the manifest variety of the possible ways of counting and numbering groups of things—particularly such concrete ways as are exemplified by the abacus in its many forms.

In the next chapter we shall explore more closely the structure of modern numeration systems.

Problem Set 4

1. Table 1-6 shows names used today starting with billion. For example, one billion = 1,000,000,000 = 10^9; and one trillion = 1,000,000,000,000 = 10^{12}. Using this table and your knowledge of names for numbers less than one billion, write word names for the following numbers:

   (a) 600,750,017,064,802,500,003
   (b) 9,008,003,213,370,285,970,000,070

Table 1-6

NUMBER WORD	LATIN ROOT	NUMERICAL EQUIVALENT OF ROOT
Billion	Bi-	2
Trillion	Tri-	3
Quadrillion	Quater	4
Quintillion	Quintus	5
Sextillion	Sex	6
Septillion	Septem	7
Octillion	Octo	8
Nonillion	Novem	9
Decillion	Decem	10
Undecillion	Undecim	11
Duodecillion	Duodecim	12
Tredecillion	Tredecim	13
Quatturodecillion	Quattuordecim	14
Quindecillion	Quindecim	15
Sexdecillion	Sexdecim	16
Septendecillion	Septendecim	17
Octodecillion	Octodecim	18
Novemdecillion	Novemdecim	19
Vigintillion	Viginti	20

2. In England, after a million, only the successive powers of one million are named, a million million being called a billion, and a million billion a trillion. How would an Englishman read the two numerals in Problem 1?
3. Multiply on your fingers, using the times table only up to 5×5, by the European peasant method.

(a) 6×6 (b) 6×8 (c) 7×7 (d) 7×9 (e) 8×9
(f) 6×7 (g) 6×9 (h) 7×8 (i) 8×8 (j) 9×9

4. In the following bibliographic references, choose one of the outstanding men of mathematics of the past and write a brief essay describing his main contribution to mathematics.

BIBLIOGRAPHY

Bell, E. T., *The Development of Mathematics*, 2d ed. New York: McGraw-Hill Book Company, Inc., 1945.
———, *Mathematics, Queen and Servant of Science*. New York: McGraw-Hill Book Company, Inc., 1951.
———, *Men of Mathematics*. New York: Simon and Schuster, Inc., 1937.
Cajori, Florian, *A History of Elementary Mathematics*, rev. ed. New York: The Macmillan Company, 1924.
———, *A History of Mathematics*, 2d ed. New York: The Macmillan Company, 1961.

Dantzig, Tobias, *Number, The Language of Science*, 4th ed., revised and augmented. New York: The MacMillan Company, 1956.

Eves, Howard, *An Introduction to the History of Mathematics*, rev. ed. New York: Holt, Rinehart and Winston, Inc., 1964.

Kline, Morris, *Mathematics—A Cultural Approach*. Palo Alto: Addison Wesley Publishing Company, Inc., 1962, pp. 11–28.

Neugebauer, Otto, *The Exact Sciences in Antiquity*. Princeton: Princeton University Press, 1952.

Sanford, Vera, *A Short History of Mathematics*. Boston: Houghton Mifflin Company, 1930.

Smith, David Eugene, *History of Mathematics*, vol. I. New York: Dover Publications, Inc., 1958.

Struik, Dirk J., *A Concise History of Mathematics*. New York: Dover Publications, Inc., 1948.

Van Der Waerden, B. L., *Science Awakening*. Noordhoff, Holland: 1954.

2

POSITIONAL
NUMERATION
SYSTEMS

1. SOME PRIMITIVE SCHEMES

A tribe living along the Belyando River in Australia counts like this:

1. Wogin	3. Booleroo wogin	(= 2 + 1)
2. Booleroo	4. Booleroo booleroo	(= 2 + 2)

Had a tribesman occasion to count beyond four, he might continue with "booleroo booleroo wogin, booleroo booleroo booleroo." In the Torres Straits a tribe does count to six in just such a way, using *urapan* and *okasa* for "one" and "two"; this tribe calls anything larger than six *ras*, which might be translated "a lot of."

These schemes are scarcely worthy of being termed numeration systems, being little more than devices of abbreviation and not involving *powers* of a base. In this chapter we shall study the structures of positional systems having various bases.

An Australian tribe called the *Kamilaroi* counts on a mixed binary-ternary scale:

1. Mal	4. Bular bular	(= 2 + 2)
2. Bular	5. Bular guliba	(= 2 + 3)
3. Guliba	6. Guliba guliba	(= 3 + 3)

The Luli of Paraguay have a mixed scheme:

1. Alapea	2. Tamop	3. Tamlip	4. Lokep

5. Lokep moile alapea (*or* is alapea)   (= 4 + 1 or 1 hand)
6. Lokep moile tamep   (= 4 + 2)
7. Lokep moile tamlip   (= 4 + 3)
8. Lokep moile lokep   (= 4 + 4)

9. Lokep moile lokep alapea	$(= 4 + 4 + 1)$
10. Is yaoum	(both hands)
11. Is yaoum moile alapea	(hands + 1)
20. Is eln yaoum	(hands, feet)
30. Is eln yaoum moile is yaoum	(hands, feet, hands)

Here we may note an initial preference for counting by fours. But once ten is reached, the scale of ten thereafter dominates.

In numeration systems a wide variety of bases have been found to be in current use in obscure portions of the world. (See L. L. Conant, *The Number Concept*, Macmillan, New York, 1896.) The scales come in twos, threes, fours, sixes, eights, tens—even in twenties and sixties, if some systems of older times are included (Mayan, Babylonian). All well-developed systems, however, have placed special emphasis on *ten*. Most, like our own, have been wholly based on ten.

Much has been written to tell how the evolutionary development of the human hand, with its opposed thumb, has spurred the cultural growth of man—how hand and brain have joined to create our human way of life. That our numeration system mirrors our hands is but one token of the profound respect we have for these, our basic tools, the fingers of our hands.

As far as our numeration system is concerned, it may be unfortunate that we have ten fingers rather than six or eight or twelve. A system based on any of these numbers would be superior to our tens, or decimal, system. A preference for bases other than ten may be discerned among our scales of weights and measures.

There are *twelve* inches in a foot, and we commonly use *two, four, eight,* or *sixteen* divisions of the inch. Quantities are often purchased by the *dozen* or by the *gross*. The ordinary pound has *sixteen* ounces. Liquid volume measures go by *twos;* cup (half-pint), pint, quart, half-gallon, gallon.

The arithmetic of everyday life, used by the housewife, the baker, the carpenter, etc., would be substantially simpler if our number scale and our measurement scales agree. Various reformists have urged the legislation of such agreement, usually arguing that the United States should adopt the *metric* system of measure. Some groups would have us change the numeration system instead, basing it on the twelve or *duodecimal* scale.

2. QUINARY NUMERATION SYSTEM: BASE FIVE

It is excellent training for a future teacher to practice simple arithmetic computation in different bases. The work may help him spot gaps in his understanding and application of the common arithmetic processes. Further, it may give him useful insight into the kinds of difficulties that

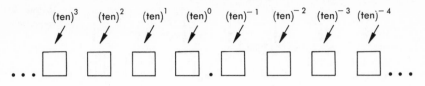

Fig. 2-1

will later trouble his own pupils as they learn to use a system unfamiliar to them. What is more, it is *fun* to deal with strange arithmetics—to add 3 and 4 and get 12, to multiply 4 by 4 and get 31. Furthermore, one cannot ignore the fact that the modern world of technology makes use of systems in bases different from ten. For example, electronic computers carry out operations using base two.

Let us observe the structure of our base-ten numeration system in relation to its base—the number ten. The values of the *positions* are shown in Figure 2-1. Note that the pattern in Figure 2-1 continues to the left and to the right. Thus,

$$5{,}329.1876_{ten}$$

may be *expanded* to show the value of each place as follows:

$$5{,}329.1876_{ten} = 5 \times 10^3 + 3 \times 10^2 + 2 \times 10^1 + 9 \times 10^0$$
$$+ 1 \times 10^{-1} + 8 \times 10^{-2} + 7 \times 10^{-3} + 6 \times 10^{-4}.$$

That the powers of ten present a consistent pattern can be seen from the following:

$$\vdots$$

$$10^3 = 1{,}000$$
$$10^2 = 100$$
$$10^1 = 10$$
$$10^0 = 1$$
$$10^{-1} = \frac{1}{10}$$
$$10^{-2} = \frac{1}{100}$$
$$10^{-3} = \frac{1}{1{,}000}$$

$$\vdots$$

In the base-ten numeration system, we employ ten *basic numerals* or **digits**: 0, 1, 2, 3, 4, 5, 6, 7, 8, 9. Using these basic numerals, we can write a name for any number.

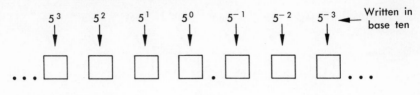

Fig. 2-2

The numeration system in *base five*, the **quinary** system, employs five basic numerals or digits: 0, 1, 2, 3, 4. The place values of this system are based on the powers of five, and its structure (see Fig. 2-2) is exactly analogous to the structure of the base-ten numeration system. Thus, the quinary numeral 3210.413_{five} would be expanded as:

$$3210.413_{\text{five}} = 3 \times 5^3 + 2 \times 5^2 + 1 \times 5^1 + 0 \times 5^0$$
$$+ 4 \times 5^{-1} + 1 \times 5^{-2} + 3 \times 5^{-3}.$$

To find the base-ten numeral for this number, we continue:

$$= 3 \times 125 + 2 \times 25 + 1 \times 5 + 4 \times \frac{1}{5} + \frac{1}{25} + 3 \times \frac{1}{125}$$

$$= 375 + 50 + 5 + \frac{4}{5} + \frac{1}{25} + \frac{3}{125}$$

$$= 430 + \frac{8}{10} + \frac{4}{100} + \frac{24}{1,000}$$

$$= 430 + \frac{8}{10} + \frac{6}{100} + \frac{4}{1,000}$$

$$= 430.864.$$

Therefore, $3210.413_{\text{five}} = 430.864_{\text{ten}}$.

A partial record of counting in base five would look like this:

1	21	41	111
2	22	42	.
3	23	43	.
4	24	44 (twenty-four)	.
10 (five)	30	100 (twenty-five)	444 (one hundred twenty-four)
11	31	101	1000 (one hundred twenty-five)
12	32	102	.
13	33	103	.
14	34	104	.
20 (ten)	40	110 (thirty)	4444 (six hundred twenty-four)
↑			10000 (six hundred twenty-five)

Read: two-zero in base five.

It is important that we read 432_{five} as "four-three-two in base five," since it is *not* four hundred thirty-two:

$$432_{\text{five}} = 4 \times 5^2 + 3 \times 5^1 + 2 \times 5^0$$
$$= 4 \times 25 + 3 \times 5 + 2 \times 1$$
$$= 100 + 15 + 2$$
$$= 117_{\text{ten}}.$$

Problem Set 1

1. What name would a tribesman from Belyando River in Australia use for

   (a) seven   (b) eight   (c) nine

2. What name would a Kamilaroi tribesman use for

   (a) seven   (b) eight   (c) nine

3. The *Ngarrimowro* (Australia) count on a binary scale, their number names for one and two being *warrangen* and *platir*, respectively. How do they say "three" and "four"? Check your answer on page 110 of Conant's *The Number Concept*.

4. What base is associated with the sequence of time units, *second, minute, hour?* With the sequence of angle units, *second, minute, degree?*

5. Expand each of the following by powers of ten:

   (a) 25
   (b) 3,762
   (c) 367,031
   (d) 27,018,653
   (e) 4,683.25
   (f) 368,750.029

6. Give the next three entries to fit into each of the following patterns:

   (a) $5^5 = 3,125$ 6 25 5
   $$\Big\}\text{ divide by 5}$$
       $5^4 = 625$ 125
   $$\Big\}\text{ divide by 5}$$
       $5^3 = 125$ 25
   $$\Big\}\text{ divide by 5}$$
       $5^2 = 25$ 5

   (b) $8^5 = 32,768$ 4,09 6
   $$\Big\}\text{ divide by 8}$$
       $8^4 = 4,096$ 512
   $$\Big\}\text{ divide by 8}$$
       $8^3 = 512$ 64
   $$\Big\}\text{ divide by 8}$$
       $8^2 = 64$ 8

   (c) $7^5 = 16,807$ 2401
   $$\Big\}\text{ divide by 7}$$
       $7^4 = 2,401$ 343
   $$\Big\}\text{ divide by 7}$$
       $7^3 = 343$ 49
   $$\Big\}\text{ divide by 7}$$
       $7^2 = 49$ 7

   (d) $2^5 = 32$ 16
   $$\Big\}\text{ divide by 2}$$
       $2^4 = 16$ 8
   $$\Big\}\text{ divide by 2}$$
       $2^3 = 8$ 4
   $$\Big\}\text{ divide by 2}$$
       $2^2 = 4$ 2

7. Prove each of the following:

   (a) $10^0 = 5^0$
   (b) $10^0 = 2^0$
   (c) $7^5 = 8^0$
   (d) $195^0 = 23^0$

8. Are we justified to conclude that, for any nonzero number n, $n^0 = 1$?
9. Expand each of the following by powers of five:

(a) 32_{five}　　　　　　　　　　(d) 23.11_{five}

(b) 2340_{five}　　　　　　　　　(e) 104.34_{five}

(c) 120324_{five}　　　　　　　　(f) 231.111_{five}

10. For each number in Problem 9, give its name in base ten.
11. Give the base-five names for the seven numbers between 111_{five} and 124_{five}.
12. Explain how the three-digit numerals in base five can be used to reflect our money system as far as pennies, nickels, and quarters are concerned.
13. Give the next three entries in the following count by fives:

$$10_{\text{five}}, \ 20_{\text{five}}, \ 30_{\text{five}}, \ \cdot \ \cdot \ \cdot$$

14. 12_{five} is an odd number (seven). Tell whether each of the following is an even or an odd number.

(a) 11_{five}　*even*　　　　　　　(f) 31_{five}　*even*

(b) 13_{five}　*even*　　　　　　　(g) 32_{five}　*odd*

(c) 14_{five}　*odd*　　　　　　　(h) 111_{five}　*even*

(d) 21_{five}　*even*　　　　　　　(i) 112_{five}　*odd*

(e) 24_{five}　*odd*　　　　　　　(j) 341_{five}　*even*

15. On the basis of your answers to Problem 14, formulate a rule for telling whether a number given in base five is even or odd.

3. PERFORMING OPERATIONS IN BASE FIVE

We construct the addition table (Table 2-1) for base five. A similar table for base ten would have 100 entries. How many entries are there in a base-five table? How many entries would a similar table for base seven have? Base twelve? Base two?

Table 2-1
ADDITION TABLE: BASE FIVE

	0	1	2	3	4
0	0	1	2	3	4
1	1	2	3	4	10
2	2	3	4	10	11
3	3	4	10	11	12
4	4	10	11	12	13

Now study these examples to see how addition is done in base five. Keep in mind that regrouping is done by fives.

Example 1 12_{five} $[2 + 4 = (4 + 1) + 1 = 11_{\text{five}}]$
            $+\ 24_{\text{five}}$
            $\overline{41_{\text{five}}}$ one group
                        of five

Example 2 33_{five}
            $+\ 24_{\text{five}}$
            $\overline{112_{\text{five}}}$

Example 3 144_{five} $[4 + 4 = (4 + 1) + 3 = 13_{\text{five}}]$
            $+144_{\text{five}}$
            $\overline{343_{\text{five}}}$ one group
                        of five

The examples below illustrate subtraction in base five.

                $1 \longleftarrow$ (Regroup 2 fives as 1 five and 5 ones.
Example 4 $2\!\!\!/3_{\text{five}}$ Five ones and 3 ones give 8 ones.)
            $-\ 14_{\text{five}}$
            $\overline{4_{\text{five}}}$

            32
Example 5 $4\!\!\!/3\!\!\!/1_{\text{five}}$
            $-\ 143_{\text{five}}$
            $\overline{233_{\text{five}}}$

            24 (Regroup 1 twenty-five as 4 fives and 5 ones.)
Example 6 $3\!\!\!/0\!\!\!/2_{\text{five}}$
            $-\ 133_{\text{five}}$
            $\overline{114_{\text{five}}}$

Table 2-2
MULTIPLICATION TABLE: BASE FIVE

	0	1	2	3	4
0	0	0	0	0	0
1	0	1	2	3	4
2	0	2	4	11	13
3	0	3	11	14	22
4	0	4	13	22	31

We can use Table 2-2 in performing multiplication of numbers whose names in base five have more than one digit.

Example 7 31_{five}
          $\times 23_{\text{five}}$
          143
          112
          1313_{five}

Example 8 134_{five}
          $\times\ \ 24_{\text{five}}$
          1201
          323
          4431_{five}

Example 9 402_{five}
          $\times\ 310_{\text{five}}$
          4020
         2211
          230120_{five}

Knowing how to multiply and to subtract in base five will enable us to divide.

Example 10 341_{five} over $12_{\text{five}})\overline{10142_{\text{five}}}$ We can check by multiplying:

          41   341_{five}
          104                               $\times\ 12_{\text{five}}$
          103   1232
           12   341
           12   10142_{five}
            0

Example 11 403, Remainder 4_{five} over $103_{\text{five}})\overline{43023_{\text{five}}}$ Check by multiplication:

          422   403_{five} 43014_{five}
          323                        $\times\ 103_{\text{five}}$ $+\ \ \ 4_{\text{five}}$
          314   2214 43023_{five}
            4   403
                                     43014_{five}

Problem Set 2

1. Rewrite preceding Examples 1 through 11 in base ten. Check whether the answers agree.

2. Compute the sums:

(a) 31_{five}
      $+23_{\text{five}}$

(b) 204_{five}
      $+241_{\text{five}}$

(c) 3420_{five}
      $+2444_{\text{five}}$

(d) 4040_{five}
      $+13044_{\text{five}}$

3. Compute the differences:

(a) 432_{five}
      $-\ 13_{\text{five}}$

(b) 423_{five}
      $-\ 34_{\text{five}}$

(c) 310_{five}
      $-\ 43_{\text{five}}$

(d) 402_{five}
      -244_{five}

4. Compute the products:

(a) 23_{five}
      $\times 41_{\text{five}}$

(b) 413_{five}
      $\times 212_{\text{five}}$

(c) 403_{five}
      $\times 44_{\text{five}}$

(d) 3004_{five}
      $\times\ 341_{\text{five}}$

5. Compute the quotients. All numerals are in base five.

(a) $23\overline{)2403}$
(b) $101\overline{)11144}$

(c) $34\overline{)34412}$
(d) $304\overline{)442302}$

4. DUODECIMAL NUMERATION SYSTEM: BASE TWELVE

In the **duodecimal** or **dozen** system, there are twelve digits. It is convenient to use our usual digits: 0, 1, 2, 3, . . . , but we need two extra digits. Rather than to devise new typographical forms that might be hard to remember, we choose T for ten and E for eleven, so that the twelve duodecimal digits become:

$$0, 1, 2, 3, 4, 5, 6, 7, 8, 9, \text{T}, \text{E}.$$

We now name the next number *dozen*, and write "10" (read: "one-zero" and *not* "ten"), meaning "1 dozen plus 0 units." Similarly, "11" (read: "one-one") means "1 dozen plus 1 unit." We continue counting systematically:

$$12 = 1 \text{ dozen} + 2 \text{ units} = 14_{\text{ten}}$$
$$13 = 1 \text{ dozen} + 3 \text{ units} = 15_{\text{ten}}$$
$$\cdot \ \cdot \ \cdot$$
$$19 = 1 \text{ dozen} + 9 \text{ units} = 21_{\text{ten}}$$
$$1\text{T} = 1 \text{ dozen} + \text{T} \text{ units} = 22_{\text{ten}}$$
$$1\text{E} = 1 \text{ dozen} + \text{E} \text{ units} = 23_{\text{ten}}$$
$$20 = 2 \text{ dozen} + 0 \text{ units} = 24_{\text{ten}}$$

$$99 = 9 \text{ dozen} + 9 \text{ units} = 117_{\text{ten}}$$
$$9T = 9 \text{ dozen} + T \text{ units} = 118_{\text{ten}}$$
$$9E = 9 \text{ dozen} + E \text{ units} = 119_{\text{ten}}$$
$$T0 = T \text{ dozen} + 0 \text{ units} = 120_{\text{ten}}$$

. . .

$$EE = E \text{ dozen} + E \text{ units} = 143_{\text{ten}}$$
$$100 = 1 \text{ gross} = 144_{\text{ten}}$$

. . .

$$EEE = E \text{ gross} + E \text{ dozen} + E \text{ units} = 1727_{\text{ten}}$$
$$1000 = 1 \text{ great gross} = 1728_{\text{ten}}$$

It is vital to realize just what the above statements mean: that a user of the duodecimal system, for example, in writing "1E" is referring to the *same natural number* as is the decimal-system user who writes "23." If both count simultaneously along a line of people, the "twelves" counter will be saying "one-E" at the same time the "tens" counter is saying "two-three," and both of them will be pointing at the same person in the line.

5. CONVERSION BETWEEN BASES

It is easy to find the base-ten numeral for the number given in base twelve. Each digit in the duodecimal numeral has a value by virtue of its position in the numeral. Thus, according to the duodecimal system:

$$3T07E_{\text{twelve}} = 3 \times 10000_{\text{twelve}} + T \times 1000_{\text{twelve}} + 0 \times 100_{\text{twelve}}$$
$$+ 7 \times 10_{\text{twelve}} + E \times 1.$$

To convert to tens, just re-express these values in the tens system, and add:

TWELVES		TENS		
$E \times 1$	=	$11 \times$	1	=	11
7×10	=	$7 \times$	12	=	84
0×100	=	$0 \times$	144	=	0
$T \times 1000$	=	$10 \times$	$1,728$	=	$17,280$
3×10000	=	$3 \times$	$20,736$	=	$62,208$
					$79,583$

Therefore, $3T07E_{\text{twelve}} = 79,583_{\text{ten}}$.

A decimal numeral may be converted to a duodecimal numeral by a similar procedure, but the re-expression of values is more difficult (10_{ten} replaced by T, 100_{ten} by 84_{twelve}, etc.), and the subsequent work has to be carried out within the duodecimal system.

A small decimal numeral may be converted to a duodecimal numeral by grouping into dozens and units. How many dozens are there in 41? This is a simple division problem. There are three dozen, and five units left over:

$$\begin{array}{r} 3 \\ 12\overline{)41} \\ 36 \\ \hline 5 \end{array} \qquad 41 = 3 \times 12 + 5.$$

$$41_{\text{ten}} = 35_{\text{twelve}}.$$

Consider 524_{ten}. Division by 12 shows:

$$524 = 43 \times 12 + 8.$$

We must separate out groups of twelve 12's from the forty-three 12's. Dividing 43 by 12 shows

$$43 = 3 \times 12 + 7.$$

Hence

$$524 = 3 \times 144 + 7 \times 12 + 8.$$
$$524_{\text{ten}} = 378_{\text{twelve}}.$$

The work may be conveniently arranged in successive division form:

$$\begin{array}{ll} 12\underline{)524} & \\ 12\underline{)43} & \text{R8} \\ 12\underline{)3} & \text{R7} \\ 0 & \text{R3} \end{array} \quad \begin{array}{l} \text{Read the answer up} \\ \text{along this column} \\ \text{of remainders.} \end{array}$$

The given number is divided by 12, the quotient being written below and the remainder at its right. The operation is repeated upon that quotient, and the work goes on until a zero quotient is reached. The column of remainders *read upward* gives the corresponding duodecimal numeral. Note how in the example at the right the original 11 and 10 remainders had to be rewritten as the duodecimal-system digits E and T.

$$\begin{array}{ll} 12\underline{)79583} & \\ 12\underline{)6631} & \text{RE} \\ 12\underline{)552} & \text{R7} \\ 12\underline{)46} & \text{R0} \\ 12\underline{)3} & \text{RT} \\ 0 & \text{R3} \end{array}$$

Answer: 3T07E

Problem Set 3

1. Find the duodecimal numeral for each of the following by first dividing by 144, then dividing the remainder by 12.

Example 479_{ten}.

$$\begin{array}{r} 3 \\ 144\overline{)479} \\ 432 \\ \hline 47 \end{array} \qquad \text{There are three 144's in 479}$$

$$\begin{array}{r} 3 \\ 12\overline{)47} \\ 36 \\ \hline 9E \end{array} \qquad \text{There are three 12's in 47.}$$

There are 9 units left over.

Therefore, $479_{\text{ten}} = 339_{\text{twelve}}$.

(a) 683_{ten} (b) 1450_{ten} (c) 1726_{ten}

2. Find the duodecimal numeral for each of the following by dividing first by 1728, then dividing the remainder by 144, then dividing the next remainder by 12.

(a) $2,078_{ten}$ (b) $11,395_{ten}$

3. Mentally find the duodecimal numeral for each of the following:

Example 40_{ten}.
Think: 36 is 3 dozen, so 40 is 3 dozen plus 4. Thus, $40_{ten} = 34_{twelve}$.

(a) 30_{ten} (b) 60_{ten} (c) 84_{ten} (d) 143_{ten}

4. Give the base-ten numeral for each of the following:

(a) 57_{twelve} (c) 590_{twelve} (e) $1,726_{twelve}$
(b) 143_{twelve} (d) $1,684_{twelve}$ (f) $3,562_{twelve}$

6. DUODECIMAL ARITHMETIC

Numbers given by a single digit may easily be added mentally. Consider $7 + 9$. Either of the following methods may be used:

METHOD A	METHOD B
Add in tens system and convert	*Group into dozens and units*

$$7 + 9 = 16_{ten}$$
$$= 1 \text{ dozen} + 4 = 14_{twelve}$$

$$7 + 9 = (7 + 5) + 4$$
$$= 1 \text{ dozen} + 4 = 14_{twelve}$$

Knowing how to add with one-digit numerals, we may now add any numbers given in the duodecimal system as follows:

(5)	(4)	(3)	(2)	(1)		STEPS
7	E	T	3	2		(1) $3 + 2 = 5$. Write 5.
+	5	1	9	3		(2) $9 + 3 = 1$ dozen $= 10$. Write 0, remember ①.
8	5	0	0	5		(3) ① $+ 1 + T = 1$ dozen $= 10$. Write 0, remember ①.

(4) ① $+ 5 + E = 1$ dozen $+ 5 = 15$. Write 5, remember ①.
(5) ① $+ 7 = 8$. Write 8.

We may subtract by any common procedure. Study the following example:

(3)	(2)	(1)		STEPS
2	3	6		(1) $16 - 9 = (1 \text{ dozen} - 9) + 6 = 3 + 6 = 9$.
−	T	9		(2) $12 - T = (1 \text{ dozen} - T) + 2 = 2 + 2 = 4$.
1	4	9		(3) $1 - 0 = 1$.

Table 2-3
MULTIPLICATION TABLE: BASE TWELVE

	0	1	2	3	4	5	6	7	8	9	T	E	
0	0	0	0	0	0	0	0	0	0	0	0	0	0
1		1	2	3	4	5	6	7	8	9	T	E	1
2			4	6	8	T	10	12	14	16	18	1T	2
3				9	10	13	16	19	20	23	26	29	3
4					14	18	20	24	28	30	34	38	4
5						21	26	2E	34	39	42	47	5
6							30	36	40	46	50	56	6
7								41	48	53	5T	65	7
8									54	60	68	74	8
9										69	76	83	9
T											84	92	T
E												T1	E
	0	1	2	3	4	5	6	7	8	9	T	E	

For efficient multiplication and division, a multiplication table is needed. This is supplied in Table 2-3. However, the student would do well to make his own, to ensure that he understands its construction. Successive addition may be used. To list the multiples of 8, for example, add 8 to 8 to get $2 \times 8 = 14$. Add 8 to this to get $3 \times 8 = 20$, etc., up to $E \times 8 = 74$. (Remember that all numerals are written in base twelve.)

In the examples that follow, the corresponding problems are also shown in base ten. In problem assignments, the student may be asked to check his work by converting to base ten, because this will give him practice in converting and in comparing the answer given in two numeration systems, and will also serve to bolster his confidence in the correctness of the work.

Example 1 23×78.

Base twelve	*Base ten*
78	92
× 23	× 27
1E0	644
134	184
1,530	2,484

To get 3×78: According to the multiplication table, $3 \times 8 = 20$. Write 0 and remember ②. Again, $3 \times 7 = 19$. Add the ②, getting 1E, which is written down. The other partial product, $2 \times 78 = 134$ (in actual value 1340), is found in the same way, and the two values are added.

Example 2 290E5 ÷ 57.

Base twelve	*Base ten*
5E1 RT	853 R10
57)290E5	67)57161
23E	536
51E	356
515	335
65	211
57	201
T	10

To estimate how many times 57 is contained in 290, test 60 into 290, or 6 into 29. According to the multiplication table, $6 \times 5 = 26$ and $6 \times 6 = 30$. So 5 is taken as a trial quotient. Subtracting $5 \times 57 = 23E$ from 290, we get 51, and the E is brought down. The work continues, in the pattern of our usual division procedure.

A duodecimal abacus is easily made in either rod or line form. The rod abacus has 11 or 12 beads on each rod (just as the base-ten simple abacus bears nine or ten). The line abacus is our former one, unchanged: a sheet ruled with several lines marked with the values 1, 10, 100, etc. (i.e., one, dozen, gross). The new rule for the line abacus is: A dozen counters on a line are equivalent to a single counter on the line above, as shown in Figure 2-3.

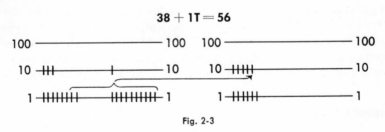

Fig. 2-3

7. DUODECIMAL FRACTIONAL NUMERALS

When the numbers involved in an arithmetic problem have many divisors (factors), the work is likely to go easily, since many simplifications can be achieved through division by common factors. Expressions containing names for numbers like 6, 8, 12 are simplified more easily than if the numbers are like 7, 11, 13.

It is especially advantageous for the numeration system to have a base with many divisors. Besides 1 and itself, 12 has four divisors: 2, 3, 4, and 6. Ten has only two: 2 and 5. Arithmetic in the duodecimal system is therefore generally easier than in the decimal system. In particular, it is much easier to handle the simple fractional numbers that so frequently turn up in the day-by-day use of arithmetic (in kitchen, store, shop, office, and easy-chair) when the base-twelve system is used.

Here are some duodecimal equivalents. Remember that each numeral is written in base twelve. Thus,

$$.1_{\text{twelve}} = \left(\tfrac{1}{12}\right)_{\text{ten}} = \left(\tfrac{1}{10}\right)_{\text{twelve}}.$$
$$.16_{\text{twelve}} = \left(\tfrac{1}{12} + \tfrac{6}{144}\right)_{\text{ten}} = \left(\tfrac{18}{144}\right)_{\text{ten}} = \left(\tfrac{1}{8}\right)_{\text{ten}} = \left(\tfrac{1}{8}\right)_{\text{twelve}}.$$

$.1 = \tfrac{1}{10}$	$.4 = \tfrac{1}{3}$	$.16 = \tfrac{1}{8}$
$.2 = \tfrac{1}{6}$	$.6 = \tfrac{1}{2}$	$.09 = \tfrac{1}{14}$
$.3 = \tfrac{1}{4}$	$.8 = \tfrac{2}{3}$	$.046 = \tfrac{1}{28}$

The rightmost column shows the equivalents corresponding to the usual ruler graduation into eighths, sixteenths, and thirty-seconds. The corresponding decimals are $\tfrac{1}{8} = .125$, $\tfrac{1}{16} = .0625$, $\tfrac{1}{32} = .03125$.

Problem Set 4

1. In Problems (a) to (v), every number is given in base twelve. Carry out the indicated computations. For practice in conversion, check your work as follows: Convert to base ten and do the indicated computation. Convert the result to base twelve and compare with your earlier answer.

(a) $\begin{array}{r} 4E \\ +T5 \\ \hline \end{array}$

(b) $\begin{array}{r} 305 \\ +70T \\ \hline \end{array}$

(c) $\begin{array}{r} 1072 \\ +19ET8 \\ \hline \end{array}$

(d) $\begin{array}{r} 19ET8 \\ +7ET04 \\ \hline \end{array}$

(e) $\begin{array}{r} 70T \\ - \ \ T5 \\ \hline \end{array}$

(f) $\begin{array}{r} 214 \\ - \ T5 \\ \hline \end{array}$

(g) $\begin{array}{r} 19ET8 \\ - \ \ 70T \\ \hline \end{array}$

(h) $\begin{array}{r} 7ET04 \\ -19ET8 \\ \hline \end{array}$

(i) $\begin{array}{r} 4E \\ \times T5 \\ \hline \end{array}$

(j) $\begin{array}{r} 4E \\ \times 214 \\ \hline \end{array}$

(k) $\begin{array}{r} T5 \\ \times 19ET8 \\ \hline \end{array}$

(l) $\begin{array}{r} 214 \\ \times 70T \\ \hline \end{array}$

(m) $\begin{array}{r} 214 \\ \times 19ET8 \\ \hline \end{array}$

(n) $\begin{array}{r} 70T \\ \times 19ET8 \\ \hline \end{array}$

(o) $\begin{array}{r} 70T \\ \times 7ET04 \\ \hline \end{array}$

(p) $5)\overline{4E}$

(q) $5)\overline{T5}$

(r) $4E)\overline{214}$

(s) $214)\overline{1072}$

(t) $4E)\overline{19ET8}$

(u) $T5)\overline{19ET8}$

(v) $214)\overline{19ET8}$

2. Give the duodecimals .1, .2, .3, .4, .5, .6, .7, .8, .9, .T, .E as fractional numerals in base twelve.
3. Proceed as in Problem 2 for .01, .02, .03, .04, .05, .06, .07, .08, .09, .0T, .0E.

8. THE BINARY SYSTEM: BASE TWO

The one disadvantage of the duodecimal system with respect to the base-ten system is that two extra digits are needed. Instead of a 10 by 10 addition table with $10 \times 10 = 100$ entries, a 12 by 12 table with 144 entries must be learned.

On the lower side of ten, 6 and 8 are good candidates for bases. The resulting **hexal** and **octal** numeration systems are both superior to the decimal system. How small a base may be used? There can be no base-one system, for this would have only one digit, and would amount to the same as tallying. The **base-two** or **binary** system is thus the system with the least possible base.

The only digits in the binary system are 0 and 1, so that the basic tables become nearly trivial (see Table 2-4). In other words, for binary arithmetic a pupil need learn, besides the usual zero properties, only the two "facts"

$$1 + 1 = 10 \quad \text{and} \quad 1 \times 1 = 1.$$

Table 2-4

+	0	1
0	0	1
1	1	10

×	0	1
0	0	0
1	0	1

So ultrasimple is the binary system that even *counting* in it is apt at first to be confusing. For no sooner is the *first* digit (0) passed than the *last* digit (1) is met, whereupon a change of form to two places (10) is at once in order. The number following 1111 is 10000, just as in the decimal system 9,999 is followed by 10,000.

The first sixteen numbers given in the binary system are:

1.	1	5.	101	9.	1001	13.	1101
2.	10	6.	110	10.	1010	14.	1110
3.	11	7.	111	11.	1011	15.	1111
4.	100	8.	1000	12.	1100	16.	10000

The rules for converting from base two to base ten, and vice versa, are like the ones used with base twelve. Binary place values are *powers of two;* 1, 2, 4, 8, ... At the left below is shown the conversion of the binary numeral 1011001 into the equivalent decimal numeral 89. At the right is shown the reverse conversion, from 89 to 1011001, accomplished through successive division by 2.

1	×	1	=	1	2)89		
0	×	2			2)44	1	↑
0	×	4			2)22	0	
1	×	8	=	8	2)11	0	
1	×	16	=	16	2)5	1	
0	×	32			2)2	1	
1	×	64	=	64	2)1	0	
				89	0	1	

A binary rod abacus needs only one bead per rod, but needs quite a few rods. For the line abacus, the rule is: a pair of counters on a line is equivalent to a single counter on the line above.

Addition using binary system is illustrated in the next example.

Example

(*3*)	(*2*)	(*1*)		STEPS
1	0	1		(*1*) 1 plus 1 gives 10. Write 0; remember ①.
+	1	1		(*2*) ① + 1 gives 10. Write 0; remember ①.
1	0	0	0	(*3*) ① + 1 gives 10. Write 0; remember ①.
				(*4*) ① + 0 gives 1. Write 1.

The corresponding problem in base ten would be:

$$\begin{array}{r} 5 \\ 3 \\ \hline 8 \end{array}$$

Adding several numbers given in binary notation is a bit tricky. Study the following example and the explanation to its right:

(*8*)	(*7*)	(*6*)	(*5*)	(*4*)	(*3*)	(*2*)	(*1*)
			1	0	1	1	0	1
				1	1	0	1	1
				1	0	1	1	0
			1	0	0	1	1	1
+					1	1	1	0
1	0	0	1	0	0	1	1

STEPS

(*1*) 1 plus 1 gives 10, plus 1 gives 11. Write 1; remember ①.

(*2*) ① plus 1 gives 10, plus 1 gives 11, plus 1 gives 100, plus 1 gives 101. Write 1; remember ⑩.

(*3*) ⑩ plus 1 gives 11, plus 1 gives 100, plus 1 gives 101, plus 1 gives 110. Write 0; remember ⑪.

Etc.

Another way to show this problem would be to write 1 in the next column to the left for each 1 + 1 of the preceding column. This is:

(8)	(7)	(6)	(5)	(4)	(3)	(2)	(1)
					1	1	
		1	1	1	1	1	
1	1	1	1	1	1	1	
			1	0	1	1	0	1
				1	1	0	1	1
			1	0	1	1	0	
		1	0	0	1	1	1	
				1	1	1	0	
1	0	0	1	0	0	1	1	

STEPS

(*1*) Since there are two 1's in column (*1*), we write one 1 in the second column to the left. Since there is one more 1, we write 1 for the sum below.

(*2*) There are two groups of two 1's, so we write two 1's in column (*3*). Since there is one more 1 left over, we write 1 for the sum below.

Etc.

The corresponding addition in base ten would be:

$$\begin{array}{r} 45 \\ 27 \\ 22 \\ 39 \\ \underline{14} \\ 147 \end{array}$$

In division with binary numerals, there is no need to estimate trial quotients. The divisor is either contained one time in the dividend or it is not. If not, move (in the dividend) one more place to the right.

The corresponding division in base ten would be:

$$\begin{array}{r} 25 \quad \text{R6} \\ 26\overline{)656} \\ \underline{52} \\ 136 \\ \underline{130} \\ 6 \end{array}$$

$$\begin{array}{r} 11001 \quad \text{R110} \\ 11010\overline{)1010010000} \\ \underline{11010} \\ 11110 \\ \underline{11010} \\ 100000 \\ \underline{11010} \\ 110 \end{array}$$

Is it true that $11001_{two} = 25_{ten}$ and $110_{two} = 6_{ten}$?

The distinguished mathematician and philosopher Gottfried Wilhelm Leibniz (1646–1716) seriously urged that we discard the decimal system in favor of the binary. Were we to do this, children would romp through arithmetic in the early grades; and long division would no longer be a "bogie" for them. It is tedious, however, to read and to write lengthy binary numerals. Since the length of numerals is not of much serious consequence to machines, the electronic computers employ the binary system. Having to deal with only two digits outweighs all other disadvantages. It permits the electronic computers to perform operations with astounding rapidity (up to 1 million operations in 1 second).

Leibniz was intrigued by his own mystical interpretation of the binary system. He glimpsed in it the "image of creation": the Universe symbolically fashioned from the Void (0) by the Supreme Being (1 = Unity). This metaphysical enchantment lured him to advocate the binary system.

Problem Set 5

1. For each binary numeral give the corresponding base-ten numeral.

(a) 101   (e) 10011001
(b) 1001   (f) 1100101001
(c) 1111   (g) 1111111111
(d) 10100   (h) 10000000000

2. A small number given in base ten can be quickly named by a base-two numeral by first showing it as a sum of powers of 2. Thus,

$$21 = 16 + 4 + 1.$$

Therefore,

$$21_{ten} = \begin{matrix} 1 & 0 & 1 & 0 & 1 \\ \uparrow & \uparrow & \uparrow & \uparrow & \uparrow \\ 2^4 & 2^3 & 2^2 & 2^1 & 2^0 \end{matrix}$$

Show each number as a sum of powers of 2, then write the binary numeral for it.

(a) 15   (c) 39   (e) 63
(b) 29   (d) 48   (f) 127

3. Using repeated division by 2, find the base-two numerals corresponding to the following base-ten numerals:

(a) 19   (d) 100   (g) 572
(b) 35   (e) 1,000   (h) 573
(c) 50   (f) 10,000   (i) 574

4. Carry out the indicated operations. All numerals are in base two.

(a)   101
   1000
   1010
 +1101

(b)   1010
    1101
   10110
 +101000

(c)   1101
   101100
  1001011
 +1101000

(d)   1101
 −1010

(e) 10100
 − 1101

(f) 1101000
 −1000001

(g)   1101
 × 101

(h)   1101
 ×1011

(i)   101010
 × 1101

(j)   1101000
 ×   1101

(k) $101\overline{)1010}$

(l) $101\overline{)1101}$

(m) $1011\overline{)101000}$

(n) $101\overline{)1000001}$

5. Notice that

$$32_{\text{ten}} = 100000_{\text{two}}.$$

Thus, in base ten, thirty-two is named by a two-digit numeral, and in base two thirty-two is named by a six-digit numeral. Using this as a guide explain the meaning of the following statement:

Digitness is not the property of numbers, rather it is the property of numerals.

6.* In base ten the following statements are true:

$$\tfrac{1}{2} = .5$$
$$\tfrac{1}{4} = .25$$
$$\tfrac{1}{8} = .125$$

In base two the following are true:

$$\tfrac{1}{10} = .1 \qquad (\tfrac{1}{2})$$
$$\tfrac{1}{100} = .01 \qquad (\tfrac{1}{4})$$
$$\tfrac{1}{1000} = .001 \qquad (\tfrac{1}{8})$$

Similarly, give names for the following in base two:

(a) $\frac{11}{1000}$

(b) $\frac{101}{1000}$

(c) $\frac{1}{10000}$

(d) $\frac{111}{10000}$

(e) $\frac{1}{100000}$

(f) $\frac{1111}{100000}$

9. APPLICATIONS OF BINARY NUMERALS

The applications of binary numerals are many and varied. They are used in statistical investigations and in problems involving probabilities. They facilitate the analysis and explanation of the strategy and play of various simple games and puzzles. They are sometimes used in proving theorems of pure mathematics. They are put to more plebian use by the giant electronic "brains" of today, which compute in terms of them and which accelerate calculations to solve in hours scientific and industrial problems that would otherwise take years.

Many important events and decisions in everyday life and in social, industrial, or scientific work depend upon successive dual choices of alternatives: yes or no, on or off, present or absent, etc. The two choices may be symbolized by 0 and 1, respectively. A succession of choices then generates a binary numeral. Thus, the coin-tossing sequence *head, head, tail, tail, tail, head, tail* could be coded as 1100010. A transformation of this sort may greatly simplify the analysis of a problem.

Example 1 How many subsets has a set of five objects? (**Set** means a **collection;** a set A is said to be a subset of set B if every object that is in set A is also in set B. If an object is found in set A, then we say that this object is an **element** of set A. **Empty set** is a set that has no elements. Sets are discussed in the next chapter in more detail.)

Let the objects be thought of as numbered 1, 2, 3, 4, 5, and associated with the five boxes labeled as in Figure 2-4.

Fig. 2-4

Any particular subset can now be coded as follows: If the subset contains object no. 1, write 1 in box no. 1; if the subset does not contain object no. 1, write 0 in box no. 1. Likewise, write 1 or 0 in box no. 2 depending on whether object no. 2 is an element of the subset. Continue. The resulting sequence of 1's and 0's is a binary numeral, like 10110 or 00101 (= 101). The various subsets, empty set included, are thus matched with the binary numerals from 00000 to 11111, inclusive. Add 1 at each end: 1 to 100000. Hence the number of subsets is 100000. In base ten this is $2^5 = 32$.

Example 2 A monetary system is based upon some smallest or unit coin (penny) and other coins or denominations that are multiples of the unit (nickel, quarter, ten-dollar bill). With an efficiently arranged system, a person should not have to carry many coins to take care of his everyday transactions. There must be neither too few nor too many denominations.

The most efficient scheme is the binary, with coins of value 1, 2, 4, 8,

16, 32, 64, etc. With it, any given amount can be put together using no more than one coin of each denomination. Suppose that an amount of 89¢ is needed. The binary numeral that corresponds to 89 is 1011001. Hence.

$$89 = 1 + 8 + 16 + 64,$$

so that the four coins having these values make up the required sum. (In a true decimal system, with denominations 1, 10, 100, etc., $8 + 9 = 17$ coins would be needed.)

United States coinage follows the binary pattern as best it can, being hampered by the decimal restriction that 10 and 100 (one dollar) must be among the denominations. Each denomination has nearly twice the value of the one before:

$$1, -, 5, 10, 25, 50, 100.$$

The gap is reserved for our nonexistent two-cent piece.

True binary "coins" can be constructed by placing the amounts 1¢, 2¢, 4¢, 8¢, 16¢, 32¢, 64¢, $1.28, $2.56 into nine envelopes. With these nine envelopes, a person can guarantee to furnish any amount from 1¢ to $5.00, say (actually to $5.11). Thus if 89¢ is called for (1011001), the four envelopes of values 1¢, 8¢, 16¢, 64¢ may be given. The demonstration can be made a fairly effective "magic" act if given a good build-up.

Example 3 "Age cards" were once popular, and are still seen. Four cards bear numerals as in Figure 2-5. A child is shown the cards and asked

Card A		Card B		Card C		Card D	
8	12	4	12	2	10	1	9
9	13	5	13	3	11	3	11
10	14	6	14	6	14	5	13
11	15	7	15	7	15	7	15

Fig. 2-5

which ones have his age on them. Suppose he answers A, C, D. When the numbers given in the upper left-hand corners of these cards are added, his age is found: $8 + 2 + 1 = 11$. It is left to the student to figure out the "why" of the cards. (*Hint:* Write down the first fifteen binary numerals. Regard the list as a code.)

Example 4 An inspector of weights and measures carries a set of standard weights. These are on the binary pattern: 1 oz., 2 oz., 4 oz., 8 oz., etc. Imagine using them with a "seesaw" type balance, consisting of a bar supported on a knife-edge at its middle and bearing a pan at each end. With a 13-oz. object in a pan, what weights must be placed in the other pan in order to balance? The binary numeral corresponding to 13 is 1101, so that $13 = 1 + 4 + 8$. (*Answer:* 1 oz., 4 oz., 8 oz.)

Table 2-5
NUMBER NAMES IN DIFFERENT BASES

In each row of this table are shown different names for the same number. On the average, the numbers of digits required to represent the same whole number in two different systems compare as the logarithms of the bases of the systems. Since the common logarithms of 10 and 2 are 1 and .30 . . . , respectively, it takes about 3⅓ times as many digits to represent numbers dyadically instead of decimally.

DECIMAL *Ten*	BINARY OR DYADIC *Two*	TERNARY *Three*	HEXAL *Six*	OCTAL *Eight*	DUODECIMAL *Twelve*
1	1	1	1	1	1
2	10	2	2	2	2
3	11	10	3	3	3
4	100	11	4	4	4
5	101	12	5	5	5
6	110	20	10	6	6
7	111	21	11	7	7
8	1000	22	12	10	8
9	1001	100	13	11	9
10	1010	101	14	12	T
11	1011	102	15	13	E
12	1100	110	20	14	10
13	1101	111	21	15	11
14	1110	112	22	16	12
15	1111	120	23	17	13
16	10000	121	24	20	14
17	10001	122	25	21	15
18	10010	200	30	22	16
19	10011	201	31	23	17
20	10100	202	32	24	18
100	1100100	10201	244	144	84
1000	1111101000	1101001	4344	1750	6E4
10000	10011100010000	111201101	114144	23420	5954
½	.5	.1	.111111 . . .	.3	.4	.6
⅓	.333333 . . .	.010101 . . .	.1	.2	.252525 . . .	.4
¼	.25	.01	.020202 . . .	.13	.2	.3
⅙	.166666 . . .	.001010 . . .	.011111 . . .	.1	.125252 . . .	.2
⅛	.125	.001	.010101 . . .	.043	.1	.16
1/12	.083333 . . .	.000101 . . .	.002020 . . .	.03	.052525 . . .	.1
1/16	.0625	.0001	.001200 . . .	.0213	.04	.09
1/32	.03125	.00001	.000211 . . .	.01043	.02	.046

On a *ternary* (base-three) scale, the standard weights would be 1, 3, 9, 27, etc., ounces. *Two* of each would be required. Suppose, for example, we wish to balance 46 oz. The corresponding ternary numeral may be found by successive division by 3. It is 1201. This means that

$$46 = 1 \times 27 + 2 \times 9 + 0 \times 3 + 1 \times 1.$$

3)46
3)15   1
3) 5   0
3) 1   2
    0   1

So one 1-oz., two 9-oz., and one 27-oz. weights must be used.

If the weights may be placed *in either pan*, only one each of the standard ternary weights will be needed. Let us rewrite the ternary numeral 1021 in terms of the "signed" digits $\bar{1}$, 0, 1 (where $\bar{1} = -1$). This can be done by replacing the digit 2 by $1\bar{1}$ (since $1\bar{1}$ means $3 - 1 = 2$).

$$1201 = 2\bar{1}01 = 1\bar{1}\bar{1}01.$$

Hence we may balance a 46-oz. object by placing weights of 9 and 27 oz. in the pan with the object, and weights of 1 and 81 oz. in the other pan.

Problem Set 6

1. List the 2^3 or 8 subsets of the set whose elements are the letters a, b, c.
2. Your Christmas-card list ends with a group of ten people, and you are undecided whether to send cards to any, to some certain ones of them, or to all. In how many ways could you make up your mind?
3. A set with one element has two subsets: one consisting of the element and the empty set. Also $2^1 = 2$. A set with two elements has four subsets. Also $2^2 = 4$. A set with three elements has eight subsets—$2^3 = 8$. Using the same pattern, tell how many subsets each of the sets with the following number of elements have:

    (a) 4   (b) 5   (c) 6   (d) n

4. If we used a monetary system such that we had coins of denomination 1¢, 3¢, 9¢, etc., how many coins (minimum) would be needed to make up the sum of 77¢? Solve by converting 77 to a base-three numeral, by division.
5. Work out a mental scheme for converting a small number, like 77, to base three, i.e., expressing it as a sum of multiples (0,1,2) of powers of 3?
6. The Slobbovian coin of smallest value is the "scent." Other coins have these values: 4 scents = 1 neck; 4 necks = 1 dyme; 4 dymes = 1 qwat; 4 qwats = 1 haf; 4 hafs = 1 doll. What coins are needed (minimum number) to pay for an item costing 3,597 scents?
7. Make up a set of five "age cards" covering the range 1 to 31.
8. What combination of standard weights (base two: 1 oz., 2 oz., 4 oz., etc.) is needed to balance an item weighing 361 oz.?
9. What combination of base-three scale weights (2 each: 1 oz., 3 oz., 9 oz., etc.) is needed to balance an item weighing 139 oz.? 524 oz.?
10. If weights may be put in both pans, what combination of base-three scale weights (*one* each: 1 oz., 3 oz., 9 oz., etc.) is needed to balance an item weighing 139 oz.? 524 oz.?

11. The values in the British monetary system are:

$$
\begin{aligned}
1 \text{ sixpence} &= 6 \text{ pennies} \\
1 \text{ shilling} &= 12 \text{ pennies} \\
1 \text{ florin} &= 2 \text{ shillings} \\
1 \text{ half-crown} &= 2 \text{ shillings and sixpence} \\
1 \text{ crown} &= 5 \text{ shillings} \\
1 \text{ ten bob note} &= 10 \text{ shillings} \\
1 \text{ pound } (£1) &= 20 \text{ shillings}
\end{aligned}
$$

(a) How many sixpence in 1 shilling?
(b) How many pennies in 1 florin?
(c) How many pennies in 1 half-crown?
(d) How many crowns in 1 ten-bob note?
(e) How many pennies in 1 pound?
(f) Does the British monetary system have one consistent base?

12.* *Nim* is a clever game played with piles of coins, matches, etc. Its theory is best explained in terms of binary numerals and is set forth in several popular mathematics books and texts, such as Burton W. Jones, *Elementary Concepts of Mathematics*. As a minor project, learn the theory of the game and explain it to the class.

13.* Write a report on the electronic computers of today and on their future impact on our society.[1]

Bibliography

Boehm, George A. W., *The New World of Math*. New York: The Dial Press, 1959, pp. 76–96, 100–103.

Booth, Andrew D., *Automation and Computing*. New York: The Macmillan Company, 1959.

Eves, Howard, *An Introduction to the History of Mathematics*, rev. ed. New York: Holt, Rinehart and Winston, 1964, Chap. 1.

Hollingdale, S. H., *High Speed Computing*. New York: The Macmillan Company, 1959.

Johnson, Donovan A., and William H. Glenn, *Understanding Numeration Systems*. St. Louis: Webster Publishing Co., 1960.

Jones, Burton W., *Elementary Concepts of Mathematics*. New York: The Macmillan Company, 1964.

Kraitchik, Maurice, *Mathematical Recreations*. New York: Dover Publications, Inc., 1942, pp. 44–58.

Meyer, Jerome S., *Fun with Mathematics*. New York: Fawcett Publications, 1958, pp. 24–40.

Nichols, Eugene D., *Pre-Algebra Mathematics*. New York: Holt, Rinehart and Winston, 1965, Chaps. 1, 2.

School Mathematics Study Group, *Studies in Mathematics*, Vol. VI. New Haven: Yale University Press, 1961, Chap. 2.

Trakhtenbrot, B. A., *Algorithms and Automatic Computing Machines*, Chicago: D. C. Heath Publishing Co., 1963 (translated from the Russian).

[1] Among others, these references may prove helpful: Edmund C. Berkeley, *Giant Brains* (New York: Wiley, 1949); Norbert Wiener, *The Human Use of Human Beings* (Boston: Houghton Mifflin, 1950).

3

SETS
AND
NUMBERS

1. BASIC NUMBER NOTIONS

In Chapter 2 we referred to the ideas of a set, subset, and membership in a set. In this chapter we shall explore these in some depth. The idea of a set is basic and central to all of mathematics. The language of sets, as you will see in Chapter 12, simplifies and clarifies communication concerning geometric concepts. Sets underlie all number work in the elementary school.

Long before he enters a schoolroom, a child begins to form crude number notions. Playing with blocks, crayons, and other objects, he comes to recognize differences in sizes of groups as well as differences in sizes of individual objects. He may even learn to count a little. In these activities, he has begun to acquire *three* separate number concepts.

Size of an object is a measurement concept. Eventually the child will learn to use a ruler and will gradually become acquainted with the idea of a continuous *number line*. This is a fairly sophisticated concept. In our treatment we shall have little to do with it for some time (Chap. 9).

The other two primary number concepts are termed **cardinal** and **ordinal.** A cardinal number tells the size of a group. An ordinal number is used in counting. (In common usage, cardinal means "most basic" or "most important." Ordinal is derived from a Latin word meaning "order.")

When do two sets have the same number of members? Sometimes an equality can be recognized instantly. When a child places his *hands* on his *ears*, he discovers that he has the same number of each, though he may not yet have learned to say "two." In any group of people there are surely as many mouths as there are heads, each mouth being associated with a particular head, and vice versa. Such a comparison process may be called *matching*.

54 /

It is thus the processes of *matching* and *counting* upon which our simplest number ideas, cardinal and ordinal, are based. Distinct as they are, these processes become so interlinked in application that it is hard to put our attention to just one of them without the other slyly intruding. No peoples of the earth appear to have developed the one approach to numbers without at the same time having developed the other.

2. SETS

The English language displays a rich variety of collective words: set, collection, group, class, assembly, family, flock, herd, and many others. The mathematician prefers the simplest, the term **set,** though he may occasionally use synonyms, especially *collection* and *class*. The objects making up the set are said to be *in* it or to *belong* to it, and are called **members** or **elements** of the set.

One way to describe a set is to list its elements within braces, { }. Suppose, for example, that we wish to think about or to talk about seven things that are in a room. Three are people, named Bob, Dave, and Mary. There are also a dog, a book, a chair, and a sofa. We shall employ this set of seven things in several illustrations. We show this set of seven things as {Bob, Dave, Mary, Dog, Book, Chair, Sofa}.

In talking about the seven things, we single out certain among them. Thus, we may speak of the people. These constitute a set of three objects, each an element of the original set of seven. This new set is part of the original. It is called a **subset** of the original set and is said to be *contained* in the original set. To show that {Bob, Dave, Mary} is a subset of the original set we write

{Bob, Dave, Mary} ⊆ {Bob, Dave, Mary, Dog, Book, Chair, Sofa}.

Thus, the symbol for "is a subset of" is ⊆. Here is a list of several such subsets, to be used in further discussion:

Illustrative Sets

$$\text{set } A = \{\text{Bob, Dave, Mary}\}$$
$$\text{set } B = \{\text{Dog, Book, Chair}\}$$
$$\text{set } C = \{\text{Chair, Sofa}\}$$

The applications of the set concept now to be developed are widespread. They pervade our talk, our thought, and our action. Every noun that we use refers to some set of objects or entities. We determine subsets of these sets whenever we refer to a set consisting of some or all (but not others) of the elements found in the original set.

Since the braces indicate that we refer to a set, we do not need to state "set A"; we may simply write:

$$A = \{\text{Bob, Dave, Mary}\}.$$

If we name the original set of seven objects by the letter U, we may state, "set A is a subset of set U," as

$$A \subseteq U.$$

We shall also admit the notion of the **empty set,** a set with no elements in it and *agree that the empty set is a subset of every set*. We shall use the symbol $\emptyset$ for the empty set.

3. MATCHING SETS

Consider sets A and B of the list in Section 2:

$$A = \{\text{Bob, Dave, Mary}\}$$
$$B = \{\text{Dog, Book, Chair}\}.$$

The elements of these two sets may be paired with each other: Bob with Dog, Dave with Book, Mary with Chair. In this case sets A and B are said to *match*. We say that a **one-to-one correspondence** has been set up between the two sets.

If Bob, Dave, etc., were present in person, we could construct a physical model of the matching by running a cord from Bob to the dog, another from Dave to the book, etc.—or we could have Dave hold the book, Mary seated in the chair, etc. It is important that student practice demonstrating actual matchings of sets in such ways, trivial as the procedure may seem, in order that the basic concept will become part and parcel of his thinking (Fig. 3-1).

Properly, we should say that the two sets *match one-to-one* instead of just that they *match*. The simpler terminology will not usually be mis-

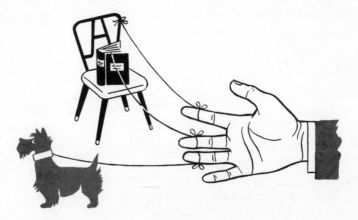

Fig. 3-1 Demonstrating a Matching

leading, however, since we shall seldom have occasion in our treatment to discuss a many-to-one or a one-to-many matching. An example of a one-to-many matching is that from a set of fathers to the set of their children, each father corresponding to his own children. We shall occasionally use the symbol "1-1" as a shorthand for one-to-one.

There are six different ways to exhibit a 1-1 matching between set A and set B. The one originally described may be shown as in Table 3-1. We may instead pair Dave with Chair and Mary with Book, obtaining another matching, Table 3-2. In both these matchings, Bob is paired with Dog. There will similarly be two matchings in which Bob is paired with Chair, and two more in which Bob is paired with Book.

Table 3-1

SET A		SET B
Bob	$\longleftrightarrow$	Dog
Dave	$\longleftrightarrow$	Book
Mary	$\longleftrightarrow$	Chair

Table 3-2

SET A		SET B
Bob	$\longleftrightarrow$	Dog
Dave	$\longleftrightarrow$	Chair
Mary	$\longleftrightarrow$	Book

Example 1 Display the six ways of matching $\{a,b,c\}$ with $\{1,2,3\}$.

The array below, looked at from left to right, shows a systematic way of deriving the matchings. The six matchings are shown in Figure 3-2.

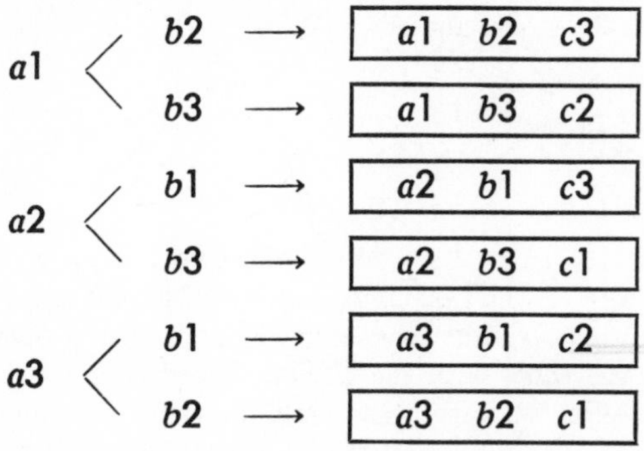

Fig. 3-2

Example 2 In how many ways can a matching be displayed between $\{a,b,c,d\}$ and $(1,2,3,4)$?

In the various matchings, the letter a can be paired with any of the *four* numbers. For each such pairing, the letter b can be paired with any one of the *three* remaining numbers. For each such pairing of a and b, the letter c can be paired with either of the *two* remaining numbers. With a, b, and c paired, d must be paired with the *one* remaining number. The total number of ways of matching is

$$4 \times 3 \times 2 \times 1 \qquad \text{or} \qquad 24.$$

Using the list of illustrative sets in Section 2, can we match sets A and C?

$$A = \{\text{Bob, Dave, Mary}\}.$$
$$C = \{\text{Chair, Sofa}\}.$$

If we try pairing Bob with Chair, we must pair Dave with Sofa, and Mary is left dangling. In this futile attempt at matching the sets, what we have done is to match set C with a part of set A. Thus, sets A and C are not matching sets. Note that we are, at present, considering only **finite** sets (having finite number of elements), as distinguished from **infinite** sets.

Our aim is to base the idea of number upon the idea of set. Two finite sets that *match* will have the *same* number associated with them. A counting number may be defined as a set of all sets that match a given set. For example, the counting number 2 is a set of all sets that match the set $\{*, \circ\}$.

Problem Set 1

1. How can you demonstrate to a friend, without speaking or counting, that you have the same number of fingers on each hand?

2. Do you need to count the cars in a parking lot to tell whether there is a 1-1 correspondence between the set of cars and the set of parking places?

3. When the dinner table has been arranged, need you count to tell if there are as many cups as saucers?

4. Given $U = \{1,2,3,4,5,6\}$ and $A = \{2,4,6\}$,

   (a) describe U in words.
   (b) describe A in words.
   (c) is $A \subseteq U$?
   (d) is $U \subseteq A$?

5. Draw four circles (each about 2 in. in diameter) in a row on a sheet of paper. Label them a, b, c, d. Take four coins of different denominations: penny, nickel, dime, quarter. Put a coin inside each circle, thus demonstrating a matching of the coins with the circles. If the penny is inside circle a, the nickel inside circle b, etc., you could describe this matching in "code": $(a1, b2, c3, d4)$. Now make all the 24 possible matchings, jotting down the

code of each. Do the work systematically, on the pattern of Examples 1 and 2 of Section 3.

6. Verify (by reasoning, as in Example 2, Section 3) that there are 120 ways of matching a set of five elements with a set of five elements.

7. There are 3,628,800 ways to match a set of ten people and the set of their noses. Can you verify this assertion? $1 \times 2 \times 3 \times 4 \times 5 \times 6 \times 7 \times 8 \times 9 \times 10 = 3,628,800$ ways

8. Give all subsets of set A of Section 2 (do not forget the empty set). Does their number agree with the formula 2^x, where x is the number of elements of the given set?

9. Proceed as in Problem 8, using set C.

4. NUMBER OF A SET

The notions of set and matching of sets are basic or *primitive* concepts that are part of everyone's experience, from babyhood on. Out of these have grown our ideas about numbers.

Take some particular set, such as set A of the list in Section 2: {Bob, Dave, Mary}. We may compare any other set with set A, then say of the new set either that it matches set A or that it does not, as the case may be.

Let us imagine that a tag or label is associated with set A. We shall call this label a *number*. We mentally attach this same label, or number, to *any* set that matches set A, but to no other set. [As children, of course, we "agreed" (upon persuasion from parents, teachers, books, etc.) to use the symbol "3" to name this particular number.]

To any given finite set is attached a label, called a number. The same label is attached to all those sets (and only those) which are in 1-1 correspondence with the given set.

Our fingers make handy basic sets with which to compare others. Extend your right forefinger and tell yourself that the number 1 is associated not only with the set consisting of that finger but also with every set whatsoever that matches it. Should you point the finger at this book, then this matching will show that 1 is also the number of the set consisting of this book.

Example Myrtle Smudge used the fingers of her right hand as a basic set to which to attach the label 5. Ho San, in Shanghai, used the toes of his left foot. Show that Myrtle's concept of the number 5 is the same as Ho San's.

Let F denote the set of the fingers of Myrtle's right hand, and T the set of toes of Ho San's left foot. We are told that F and T match, and we may picture in our minds a set of imaginary cords linking Myrtle's fingers

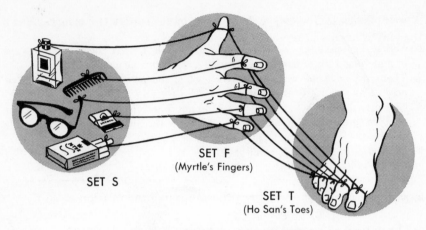

Fig. 3-3   Set S Matches Set T via Set F

to Ho San's toes, thumb to big toe, and so on (Fig. 3-3). Now suppose that S is any set that Myrtle would label 5. Then S matches F, and we may imagine a second set of cords linking the individual elements of S to Myrtle's fingers. Now think of the two sets of cords as one. The new set of cords joins the elements of S with Ho San's toes (via Myrtle's fingers). Hence S matches T, and Ho San would likewise apply the label 5 (in his own language terms) to the set S.

What we have shown so far is that every set labeled 5 by Myrtle is also labeled 5 by Ho San. By interchanging the roles of Myrtle and Ho San and repeating the argument, we can show that every set labeled 5 by Ho San will also be labeled 5 by Myrtle. The concepts of the number 5 held by Myrtle and by Ho San are thus identical.

5. NOTATION

We have begun using capital letters to designate sets, and shall continue this practice. For the time being, we shall use small letters to denote numbers. Thus the number of a set X may be denoted by x. We also use the abbreviation:

$$\text{n}(X) \qquad \text{for} \qquad \textbf{The number of the set X.}$$

For short, we may read "$n(X)$" as "the number of X" or even just "n of X."

If X and Y both denote the *same set*, then we write the equation:

$$X = Y.$$

X and Y are the same set if and only if they have exactly the same elements. For example, if $X = \{2,5,9\}$ and $Y = \{8 + 1, 1 + 1, 7 - 2\}$, then

$X = Y$, because $2 = 1 + 1$, $5 = 7 - 2$, and $9 = 8 + 1$, and these are the only elements present in each set.

You should observe that it may be true that $X \neq Y$ (X is not equal to Y), while $n(X) = n(Y)$. This is the case, for example, if $X = \{1,2,3\}$ and $Y = \{5,10,15\}$. Explain. Is it true for all sets X and Y that, if $X = Y$, then $n(X) = n(Y)$?

It is often a matter of great practical importance to demonstrate that two sets, described in different ways, and therefore symbolized differently, are actually one and the same set. Set X, for example, may be {the gang who held up the Orangeville bank}. Set Y may be {Toughy Johnson, Dick (the Drip) Murphy, and Bughead Jones}. The district attorney may devote weeks of effort toward establishing the relation $X = Y$.

We stated previously that, if every element of set X is also an element of set Y, then set X is a **subset** of set Y. This relation is expressed by writing

$$X \subseteq Y,$$

which is read, "X is a subset of Y."

According to the definition just given, a set is a subset of itself: for any set X, we have $X \subseteq X$. A subset that is not the whole set is called a **proper subset** of the set. For example, if $Y = \{1,3,5,7\}$ and $X = \{1,3\}$, then X is a proper subset of Y, since $X \subseteq Y$ and $X \neq Y$. To say that X is a *proper* subset of Y, we write

$$X \subset Y.$$

If a finite set X matches a proper subset of another finite set Y, then $n(X)$ is said to be less than $n(Y)$. If $n(X) = x$ and $n(Y) = y$, then we write the inequality

$$x < y,$$

which is read, "x is less than y." For any two numbers x and y, if $x < y$ is true, then $y > x$ (read: y is greater than x) is also true. For example, if $1 < 3$ is true, then $3 > 1$ is also true.

Example If $X = \{$Bob, Dave, Mary, John, Susan$\}$ and $Y = \{$Chair, Sofa, Book$\}$, show that $n(X) < n(Y)$.

Table 3-3 shows a matching between set X and a proper subset of set Y:

Table 3-3

SET X		SET Y	
Chair	$\longleftrightarrow$	Bob	
Sofa	$\longleftrightarrow$	Dave	*proper subset*
Book	$\longleftrightarrow$	Mary	
		John	
		Susan	

Problem Set 2

1. Take the set of fingers of your right hand for a given or comparison set. Describe three sets each having the same number associated with it.
2. Proceed as in Problem 1, except that the described sets are to have smaller numbers.
3. Same as Problem 1, except that the described sets are to have larger numbers.
4. How does the number of the set of all automobiles in the United States compare with the number of the set of their steering wheels?
5. How does the number of the set of all automobiles in the United States compare with the number of the set of those automobiles that have automatic transmissions?
6. Describe a relation between the set of all the automobiles in the United States and the set of all people who are at this instant driving one of these automobiles.
7. Describe a relation between the set of all the automobiles in the United States and the set of all their windows (windshields included).
8. Describe a relation between a set of books and the set of pages of the books; between a set of books and the set of their front covers.
9. Describe a relation between a set of children and a set of their mothers (living or dead).
10. In general, if set A matches set B, and set B matches set C, then set A matches set C. Show why this is so in the special case in which set B is a set of the fingers of a hand.
11. Show how the statement in Problem 10 can be used to establish the following: Given the numbers x, y, z, if $x = y$ and $y = z$, then $x = z$.
12. Devise an argument along the same lines as those you used in Problems 10 and 11 to establish the following: Given the numbers x, y, z, if $x < y$ and $y < z$, then $x < z$.
13. Given the sets:

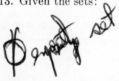

$$A = \{1,3,5,7\}$$
$$B = \{2,4,6,8\}$$
$$C = \{7,9,11\}$$
$$D = \{8,9,10\}$$
$$E = \{10\},$$

$\neq$ not equal

tell whether each statement is true or false.

(a) $E \subseteq D$ — *C is a subset of D*
(b) $E \subset D$ — *C is a proper set of D*
(c) $n(A) \neq n(B)$ — *the number of the set A is not equal to the number of the set B*
(d) $n(C) > n(B)$ — *the number of the set C is greater than the number of*
(e) $n(C) = n(D)$
(f) $D \subseteq A$ — *is less than*
(g) $n(E) < n(C) < n(A)$
(h) $n(E) > n(A)$ — *is greater*
(i) $n(B) = 8$
(j) $n(10) = 1$

$\geq$ *is greater than or equal to*

6. COUNTING

We use the relation *is less than* in *ordering* the numbers associated with sets.

The number 1 is the smallest. This is the number that labels the set S consisting of your right forefinger. Given any other set X, you may point to some element of it with your forefinger, and by this pairing demonstrate a matching between S and a subset of X. For every set X, therefore, $n(X) \geq 1$ (i.e., $n(X) > 1$ or $n(X) = 1$; read, "n of X is greater than or equal to 1").

Extend the next finger to join the forefinger. We agree to use the symbol 2 for the number of the set composed of both fingers (as well as for the number of any matching set).

Extend the next finger with the others, and you have a set whose number we call 3. This process can be continued *without end*. You will run out of fingers, to be sure, but may substitute tally marks on a sheet of paper or just conceive mentally of this "and one more" succession as going on and on.

In this way we obtain an unending *sequence* of numbers:

$$1, 2, 3, 4, 5, 6, 7, 8, 9, 10, 11, \ldots .$$

The three dots on the right indicate that the sequence continues without end. The numbers of the sequence are called **natural numbers**. We use natural numbers for counting the elements of any finite set.

The set of all natural numbers is an **infinite set**. That is, there is no greatest natural number. And each natural number has a **successor**. For any natural number k, $k + 1$ is its successor.

Once the set of natural numbers is ordered as shown above, we may consider each natural number in this sequence to be the number of the set whose members are all the natural numbers up to and including it.

For example, 3 is the number of the set consisting of the numbers 1, 2, 3. Suppose we denote this set by S_3. That is, $S_3 = \{1,2,3\}$. Then $n(S_3) = 3$. Similarly, $S_1 = \{1\}$ and $n(S_1) = 1$; $S_2 = \{1,2\}$ and $n(S_2) = 2$. And, generally, $S_k = \{1, 2, 3, \ldots, k - 1, k\}$ and $n(S_k) = k$.

Example Show that $5 < 8$.
Consider the sets

$$S_5 = \{1,2,3,4,5\}.$$
$$S_8 = \{1,2,3,4,5,6,7,8\}.$$

Since $S_5 \subset S_8$, $n(S_5) < n(S_8)$, and also $n(S_5) = 5$ and $n(S_8) = 8$, we have $5 < 8$.

Counting is a matching between a given finite set and one of the natural number sets S_1 or S_2 or S_3, etc., whichever one turns out to match the given set.

Let us count $C = \{$Bob, Dave, Mary, Dog$\}$. We show the counting by numbered tags affixed to the elements of C:

$$\text{Set } C = \{\text{Bob, Dave, Mary, Dog}\}$$
$$\uparrow \qquad \uparrow \qquad \uparrow \qquad \uparrow$$
$$\text{Set } S_4 = \{\ ①\ ,\quad ②\ ,\quad ③\ ,\quad ④\ \}.$$

The counting has matched set C with the set S_4, which consists of the natural numbers 1, 2, 3, 4. Since $n(S_4) = 4$, this is the number of the set C. It is also the last number named in the counting procedure; $n(C) = 4$.

In general, as we count the elements of a set, at any stage of the counting we have matched the subset so far counted with the set of natural numbers up to and including the last one named. The final number named at the end of the count must therefore be the number of the whole set.

Problem Set 3

1. By comparing the numbers of sets S_3 and S_5, show that $3 < 5$.
2. Compare the numbers of S_6 and S_7, showing that $6 < 7$.
3. Compare the numbers of S_{562} and S_{564}, showing that $562 < 564$.
4. Assuming that $n(S_5) = 5$ and using the definition $6 = 5 + 1$, prove that $n(S_6) = 6$.
5. Assuming that $n(S_m) = m$, where m is some natural number, prove that $n(S_{m+1}) = m + 1$.
6. The process of counting the elements of any set will result in the same number (fortunately!), no matter how we order the elements. For example,

$$A = \{\text{Bob, Dave}\}$$
$$\uparrow \qquad \uparrow$$
$$B = \{\ ①\ ,\quad ②\ \}.$$

Thus, $n(A) = 2$. A different ordering

$$A = \{\text{Dave, Bob}\}$$
$$\uparrow \qquad \uparrow$$
$$B = \{\ ①\ ,\quad ②\ \}.$$

also leads to $n(A) = 2$.

We see that a set having two elements can be counted in two different ways. In how many ways can a set of three objects be counted?
7. In how many ways can a set of four objects be counted?
8. In how many ways can a set of five objects be counted?
9. Why is it that two different ways of counting a given set must give the same result?
10. In place of $4 \leq 4$, write a statement that means the same and that contains the word "or."
11. List the elements of S_{k-2} by listing the first three elements, then three dots, followed by the last three elements.

7. MORE ABOUT SETS

In developing basic number ideas, we referred in illustration and discussion to sets of physical objects of various kinds. The student has been urged to practice with such sets, so as to learn what the number of a set, matching, etc., mean on the level of his physical sense experience.

In developing number ideas with children, it is surely even more important to make extensive use of sets of actual objects, objects that can be seen and handled—blocks, crayons, chairs, fingers. Furthermore, the objects in a given set should at first be physically grouped, that is, placed close together in a heap or stack, for example.

Yet where important ideas are concerned, the concrete level of discussion is always only a beginning. Without generalization and abstraction, deep understandings cannot be attained.

An element of a set need not be a material object. It may be a thought, a fictional character, a perception. Elements of sets may be placed far apart or they may be dissimilar; they need not be grouped in space. There may be several heaps of blocks in parts of the room. The teacher may ask the children to collect all the *red* blocks. This new set may be composed of blocks scattered among many heaps, and the child may conceive of it as being a set before the gathering is done.

Anything that can be talked about is potentially an element of a set. Consider the items:

> a girl
> her last night's dream
> a unicorn
> the Taj Mahal

Can they *naturally* be grouped together in some context? We need but imagine the girl saying, "Last night I dreamed I rode on a unicorn before the Taj Mahal." It is usually easy to make up an imaginary conversation in which any given group of items are the ones talked about.

The formation of a set is thus a purely mental process, an arbitrary association of things of any sort—objects, activities, fancies, and concepts. As we talk, we continually form and dissolve sets. In one sentence, a certain object may occur as an element of a set. In the next sentence the same object may be referred to as an element of a different set. Being an element of a set is not an inherent property of an entity: it becomes an element of a set solely by virtue of the point of view from which we discuss it.

The recognition that a set is a mental concept will aid the student in answering various puzzling questions that may arise in his own mind or be put to him by others. Since the kind of existence or reality of a set may be different from that of its elements, a set may have properties that its elements do not, or cannot, have. A set of small towns may be large, although its elements are small. A set consisting of one red apple is not red (color is not the sort of property we assign to sets), although its element is red.

In ordinary usage, sets are more often specified by *descriptions* rather than by direct listings of their elements. There is probably nowhere a list of all the *red-haired men* in the United States, nor do we need the list to discuss the set. *Mammals* form a certain subset of the set of animals; this subset is quite satisfactorily defined by requiring its elements to be "animals whose females possess milk-secreting organs for suckling their young."

It frequently happens that a described set has no elements, by accident or by necessity. Up to the moment that a man reaches into his pocket for a pack of cigarettes, he may be unaware that the set of cigarettes in his pocket is a vacuous entity (because he left them at home). A girl's specifications for her husband-to-be may have narrowed her set of suitable men to a blank without her realizing it. What of the set of green-haired men? The set of inhabitants of Mars?

The notion of a set without any elements is thus a perfectly ordinary notion, familiar to us all. In Section 2, we called this set the **empty set** and agreed to regard the empty set (∅) to be a subset of every set. Thus, for every set X,

$$\emptyset \subseteq X.$$

So long as there are any men over x years old, the set of all men over x years old is easily conceived to be a subset of the set of all men. It is reasonable to regard the subset relation as still holding even when x becomes so large, as $x = 200$, that "the set of all men over x years old" describes the empty set.

The *number* of the empty set is called **zero**: 0. Since the empty set is a proper subset of every nonempty set, zero is less than any natural number k, that is, $0 < k$.

Problem Set 4

1. Make up a plausible sentence containing these terms:

    oak tree   love
    Boy Scout knife   rain

2. Make up a plausible sentence containing these terms:

    egg beater   Times Square
    Wizard of Oz   Cadillac

3. Team up with three other students. Write a term (word or phrase, as in Problems 1, 2) at the top of a slip of paper. Fold your writing under and pass the paper to the next student, who is to do the same. When each of the

four has written a term, unfold and inspect. Each of you is now to compose a plausible sentence using the four terms.

4. The following groups define sets of playing cards (s = spades, h = hearts, d = diamonds, c = clubs). Which sets could also conveniently be defined by word descriptions, like "all red cards"?

(a) $2h$, $3s$, Kd, Jc, $8s$

(b) Qs, Qh, Qd, Qc

(c) $2d$, $3d$, $4d$, $5d$, $6d$, $7d$, $8d$, $9d$, $10d$, Jd, Qd, Kd, Ad

(d) Js, Qs, Ks, Jc, Qc, Kc

5. What are some advantages in defining sets by listing the elements instead of by word descriptions? By descriptions instead of lists?

6. Take a deck of cards, and separate the red cards from the black cards. You now have two packets: (1) the set of red cards and (2) the set of black cards. The number of the set of these two sets is 2. Now separate each packet according to suit (spades, clubs, . . .). What is the number of the new set of packets? Make up other ways of using the deck to form sets of sets.

7. If X denotes the set of all men over 100 feet tall and Y denotes the set of all winged dogs, is $X = Y$? Describe the empty set in some other ways.

8. How many elements does $\{0\}$ have?

9. Are X and Y matching sets, if $X = \{0\}$ and $Y = \{1\}$?

10. Obtain a new set B by adding 2 to each element of $A = \{2,4,6\}$. Are A and B matching sets?

11. How many elements are common to both sets A and B in Problem 10?

12. How many common elements do sets $X = \{0,2\}$ and $Y = \{0,5\}$ have?

BIBLIOGRAPHY

Breuer, Joseph, *Introduction to the Theory of Sets*, trans. by H. F. Fehr. Englewood Cliffs, N.J.: Prentice-Hall, Inc., 1958.

Dantzig, Tobias, *Number, The Language of Science*. New York: The Macmillan Company, 1954.

Fehr, Howard F., *Modern Mathematics and the High School Mathematics Curriculum*. Stillwater: Oklahoma State University, 1955.

Fraenkel, A. A., *Abstract Set Theory*. Amsterdam: North-Holland, 1953, Chaps. 1, 2.

Gray, James F., *Sets, Relations and Functions*, lessons 1–3. New York: Holt, Rinehart and Winston, 1962.

Kamke, E., *Theory of Sets*, trans. by F. Bagemihl. New York: Dover Publications, Inc., 1950.

Kemeny, J. G., J. L. Snell, and G. L. Thompson, *Introduction to Finite Mathematics*. Englewood Cliffs, N.J.: Prentice-Hall, 1957, Chap. 2.

National Council of Teachers of Mathematics, *23rd Yearbook: Insights into Modern Mathematics*. Washington, D.C., 1957, Chap. 3.

Nichols, Eugene D., *Modern Elementary Algebra*, New York: Holt, Rinehart and Winston, 1965, Chap. 1.

Nichols, E. D., R. Kaline, and H. Garland, *Introduction to Sets, A Programed Unit*. New York: Holt, Rinehart and Winston, 1962.

Northrop, E. P., and the College Mathematics Staff, *Fundamental Mathematics*, Vol. I, 3d ed. Chicago: University of Chicago Press, 1948, Chaps. 1, 2.

Suppes, Patrick, *Introduction to Logic*. Princeton, N.J.: D. Van Nostrand, 1957, Chap. 9.

Swain, Robert L., *Modern Mathematics for Secondary School Teachers of Mathematics and Science*. Stillwater: Oklahoma State University, 1958, Chap. 1.

4

NUMBER
OPERATIONS

1. ADDITION

If X and Y are any two sets, we shall denote their union by the expression $X \cup Y$. We define this to be a set consisting of all those elements that belong either just to the one or just to the other or to both of the sets X, Y. (Briefly, an element belonging to either set also belongs to their union.)

Example If $X = \{1,2,3,4\}$ and $Y = \{4,6\}$, then $X \cup Y = \{1,2,3,4,6\}$. Note that the number 4 is an element of both sets X and Y. Observe also that $n(X) = 4$, $n(Y) = 2$, and $n(X \cup Y) = 5$. Thus, $n(X \cup Y) \neq n(X) + n(Y)$. More precisely, $n(X \cup Y) < n(X) + n(Y)$.

We wish to base our definition of a *sum* of whole numbers upon this notion of **union** of sets, which represent the numbers—even as a teacher shows a child how to add 2 and 3 by combining 2 blocks and 3 blocks into a single pile (union) of 5 blocks (Fig. 4-1).

In the example we observed that, when two sets share an element, this element gets counted twice when the sets are separately enumerated, yet only once in their union. In defining number addition in terms of union of sets, therefore, we shall wish to deal only with sets that are "mutually

Fig. 4-1   Set Union

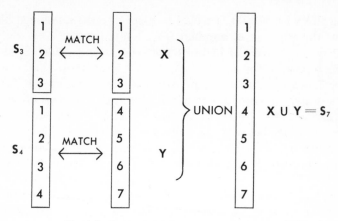

Fig. 4-2   The Sum of Two Numbers: 3 + 4 = 7

exclusive" or "nonoverlapping." We call a pair of sets **disjoint** if there is no element which belongs to both. For example, if $X = \{1,2,3\}$ and $Y = \{5,10,15,20\}$, then X and Y are disjoint sets. Explain why.

Given any two natural numbers, consider a pair of *disjoint* sets that represent them.

Definition of the Sum of Two Numbers.   The sum of the two numbers is the number of the union of the two disjoint sets.

In symbols, the definition reads: given two natural numbers x, y, let X, Y be a pair of disjoint sets such that $n(X) = x$, $n(Y) = y$. Then $x + y = n(X \cup Y)$.

To illustrate the definition and to help us see that we can always find the required pair of disjoint sets, let us take the particular case $3 + 4$. For the set X, which is to represent $x = 3$, we take S_3, which in the notation of Chapter 3 denotes the set of the numbers 1, 2, 3 of the ordered sequence of natural numbers. Then $n(X) = 3$. For the set Y, which is to represent $y = 4$, we take the set of the numbers 4, 5, 6, 7 of the ordered sequence, a set that matches S_4 but is *disjoint* from $X = S_3$. Then $n(Y) = 4$. Now the set $X \cup Y$ is S_7, the set of the numbers 1, 2, 3, 4, 5, 6, 7. Hence

$$3 + 4 = x + y = n(X \cup Y) = 7.$$

The process is pictured in Figure 4-2. It is essentially the same process a child uses to establish or to justify a basic "addition fact." It is a procedure of counting along the sequence:

$$
\begin{array}{cccccccc}
\textit{Count:} & 1 & - & 2 & - & 3 & - & 1 & - & 2 & - & 3 & - & 4. \\
& & 1 & & 2 & & 3 & & 4 & & 5 & & 6 & & 7.
\end{array}
$$

In doing this with a child, it would be helpful to use numbered blocks to represent the sequence of numbers from 1 through 7.

In the demonstration of Figure 4-2, we selected a particular pair of sets X, Y to represent the numbers 3, 4. We must show that the result, $3 + 4 = 7$, is always obtained no matter what sets are chosen. Let X', Y' denote any pair of disjoint sets which represent 3, 4, respectively. Then since $n(X') = n(X) = 3$, we know that X and X' match. So do Y and Y'. The three pairings between the individual elements of X and X' and the four pairings between the elements of Y and Y' all together provide a matching between the sets $X \cup Y$ and $X' \cup Y'$. Hence $n(X' \cup Y') = n(X \cup Y) = 7$.

The various ways in which 7 is obtained as the sum of two natural numbers can be seen by partitioning the sequence of numbers from 1 through 7 in all six possible ways. This is shown in Figure 4-3.

$$
\begin{array}{ccccccc l}
\mathbf{1} & 2 & 3 & 4 & 5 & 6 & 7 & (\mathbf{1} + 6 = 7) \\
\mathbf{1} & \mathbf{2} & 3 & 4 & 5 & 6 & 7 & (\mathbf{2} + 5 = 7) \\
\mathbf{1} & \mathbf{2} & \mathbf{3} & 4 & 5 & 6 & 7 & (\mathbf{3} + 4 = 7) \\
\mathbf{1} & \mathbf{2} & \mathbf{3} & \mathbf{4} & 5 & 6 & 7 & (\mathbf{4} + 3 = 7) \\
\mathbf{1} & \mathbf{2} & \mathbf{3} & \mathbf{4} & \mathbf{5} & 6 & 7 & (\mathbf{5} + 2 = 7) \\
\mathbf{1} & \mathbf{2} & \mathbf{3} & \mathbf{4} & \mathbf{5} & \mathbf{6} & 7 & (\mathbf{6} + 1 = 7)
\end{array}
$$

Fig. 4-3

Problem Set 1

1. Let U denote the set of fingers of your right hand, V the set of all your toes. What is the number of the set $U \cup V$?

2. Let U denote the set of fingers of your right hand, V the set of your forefingers. What is the number of the set $U \cup V$?

3. Find $n(U + V + W + Z)$, where U is the set of fingers on your right hand, V is the set of your thumbs on both hands, W is the set whose elements are all fingers of your two hands, and Z is the set consisting of your right thumb, right little finger, and right forefinger.

4. A man, his wife, his sister, his mother-in-law, his mother-in-law's only daughter, his father, and his father's only two children climbed into the family car to take a trip. Was the car overloaded? How many persons were there in the car?

5. A group composed of men, women, and children contains an equal number of each. Everyone in it is either a Republican, a Democrat, or an Independent, and there are the same number of each. Everyone is to vote for a chairman. One candidate will receive the votes of all the men, also the votes of all the Republicans. Is he sure to be elected?

6. Let U denote the set of all girls in a class, V the set of all seniors in the class. Suppose that $n(U) = 15$ and $n(V) = 10$. What is the minimum and maximum of $n(U \cup V)$?

7. A person is eligible to vote in a school election if either (a) he owns property in the district or (b) he is the parent of a child attending school in the district. Let U be the set of people fulfilling condition (a), V the set fulfilling condition (b). Would you expect U and V to be disjoint? Describe $U \cup V$.

8. Given the following sets:

$$U = \{1,2,3,4,5,6,7,8,9,10\}$$
$$A = \{1,3,5,7,9\}$$
$$B = \{2,4,6,8,10\}$$
$$C = \{2,3,5,7\}$$
$$D = \{5,10\}$$
$$E = \{3,6,9\}$$
$$F = \{4,8\}.$$

Tell whether each statement is true or false.

(a) A and B are disjoint sets.
(b) B and C are disjoint sets.
(c) $n(A \cup B) = n(A) + n(B)$
(d) $n(B \cup C) = n(B) + n(C)$
(e) $A \cup B = U$
(f) $A \cup U = U$
(g) $D \cup E =$ the set of all natural numbers less than 10, which are divisible by 3 or 5.
(h) $C \cup D \cup E \cup F = U$
(i) $n(C \cup D \cup E \cup F) = n(C) + n(D) + n(E) + n(F)$

9. Describe in words each set in Problem 8. The problem is done for set C.

$$C = \text{the set of all prime numbers less than 10.}$$

(A prime number is a natural number that has exactly two natural numbers as divisors—1 and itself.)

10. In Section 1, the addition of 3 and 4 was related to the union of the set S_3 and a set that matched set S_4. Repeat the demonstration for the addition of 5 and 2.

11. In how many ways can 300 be obtained as the sum of two natural numbers? (See Fig. 4-3.)

2. PROPERTIES OF ADDITION

From the symmetric way in which the union of two sets is defined, it is evident that the *order* of adding two numbers is inconsequential. Thus the expressions $2 + 1$ and $1 + 2$ must designate the same number, namely 3. This important property has a technical name: It is called the **Commutative Property of Addition.** In referring to this property, we shall use the abbreviation CPA.

For a collection of sets in general, the union of all the sets of the collection is defined as that set consisting of all the elements found in any set or sets of the collection. Consider, for example, three sets, so that each pair is a pair of disjoint sets:

$$X = \{a,b\}; \qquad Y = \{c,d,e\}; \qquad Z = \{f,g,h,i,j,k\}.$$

We find the union of the three sets in two different ways:

$$\begin{aligned}
(X \cup Y) \cup Z &= \{a\,b,c,d,e\} \cup \{f,g,h,i,j,k\} \\
&= \{a,b,c,d,e,f,g,h,i,j,k\}. \\
X \cup (Y \cup Z) &= \{a,b\} \cup \{c,d,e,f,g,h,i,j,k\} \\
&= \{a,b,c,d,e,f,g,h,i,j,k\}.
\end{aligned}$$

The resulting set in each case is the same.

Since $n(X) = 2$, $n(Y) = 3$, and $n(Z) = 6$, we have

$$(2 + 3) + 6 = 2 + (3 + 6).$$

This is an example of the **Associative Property of Addition,** abbreviated APA.

Our experience with natural numbers and with addition indicates that CPA and APA hold for all natural numbers. To be able to state this briefly, we introduce the symbol $\forall_{x \in N}$, which is read, "for every number x, a member of the set of natural numbers." The symbol $\in$ means "is a member of" or "belongs to." And, of course, we are using N here to denote the set of natural numbers.

Using these abbreviations, we state the two properties.

The Commutative Property of Addition (CPA):

$$\forall_{x \in N} \forall_{y \in N} \; x + y = y + x.$$

The Associative Property of Addition (APA):

$$\forall_{x \in N} \forall_{y \in N} \forall_{z \in N} (x + y) + z = x + (y + z).$$

Quite frequently we may state at the outset that we are concerned with natural numbers and state simply

$$\forall_x \forall_y \forall_z (x + y) + z = x + (y + z).$$

APA is used constantly in computation. To add 3, 2, and 4, for example, we may proceed from left to right, saying "3 + 2 gives 5; and 5 + 4 gives 9." In so doing we made use of the equality

$$3 + 2 + 4 = (3 + 2) + 4,$$

for we "associated" the 3 with the 2, added these, then added 4 to the result. We could just as well have associated the 2 with the 4, added, and then have added the result to 3, according to the alternative form: $3 + (2 + 4)$. (Fig. 4-4.)

Taken together, the commutative and associative properties of addition tell us that in adding numbers "most anything goes." No matter how we

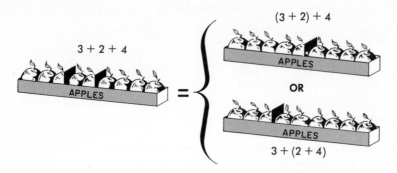

Fig. 4-4 The Associative Property of Addition—An Illustration

mix up the numbers, we get the right answer. Thus the following 18 expressions all denote the same number, 9:

$$2 + 3 + 4 \qquad (2 + 3) + 4 \qquad 2 + (3 + 4)$$
$$2 + 4 + 3 \qquad (2 + 4) + 3 \qquad 2 + (4 + 3)$$
$$3 + 2 + 4 \qquad (3 + 2) + 4 \qquad 3 + (2 + 4)$$
$$3 + 4 + 2 \qquad (3 + 4) + 2 \qquad 3 + (4 + 2)$$
$$4 + 2 + 3 \qquad (4 + 2) + 3 \qquad 4 + (2 + 3)$$
$$4 + 3 + 2 \qquad (4 + 3) + 2 \qquad 4 + (3 + 2)$$

Example Using CPA and APA, show that $(2 + 3) + 4 = 3 + (4 + 2)$.

$$(2 + 3) + 4 = (3 + 2) + 4 \qquad \text{(CPA)}$$
$$= 3 + (2 + 4) \qquad \text{(APA)}$$
$$= 3 + (4 + 2) \qquad \text{(CPA)}$$

With four numbers, the sum may be expressed in 264 different ways! One is

$$1 + [(2 + 3) + 4].$$

This directs us to add 2 and 3, getting 5, to add 4 to this, getting 9, then to add 9 to 1, obtaining 10 as the final result. Note that this is exactly the procedure in the *column addition* of 2, 3, 4, 1, as indicated at the right. Another form is $(2 + 3) + (4 + 1)$, which gives $5 + 5 = 10$, as before. (In adding many numbers, we often make such pairings to save time or to relieve monotony.)

$$\begin{matrix} 1 \\ 4 \\ 3 \\ 2 \\ \hline 10 \end{matrix} \quad \begin{matrix} \text{Add} \\ \text{upwards} \end{matrix}$$

In adding natural numbers, you have observed that the sum of any pair of natural numbers is a natural number. We call this the **Closure Property of Natural Numbers under Addition**, abbreviated ClPA:

$$\forall_{x \in N} \forall_{y \in N} (x + y) \in N.$$

We say that *the set of natural numbers is closed under addition.*

Problem Set 2

1. Let X, Y, Z and X', Y', Z' denote the following sets:

$$X = \{\text{Abe, Bess, Carol}\} \qquad X' = \{\text{Joan, Kitty, Lem}\}$$
$$Y = \{\text{Dot, Eric, Fay}\} \qquad Y' = \{\text{Joan, Mae, Ned}\}$$
$$Z = \{\text{Gene, Harry}\} \qquad Z' = \{\text{Kitty, Oscar}\}$$

   Show the construction of $X \cup (Y \cup Z)$ and $(X \cup Y) \cup Z$ in detail, verifying that $X \cup (Y \cup Z) = (X \cup Y) \cup Z$. Do the same with respect to the nondisjoint sets X', Y', Z'.

2. Put two pennies in your left hand and three in your right. Can you now think of a simple and dramatic way to put the $3 + 2 = 2 + 3$ idea across to a young pupil?

3. Put three piles of objects (pennies, blocks, etc.) on a table. In what simple way can you now demonstrate the associative property of addition?

4. Use the following star (∗) diagram to help explain $3 + 4 = 4 + 3$. (*Hint:* Consider two different ways of separating the group of stars into two groups.)

$$* \quad * \quad * \quad * \quad * \quad * \quad *$$

5. Use the following star diagram to help explain $(2 + 3) + 4 = 2 + (3 + 4)$.

$$* \quad * \quad * \quad * \quad * \quad * \quad * \quad * \quad *$$

6. As in the Example of Section 2, use the commutative and associative properties of addition to show that $2 + (4 + 3) = 4 + (3 + 2)$.

7. Use the commutative and associative properties of addition to show that $1 + [(2 + 3) + 4] = (2 + 3) + (4 + 1)$. (*Hint:* By ClPA, $(2 + 3)$ is a single natural number. Hence $(1 + 4) + (2 + 3) = 1 + [4 + (2 + 3)]$, by APA.)

8. Use the properties of addition to show that $(2 + 3 + 1) + 4 = [4 + (2 + 3)] + 1$.

9. Using a, b, c, and $\forall$, state

   (a) CPA   (b) APA   (c) ClPA

   for the set of natural numbers N.

10. For each step, identify the property that justifies it.

$$
\begin{aligned}
97 + [78 + (13 + 22)] &= 97 + [78 + (22 + 13)] \\
&= 97 + [(78 + 22) + 13] \\
&= 97 + (100 + 13) \\
&= 97 + (13 + 100) \\
&= (97 + 13) + 100 \\
&= 110 + 100 \\
&= 210.
\end{aligned}
$$

3. MULTIPLICATION

If 300 people each pay 50¢ to see a show and we wish to find the total collected from them by the use of addition, we must form the sum of three-hundred 50's: $50 + 50 + \cdots + 50$ (300 terms). It is awkward to deal with such an expression. Since situations of this kind occur frequently, it is natural to seek efficient ways of treating them.

The first step is to frame a new operation, called **multiplication.** We define 3×2 as $2 + 2 + 2$, the sum, in which 2 is used three times as an addend. Similarly, 300×50 means $50 + 50 + \cdots + 50$, the sum, in which 50 is used three-hundred times as an addend. In general, if x and y are any natural numbers, we define their *product* xy as

$$xy = \overbrace{y + y + \cdots + y}^{x \text{ times}},$$

the sum in which y is used x times as an addend.

The symbol xy may be read either as "xy" or as "x times y." The form $x \times y$ is avoided, since the symbol $\times$ may be confused with the letter x. When expressions involve two numerals, a dot is often used; $2 \cdot 3$ and 2×3 both denote the product of 2 and 3. $2a$, $2 \times a$, and $2 \cdot a$ denote the product of 2 and a.

The familiar and much used commutative and associative properties of multiplication are not obvious consequences of the definition given above. According to the definition,

$$3 \times 2 = 2 + 2 + 2, \quad \text{whereas} \quad 2 \times 3 = 3 + 3.$$

Is it obvious from an inspection of the *form alone* that $2 + 2 + 2 = 3 + 3$? (If so, then $2 \times 2 \times 2 = 3 \times 3$ should appear equally "obvious"!) It is true that, when the addition is carried out, the result 6 is obtained in both cases. Yet it is a long step from such an empirical or experimental verification in this and in other special numerical cases to a conviction that the commutative property of multiplication holds for *every* pair x, y of natural numbers: $xy = yx$.

To see the pattern on which an argument can be based, begin with the form $3 \times 2 = 2 + 2 + 2$, and represent the number $2 + 2 + 2$ by 3 groups (columns) of 2 stars each laid out as in Figure 4-5. It is plain

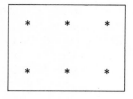

Fig. 4-5

that the set of stars in the array represents not only the number 3×2, but also the number 2×3. For the set may also be regarded as composed of 2 groups (rows) of 3 stars each $(3 + 3)$. To establish $xy = yx$, we may mentally conceive of an array with x rows and y columns of stars.

This pictorial analysis suggests the possibility of developing the idea of multiplication directly in *set* terms, instead of basing it upon addition.

Given two sets X, Y, consider the set of all pairs formed by pairing an element of X with an element of Y. Call this set of pairs the **cross-product set** $X \times Y$ (read: X cross Y) of the sets X and Y.

Example Let the elements of the set X be three boys: Bob, Dave, Ted. Let the elements of set Y be two girls: Mary, Joan. Then $X \times Y$ is the set of all six possible boy-girl pairs. {(Bob, Mary), (Bob, Joan), (Dave, Mary), (Dave, Joan), (Ted, Mary), (Ted, Joan)}. In Table 4-1, the six starred spaces correspond to these pairings. $n(X) = 3$, $n(Y) = 2$, and $n(X \times Y) = 6$. Thus, $2 \cdot 3 = 6$.

Table 4-1

Y \ X	BOB	DAVE	TED
MARY	*	*	*
JOAN	*	*	*

Now we may define the product of two numbers in terms of the cross-product set. Given any two natural numbers, consider a pair of disjoint sets that represents them. *The product of the numbers is defined as the number of the cross-product set.*

In symbols, if x and y are any two natural numbers, and X and Y a pair of disjoint sets such that $n(X) = x$ and $n(Y) = y$, then $xy = n(X \times Y)$.

Problem Set 3

1. Lay out 12 pennies in a rectangular array to show that $3 \times 4 = 4 \times 3$ (where 3×4 means $4 + 4 + 4$ and 4×3 means $3 + 3 + 3 + 3$).
2. Try to convince a friend who claims to have forgotten the multiplication tables that $37 \times 53 = 53 \times 37$ by showing him how you could lay out pennies to prove it if you had enough of them.
3. A social club has 10 members, 4 boys and 6 girls. Every night, just one of the boys dates one of the girls, while the other 8 members stay home and watch TV. It is against the club rules for a boy to date a girl twice. How long will it be before they have to change the rules?
4. If the club in Problem 3 changes its rules so as to permit a boy to date a girl only so often as he takes her to a different place of entertainment, and the town provides just 8 such places, how long can the dating go on?
5. There are three roads from Podunk Center to Mudbank, and five roads from Mudbank on to Deville. By how many routes can one drive from Podunk Center to Deville?
6. If in Problem 5 there are also two roads that lead directly from Podunk Center to Deville, by-passing Mudbank, then among how many routes can one choose?

7. If in Problem 6 one may also take a plane to Mudbank, continuing on to Deville by taxi, how many choices are there in all?

8. A combination lock has three dials, one bearing all the letters of the alphabet, the others each bearing all the digits. (*Example:* G–2–0 is one possible combination.) How many combinations are possible?

9. A signaler has five signal flags: white, black, yellow, red, green. Will he be able to arrange a code so that he can signal every number from 1 to 100 by showing three flags in succession?

10. How many 1-foot-square floor tiles are needed to cover a rectangular floor of dimensions 8 ft. by 9 ft.?

4. PROPERTIES OF MULTIPLICATION

We have seen that a product xy can be represented by a rectangular array with x rows and y columns (or x columns and y rows). *Order* is thus inconsequential in multiplying as well as in adding. We have the **Commutative Property of Multiplication,** abbreviated CPM:

$$\forall_x \forall_y \; xy = yx.$$

Likewise, there is the **Associative Property of Multiplication** (APM), which tells us that we may *group* the factors of a product in any way we wish. For any three natural numbers x, y, z:

$$xyz = (xy)z = x(yz).$$

To illustrate APM, let X, Y be the boy, girl sets of Section 3, and Z a set whose elements are Miss Prim and Miss Prude—elderly ladies who insist upon chaperoning the couples on their dates.

$$X = \{\text{Bob, Dave, Ted}\}$$
$$Y = \{\text{Mary, Joan}\}$$
$$Z = \{\text{Prim, Prude}\}.$$

Now $X \times Y \times Z$ is a set of 12 triples. A typical one of these is (Bob, Mary, Prim). Corresponding to this is an element of $(X \times Y) \times Z$ that may be shown as [(Bob, Mary), Prim], a pair. Obviously, the sets $X \times Y \times Z$ and $(X \times Y) \times Z$ match 1-1, so that $n(X \times Y \times Z) = n[(X \times Y) \times Z]$, or $xyz = (xy)z$. Similarly, an element in $X \times (Y \times Z)$, which corresponds to (Bob, Mary, Prim) in $X \times Y \times Z$, may be shown as [Bob, (Mary, Prim)]. Thus, continuing in this fashion, we arrive at $X \times Y \times Z = X \times (Y \times Z)$, resulting in $(X \times Y) \times Z = X \times (Y \times Z)$. Consequently, $n[(X \times Y) \times Z] = n[X \times (Y \times Z)]$ and, therefore, $(xy)z = x(yz)$.

APM may be illustrated in another way. Consider $2 \cdot 3 \cdot 4$ in terms of a star array as in Figure 4-6. We have $(2 \cdot 3) \cdot 4$ represented by $(2 \cdot 3)$ or

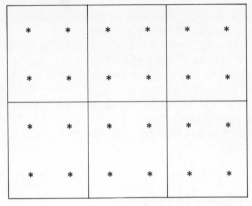

Fig. 4-6

6 rectangles of 4 stars each (see Fig. 4-6). Also, $2 \cdot (3 \cdot 4)$ is represented by 2 rectangles of $(3 \cdot 4)$ or 12 stars each (see Fig. 4-7). Since in each case the same number of stars is represented, we have

$$(2 \cdot 3) \cdot 4 = 2 \cdot (3 \cdot 4).$$

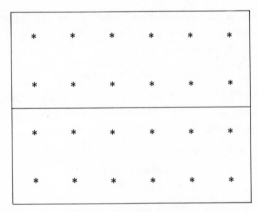

Fig. 4-7

In three dimensions, of course, a symmetrically distributed array can be formed. The elementary school teacher may use blocks in place of stars, stacking them to form a solid box whose "block dimensions" are 2 by 3 by 4, to illustrate how $2 \cdot 3 \cdot 4$ gives the number of blocks in the box (or gives its volume).

From experience we know that the product of a pair of natural numbers is a natural number; therefore, the set of natural numbers has the **Closure Property under Multiplication** (ClM):

$$\forall_{x \in N} \forall_{y \in N} (xy) \in N.$$

It is easy to demonstrate that neither subtraction nor division has the associative properties.

Example 1
$$(10 - 3) - 1 = 7 - 1 = 6$$
$$10 - (3 - 1) = 10 - 2 = 8$$

Therefore, $(10 - 3) - 1 \neq 10 - (3 - 1)$.

Example 2
$$(48 \div 4) \div 2 = 12 \div 2 = 6$$
$$48 \div (4 \div 2) = 48 \div 2 = 24$$

Therefore, $(48 \div 4) \div 2 \neq 48 \div (4 \div 2)$.

5. BASIC PROPERTIES OF NATURAL NUMBERS UNDER MULTIPLICATION AND ADDITION

The next property we shall examine links addition and multiplication. The following example illustrates this property:

$$2 \times (3 + 4) = 2 \times 7 \qquad (2 \times 3) + (2 \times 4) = 6 + 8$$
$$= 14 \qquad\qquad\qquad = 14$$

Therefore, $2 \times (3 + 4) = (2 \times 3) + (2 \times 4)$. Stated in general:

$$\forall_x \forall_y \forall_z \; x(y + z) = (xy) + (xz).$$

The name of this property is the **Left Distributive Property of Multiplication over Addition, LDPMA.**

Figure 4-8 illustrates the property for the numerical case $2 \times (3 + 4) = 2 \times 3 + 2 \times 4 = 14$.

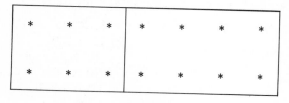

Fig. 4-8

It is left to the student to show how the set of stars in the diagram represents both $2 \times (3 + 4)$ and $(2 \times 3) + (2 \times 4)$.

Having established the *left* distributive property, we can prove the *right* distributive property, RDPMA. Supply the reason for each step in the proof:

$$(x + y)z = z(x + y) \qquad \text{Why?}$$
$$= (zx) + (zy) \qquad \text{Why?}$$
$$= (xz) + (yz) \qquad \text{Why?}$$

Thus, we have the **Right Distributive Property of Multiplication over Addition**:

$$\forall_x \forall_y \forall_z (x + y)z = (xz) + (yz) \quad \text{[RDPMA]}.$$

For future reference, we present in Table 4-2 the eight basic properties we have established for natural numbers. It will later be observed that these properties apply to all real numbers.

Table 4-2

EIGHT BASIC PROPERTIES OF NATURAL NUMBERS

	ADDITION	MULTIPLICATION
Closure	$\forall_{x \in N} \forall_{y \in N} (x + y) \in N$	$\forall_{x \in N} \forall_{y \in N} (xy) \in N$
Commutative	$\forall_x \forall_y \; x + y = y + x$	$\forall_x \forall_y \; xy = yx$
Associative	$\forall_x \forall_y \forall_z (x + y) + z = x + (y + z)$	$\forall_x \forall_y \forall_z (xy)z = x(yz)$
Distributive	$\forall_x \forall_y \forall_z \; x(y + z) = (xy) + (xz)$	
	$\forall_x \forall_y \forall_z \; (x + y)z = (xz) + (yz)$	

We can make good use of the distributive properties in simplifying computations. Study the next two examples to see how the distributive properties are helpful.

Example 1
$$\begin{aligned} 37 \times 20 &= (30 + 7) \times 20 \\ &= (30 \times 20) + (7 \times 20) \\ &= 600 + 140 \\ &= 740. \end{aligned}$$

Do you use this scheme in doing mental computations?

Example 2
$$\begin{aligned} (12 \times 185) + (12 \times 115) &= 12 \times (185 + 115) \\ &= 12 \times 300 \\ &= (10 + 2) \times 300 \\ &= (10 \times 300) + (2 \times 300) \\ &= 3{,}000 + 600 \\ &= 3{,}600. \end{aligned}$$

Problem Set 4

1. Suppose that you open a door, then cross the threshold. Can you reverse the order of these two operations? Give another example of a sequence of two operations in which reversing the order produces a different result. Also give an example in which the order is irrelevant.
2. How would you arrange 72 cubes to verify the associative property for the case $(3 \times 4) \times 6 = 3 \times (4 \times 6)$?

3. Produce a star diagram like that in Section 4 to verify the associative property for the case $(2 \times 5) \times 3 = 2 \times (5 \times 3)$.
4. Produce a star diagram like that in Section 5 to verify the distributive property for the case $3 \times (4 + 7) = (3 \times 4) + (3 \times 7)$.
5. Use the distributive properties as you would in mental computations.

   (a) 23×30 (b) 50×76
   (c) 87×40 (d) 20×99

6. Each distributive property can be extended to cover any number of addends:

$$x(y_1 + y_2 + \cdots + y_n) = (xy_1) + (xy_2) + \cdots + (xy_n)$$
$$(x_1 + x_2 + \cdots + x_2)y = (x_1y) + (x_2y) + \cdots + (x_ny).$$

Use extensions of the distributive properties as you would in mental computations.

   (a) 20×127 (b) $90 \times 2,078$
   (c) $2,365 \times 40$ (d) $5,609 \times 400$

7. Demonstrate the use of the distributive properties in the following problems:

   (a) $(17 \times 165) + (17 \times 35)$
   (b) $(317 \times 5) + (83 \times 5)$
   (c) $(995 \times 89) + (5 \times 89)$
   (d) $(1,121 \times 17) + (879 \times 17)$

8. Show the use of associative and commutative properties when multiplying mentally 300 by 400. (*Hint:* Use $300 = 3 \times 100$.)

6. SUBTRACTION AND DIVISION

Quite often, and particularly with elementary school children, we think of mathematical operations on numbers as being "activities." That is, in performing operations, some "doing" is involved. We speak of *adding* 3 to 2 to *obtain* the sum 5. Instead of just observing that the expressions $2 + 3$ and $3 + 2$ denote the same number, we are apt to say that if we *add* the numbers in the other order, we *get* the same *result*. Rather than referring to the existence of a correspondence between two sets, we have felt it to be more vivid to speak actively of *matching* the sets.

In everyday life, after we have performed an operation, we frequently do it backwards, or undo it, getting back to where we started. Having opened a door, we may shut it again. Having switched on a light, we may switch it off. The "undoing" operation is called the **inverse** of the original.

In arithmetic, we may add the number 3 to the number 2, thus performing an operation of addition to get the result 5. This implies the "existence" of an *inverse operation* (involving the same number, 3) that we are to apply to 5 in order to get back to the 2 with which we began. This we call **subtraction.** We write $5 - 3 = 2$, and may refer to the expression $5 - 3$ as the **difference,** 5 *minus* 3. Thus $5 - 3 = 2$ *because* $2 + 3 = 5$. Figure 4-9 shows the two operations.

ADD 3

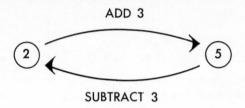

SUBTRACT 3

Fig. 4-9

To emphasize the active character of the process, we may say that we subtract 3 from 5 to get 2, or even that we *take away* 3 from 5. This last mode of description suggests many physical illustrations of the operation, such as the actual removal of 3 oranges from a group of 5 oranges, the cutting of a 3-ft. length from a 5-ft. string, etc.

In set terms, if x and y are two natural numbers and $x < y$, then if Y is some set representing y, there will be some subset X of Y such that X represents x. We may define $y - x = n(\bar{X})$, where $\bar{X}$ consists of all those elements of Y that do not belong to X. $\bar{X}$ is called the **complement** of X in Y.

The operation of multiplying 2 by 3 produces $6 : 3 \times 2 = 6$ (Fig. 4-10).

MULTIPLY BY 3

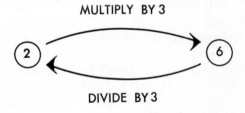

DIVIDE BY 3

Fig. 4-10

Hence we conceive of an inverse operation that, when performed on 6 with 3, gives back the 2. This we call **division** and write $6 \div 3$ (6 divided by 3) or $\frac{6}{3}$ or $6/3$ (the **quotient,** 6 "over" 3) to symbolize the operation. We have $6 \div 3 = 2$ *because* $3 \times 2 = 6$.

A set operation that corresponds to division by 3 is that of separating a set into 3 mutually matching sets. Another is that of separating a set into subsets of 3 elements each.

With respect to the system of the natural numbers, subtraction and division are limited operations. There is no natural number to which 7 can be added to give 5. Hence the operation indicated by 5 − 7 cannot be performed. We say, therefore, that the set of natural numbers is **not closed** under subtraction.

There is no natural number that, when multiplied by 3, gives 8. The indicated operation 8 ÷ 3 cannot be performed. The set of natural numbers, thus, is *not closed* under division. *With respect to the system of natural numbers*, therefore, the expressions 5 − 7 and 8 ÷ 3 are *meaningless*. In physical set terms, seven people cannot be taken away from an original group of only five, and eight people cannot split up into teams of three. As we later extend the number system, we shall increase the scope of the subtraction and division operations, until they are finally made universally possible. That is, we shall deal with a system of numbers that is *closed* under subtraction and under division.

The four operations we discussed (addition, multiplication, subtraction, division) are a very vital part of our life; we all need them to get along. It is an interesting game to invent some "compound" operations. Practice with them may aid the student to grasp the inverse operation more easily.

A compound operation is a succession of addition, multiplication, subtraction, or division operations. Let O( ), for example, signify the result of subtracting 3, then multiplying by 2, where these successive operations are to be applied to the number given in parentheses. What is O(12)? Subtract 3 from 12, getting 9, then multiply this by 2, ending with 18. So O(12) = 18. Now let O'( ) symbolize the inverse operation of O. Obviously O'(18) = 12. What is O'(8)? Proceeding backwards, we must first divide by 2, then add 3. O'(8) = 7. The operational diagram of Figure 4-11 shows the various steps.

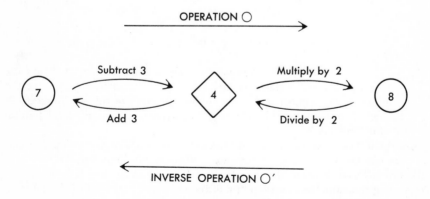

Fig. 4-11

Problem Set 5

1. Cite three everyday-life illustrations of operations and their inverses.
2. What are the inverses of the following?

   (a) Sit down   (b) Move three feet west
   (c) Get wet   (d) Stretch to double length (a spring)
   (e) Get cold   (f) 10° rise (temperature)

3. Lay two pennies on a table. Add three pennies to the two, demonstrating $2 + 3 = 5$. Now take the three pennies away again, leaving the original two, demonstrating the inverse operation $5 - 3 = 2$. Devise a similar procedure for showing how addition is inverse of subtraction.
4. Sketch an operational diagram for $6 + 8 = 14$ (taking the order $6 + 8$ as meaning that 8 is added to 6). What difference equation is associated with the inverse operation?
5. We defined $\bar{X}$ (complement of X) in Y as the set consisting of those elements that are in Y, but not in X. Choose a set Y and $X \subset Y$. Then show that, if $n(Y) = k$ and $n(X) = a$, then $n(\bar{X}) = k - a$.
6. Sketch an operational diagram for $24 \div 6 = 4$. Write the related statement showing the inverse operation.
7. As noted briefly in Section 6, dividing by 3 corresponds to the operation of separating a set into 3 mutually matching sets. Given the number 12, for example, we may take a set of 12 objects and separate it into 3 sets of 4, upon which we conclude $12 \div 3 = 4$. Upon the basis of the array of stars in Figure 4-12, can you give a general argument to show that this "partition" definition of division is equivalent to its definition as inverse of multiplication?

$$* \qquad * \qquad * \qquad \cdot \ \ \cdot \ \ \cdot \qquad *$$

$$* \qquad * \qquad * \qquad \cdot \ \ \cdot \ \ \cdot \qquad * \quad \textbf{(3 rows of } n \textbf{ stars each)}$$

$$* \qquad * \qquad * \qquad \cdot \ \ \cdot \ \ \cdot \qquad *$$

Fig. 4-12

8. Another "set definition" of division by 3 arises from the idea of separating a set into subsets of 3 elements each, the number of such subsets being the quotient of the number of the set by 3. Can you use the star diagram in Problem 7 to show that this definition is equivalent to the other set definition cited in Problem 7?
9. Explain the meaning of the following statement: "The expression $2 - 8$ is meaningless with respect to the system of the natural numbers."
10. Proceed as in Problem 9, but with "$7 \div 2$" in place of "$2 - 8$."
11. Let $\alpha(x)$ denote the operation of multiplying x by 5, then subtracting 3 from the result. Thus, $\alpha(4) = (5 \times 4) - 3 = 17$. Is this the same as first subtracting 3, then multiplying by 5? Defend your answer with an example.
12. Let $\alpha'(\ \ )$ denote the operation inverse of the operation $\alpha(\ \ )$ of Problem 11.

Verify that $\alpha'(27) = 6$, using an operational diagram as an aid. Find $\alpha'(62)$. What about $\alpha'(10)$?

13. If β and β' are inverse operations and $\beta(x)$ is the operation of adding 4 to x, then dividing the result by 3, find $\beta'(20)$.

14. To demonstrate that subtraction and division are not associative operations, compute the values of these four expressions, showing each pair to have different values:

(a) $(12 - 5) - 2 = ?$
$\quad\;\; 12 - (5 - 2) = ?$

(b) $(36 \div 6) \div 3 = ?$
$\quad\;\; 36 \div (6 \div 3) = ?$

15. Compute each of the following:

(a) $3 + (2 \times 5); (3 + 2) \times (3 + 5)$
(b) $12 \div (1 + 2); (12 \div 1) + (12 \div 2)$

16. Examine your answers to Problem 15. What can you conclude about distributivity

(a) of addition over multiplication?
(b) of division over addition?

7. ZERO

It is frequently convenient to refer to the set of numbers:

$$\{0,1,2,3,4,5, \ldots\}.$$

We call this the set of the **whole numbers.** If we denote the set of natural numbers by N and the set of whole numbers by W, we have:

$$N = \{1,2,3,4,5, \ldots\}$$
$$W = \{0,1,2,3,4, \ldots\}.$$

Observe that the only difference between the two sets is that the set of whole numbers W contains one more number, namely 0. That is, $N \cup \{0\} = W$.

We met zero previously as the number of the empty set. The properties of 0 are easily established:

$$\forall_x \; x + 0 = x \qquad \text{and} \qquad \forall_x \; 0 \cdot x = 0.$$

The property of 0 for addition, $\forall_x \; x + 0 = x$, has earned the number 0 the name of **additive identity, or identity for addition.**

Using $\emptyset$ for the empty set and X for any set, we have the following corresponding statements involving sets:

$$\forall_{\text{set } X} \; X \cup \emptyset = X \qquad \text{and} \qquad \forall_{\text{set } X} \; X \times \emptyset = \emptyset.$$

Recall that "$\times$" indicates the cross-product set. Since there are no elements in the empty set, $X \times \emptyset$ has no pairs belonging to it and thus is the empty set.

8. CARDINAL AND ORDINAL NUMBERS

As Max White waits in line at a ticket office, he may observe that he is *sixth* in line. In the pantry, a jar of preserves may be placed on the *third* shelf from the bottom. These are *ordinal* usages of number. A *cardinal number* tells the "size" of a set. An *ordinal number* designates a position in a linear (line) arrangement. See Figure 4-13.

In Chapter 3 we referred to *matching* and *counting* as cardinal and ordinal concepts, respectively. In application, however, these two processes are linked—we often find the sizes of sets by counting their elements. We count: 1, 2, 3, ... During this procedure, the named numbers are apparently to be regarded as ordinals. Upon finding the count, however, we identify the last ordinal named as the number of the counted set, a cardinal.

Because we switch back and forth so speedily and frequently between the two concepts, it is convenient to use the same symbols for the cardinals and ordinals, also to use the term *natural number* for both cardinals and ordinals.

The housewife's note to the milkman, "3 quarts homogenized," employs the number 3 as a cardinal. The "3" in the upper right-hand corner of a newspaper page denotes an ordinal. The suffix "th" is frequently attached to the ordinal numerals. They are then written "1st, 2nd, 3rd, 4th, . . . ," and read as "first, second, third, fourth, . . ." in place of "one, two, three, four, ..."

We chose to develop the theory of the natural numbers on the basis of their cardinal interpretation. The fundamental notion was then that of *set*. For the ordinals, the basic notion is that of *progression* or *sequence*. The theory of the ordinals can be developed from the idea of "matching sequences." The finite cardinals and ordinals turn out to be structurally alike, enabling us to pass from one system to the other automatically and trivially.

3 as a CARDINAL   **3 as an ORDINAL**

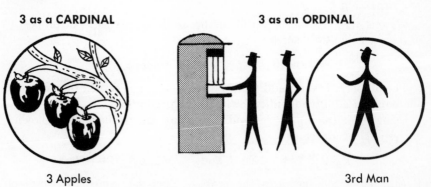

3 Apples   3rd Man

Fig. 4-13 Cardinal and Ordinal

Problem Set 6

1. Let N and W denote the set of natural numbers and the set of whole numbers, respectively. Tell whether each statement is true or false.

   (a) $N \cap W = N$
   (b) $N \cup W = N$
   (c) $0 \in W$
   (d) $0 \in N$
   (e) $W \subset N$
   (f) $N \subset W$
   (g) $N \cap \{0\} = \emptyset$
   (h) $W \cap \{0\} = \{0\}$
   (i) $N = W$

2. Explain why the statement $N \cup 0 = W$ is false.

3. We can establish a one-to-one correspondence between the set of natural numbers and the set of whole numbers as follows:

$$N = \{1, \ 2, \ 3, \ 4, \ 5, \ . \ . \ .\}$$
$$\updownarrow \ \ \updownarrow \ \ \updownarrow \ \ \updownarrow \ \ \updownarrow$$
$$W = \{0, \ 1, \ 2, \ 3, \ 4, \ . \ . \ .\}.$$

Thus, 1 in N is matched with 0 in W, 2 in N with 1 in W, and so on. For each number below, tell what number is associated with it in the other set.

   (a) with 17 in N (What number in W is associated with it?)
   (b) with 35 in W
   (c) with 36,378 in N
   (d) with 47,001 in W
   (e) with k in N
   (f) with x in W

4. Are N and W matching sets? Explain your answer.
5. What is the least natural number?
6. What is the least whole number?
7. Is there a greatest natural number?
8. Is there a greatest whole number?
9. In each case, is the number cited used in the cardinal or in the ordinal sense or in neither?

   (a) He has 10 marbles in his pocket.
   (b) The golfers did not play out on Hole No. 9.
   (c) His address is 721 Westmount Place.
   (d) He weighs 180 pounds.
   (e) This sheet is 140-count muslin.
   (f) Look out for Public Enemy No. 1!
   (g) Give me a 3¢ stamp.
   (h) Math. 432 is a popular course.
   (i) Page 37 is ink-stained.
   (j) In cadence, count: 1, 2, 3, 4; 1, 2, 3, 4.

9. THE INTEGERS

So far, the most inclusive set to which we turned our attention was the set of whole numbers W. A more inclusive set than W is the set of integers I. It consists of the positive whole numbers, 0, and the additive inverses of the positive whole numbers.

$$I = \{\ldots, -4, -3, -2, -1, 0, +1, +2, +3, +4, \ldots\}.$$

The set of natural numbers has the least member; so does the set of whole numbers. The set of integers, on the other hand, has no least member. It extends infinitely in both directions.

A child begins to become accustomed to some of the ideas underlying the system of integers long before he meets the system in explicit form. There are many games in which the player both adds to and takes away from the score, others in which a marker is moved both forward and backward. A player may sometimes be ahead and sometimes behind, and may even end a game "in the red" or "in the hole." Red and black checkers could be used to keep score in such a game, the blacks indicating additions, the reds deductions. A surplus of blacks over reds would correspond to a positive score, a surplus of reds over blacks to a negative score.

We may express the concept of the system of the integers in terms of sets by considering sets that have two different kinds of elements. What these two kinds are will depend upon the specific application being made. They could be male and female, living and dead, up and down, right and left, input and output, asset and liability. Whatever the case, we shall term the two types black and red.

A given set may have an equal number of red and black elements. It will then be called the **null set** and will have assigned to it the integer 0.

A nonnull set has a surplus of one color. The *directed number of the set* is defined as the *number of the surplus elements, with a plus or minus sign* according as the surplus elements are black or red.

Consider a set with 5 black and 2 red elements. We shall use the symbol [5B,2R] to denote the integer that is the number of the set: [5B,2R] = +3. Examples are:

$$[7B,4R] = [6B,3R] = [5B,2R] = [4B,1R] = [3B] = +3.$$
$$[3B,3R] = [2B,2R] = [1B,1R] = 0.$$
$$[4B,7R] = [3B,6R] = [2B,5R] = [1B,4R] = [3R] = -3.$$

We may define number addition in terms of set union just as in the case of the natural numbers, and may develop rules for adding and subtracting positive and negative integers.

Example 1 Find $-3 + 5$.

Select any black-red sets to represent -3 and 5. The simplest choices are [3R] and [5B]. For illustrative purposes, let us pick a less special pair, say [4B,7R] and [19B,14R]. The union of two such disjoint sets will contain $4 + 19 = 23$ *black* and $7 + 14 = 21$ *red* elements, and so will have the number $+2$. Hence: $-3 + 5 = +2$. Symbolically the work is

$$-3 + 5 = [4B,7R] + [19B,14R] = [23B,21R] = [2B] = +2.$$

Example 2 Find $-3 - 4$.

We may regard the expression $-3 - 4$ as denoting the sum of -3 and -4: $(-3) + (-4)$. We may also regard it as asking for the subtraction of 4 from -3. Here we show the work related to the latter interpretation. Let -3 be represented by a set of structure [10B,13R], 4 by a set of structure [6B,2R]. Then

$$-3 - 4 = [10B,13R] - [6B,2R] = [4B,11R] = [7R] = -7.$$

The structure of the positive integers $+1$, $+2$, $+3$, . . . is exactly the same as the structure of the natural numbers 1, 2, 3, ... That is, for any given relation involving positive integers, such as $(+2) + (+3) = +5$, there is a corresponding relation involving natural numbers, $2 + 3 = 5$, and vice versa. Hence we ordinarily write "2," whether we are thinking of the number so denoted as a member of the system of integers or as a member of the system of natural numbers. Therefore we must exercise care when we use an expression like $2 - 5$. Relative to the system of integers, this expression is meaningful, and may be replaced by -3. Relative to the system of natural numbers, the expression is meaningless.

Problem Set 7

1. In the notation of Section 9, let $+2$ be represented by a set of type [6B,4R] and $+3$ by one of type [10B,7R]. Verify that $(+2) + (+3) = +5$.
2. As in Problem 1, verify that $(-4) + (+3) = -1$, using sets of type [2B,6R] and [20B,17R].
3. Verify $(+5) - (+3) = +2$, using [8B,3R] and [5B,2R].
4. Verify $(+5) - (-3) = +8$, using [12B,7R] and [2B,5R].
5. Verify $(+6) + 0 = +6$, using [6B] and [2B,2R].
6.* Form the "product" of the sets of type [3B,1R] and [2B,5R] by writing 28 couples of elements, each containing an element from each set. Show that, if like-colored couples are called B's and unlike R's, then the set of couples will represent -6, in accordance with the usual rule $(+2) \times (-3) = -6$.
7. As a person deposits and withdraws, his bank balance gives his net position. Considered as a number of cents, is the value of this balance properly thought of as a natural number or as an integer? Explain fully.

8. Given that $I =$ the set of integers, $I_P =$ the set of positive integers, and $I_N =$ the set of negative integers, tell whether each statement is true or false.

   (a) $I_P \cup I_N = I$
   (b) $(I_P \cup \{0\}) \cup I_N = I$
   (c) $I_P \cap I_N = \emptyset$
   (d) $I_P \cap I = I$
   (e) $I_P \cup I = I$
   (f) $n(\{0\}) = 0$
   (g) $n(\{0\}) = 1$
   (h) I_P and I_N are matching sets
   (i) $\bar{I}_P = I_N \cup \{0\}$ ($\bar{I}_P$ is the complement of the set of positive integers in the set of integers.)
   (j) $\{0\} = I_P \cup I_N$

9. Show how you would establish a one-to-one correspondence between the set of

   (a) positive integers and the set of integers,
   (b) positive integers and natural numbers,
   (c) negative integers and natural numbers.

10. Consider the following sets:

$$A_1 = \{+1\}$$
$$A_2 = \{+1, +2\}$$
$$A_3 = \{+1, +2, +3\}$$
$$\text{and so on.}$$

   (a) List the first 3 elements and the last element of A_k, using three dots after the third element.
   (b) Show how you would establish a one-to-one correspondence between $A = \{A_1, A_2, A_3, \ldots\}$ and the set of positive integers. Notice that the elements of A are sets.

11. Show how you would establish a one-to-one correspondence between the set of natural numbers and the union of the set of positive integers and $\{0\}$.

Bibliography

Barnett, I. A., *Some Ideas About Number Theory.* Washington, D.C.: National Council of Teachers of Mathematics, 1961.

Dubisch, Roy, *The Nature of Number.* New York: Ronald Press, 1952.

Freitag, H. T., and A. H. Freitag, *The Number Story.* Washington, D.C.: National Council of Teachers of Mathematics, 1960.

Freund, John E., *A Modern Introduction to Mathematics.* Englewood Cliffs, N.J.: Prentice-Hall, Inc., 1956, Chaps. 1–11, 22, 23.

Jones, Burton W., *Elementary Concepts of Mathematics.* New York: Macmillan, 1947, Chaps. 1–3.

Nichols, Eugene D., Ralph T. Heimer, and Henry Garland, *Modern Intermediate Algebra.* New York: Holt, Rinehart and Winston, 1965, Chap. 1.

———, Robert Kalin, and Henry Garland, *Arithmetic of Directed Numbers* (A Programed Unit). New York: Holt, Rinehart and Winston, Inc., 1962.

Ore, Oystein, *Number Theory and Its History*. New York: The McGraw-Hill Book Company, Inc., 1948.

Ringenberg, L. A., *A Portrait of 2*. Washington, D.C.: National Council of Teachers of Mathematics, 1956.

Stewart, B. M., *Theory of Numbers*, 2d ed. New York: The Macmillan Company, 1964, Chaps. 1–9.

Thurston, H. A., *The Number-System*. New York: Wiley-Interscience, 1956.

Waisman, Friedrich, *Introduction to Mathematical Thinking*, trans. by T. J. Benac. New York: Frederick Ungar, 1951.

5

ADDITION
AND
SUBTRACTION

1. ADDITION: FIRST NOTIONS

We have now developed the logical basis of the addition operation and have established the basic properties (commutative, etc.) governing the operation. The next task is that of working out practical techniques for performing the operation efficiently. From the "why" we proceed to the "how."

An obvious way of adding is by direct counting—a favorite scheme with young children and a necessary preliminary to their later learning. To add 14 to 23, for example, we may count 1, 2, . . . , 23 and then 1, 2, . . . , 14, marking a stroke with each count. A count of the whole group of tally strokes then gives the result, 37:

IIIIIIIIIIIIIIIIIIIIIII   IIIIIIIIIIIIII

The Egyptian, Greek, and Roman numerals may be regarded as abbreviated ways of keeping the tallies. In Roman numerals, 23 and 14 appear as

XXIII   XIIII.

Pushing these together gives the result:

XXXIIIIIII = XXXVII.

Addition with Roman numerals is thus a sort of improved counting process.

With our own Hindu-Arabic numerals, the process is carried out on a more sophisticated level, as required by the position-value feature of our system, which we discussed in Chapter 2.

92 /

	0	1	2	3	4	5
0	0	1	2	3	4	
1	1	2	3	4	5	
2	2	3	4	5	6	

Fig. 5-1

Our children first learn how to add two numbers whose sum is at most 9. They establish "addition facts," like $3 + 4 = 7$, by direct counting. Eventually, they learn an entire 10 by 10, 100-entry, addition table, as shown in Figure 5-1.

It might seem that nearly half the memorization effort could be saved (table reduced to 55 entries) by applying the commutative property $2 + 1 = 1 + 2$, etc., and eliminating entries below the main diagonal from upper left to lower right corner. But a child so taught would be handicapped. Having the answer to $2 + 1$, say, on the "tip of his tongue," when confronted by $1 + 2$ he would have to mentally reverse the order of 1 and 2 before producing the answer. (A person familiar with "touch typing" can readily and dramatically prove to himself the difference between learning a response in one direction and in reverse. Shown a letter, the typist's response is immediate—a certain finger bangs down a certain key. But if someone places the typist's finger on a key and asks that the letter be named, the response will likely be quite slow.)

There is some difference of opinion as to whether young children should be taught the zero addition facts, like $0 + 3 = 3$. In summing the values of a column of digits, a child may just skip whenever he comes to a zero, so that he need not think explicitly of adding zero. But this evasion must perforce be temporary. Eventually the pupil must learn that $0 + n = n$ for every number n.

Knowing how to add the values of digits, we are ready to add a pair of numbers like 23 and 14. Even as the Hindus, we may *name* the places and proceed as follows:

$$
\begin{array}{rl}
23 = & 2 \text{ tens} + 3 \text{ units} \\
+\ 14 = & 1 \text{ ten} \ + 4 \text{ units} \\
\hline
37 = & 3 \text{ tens} + 7 \text{ units}
\end{array}
$$

Simplification—an exchange, for example, replacing 10 units by 1 ten—will often be necessary:

$$
\begin{array}{r}
27 = 2 \text{ tens} + 7 \text{ units} \\
+ 36 = 3 \text{ tens} + 6 \text{ units} \\
\hline
5 \text{ tens} + 13 \text{ units} \\
63 = 6 \text{ tens} + 3 \text{ units} \\
\hline\hline
\end{array}
$$

A child quickly learns to perform the exchange or regrouping process in rote fashion while summing in columns in right-to-left order. It is so easy to learn to do the task mechanically and without insight that the teacher must take much care to ensure that his pupils fully understand the meaning of what is done. It is of special importance that a child's early mathematical work should be fully meaningful to him. If it is not—if he merely learns the appropriate motions to go through to get the "right answer"—then he is likely to be handicapped and frustrated in all his future mathematical efforts, and the domain of mathematics may become for him an area of senseless fumblings, "school stuff" unrelated to the realities of life.

The addition procedures above may be illustrated effectively by using sets of matchsticks to represent the numbers. We sort 27 sticks into 2 bundles of ten and 7 individual sticks; 36 sticks give 3 bundles of ten and 6 loose sticks. When the sets are combined, there are 5 bundles of ten and 13 loose sticks. Ten of the latter may be grouped and a rubber band put around them to make a new bundle of ten, which is united with the 5 bundles of ten.

A somewhat more abstract type of illustration makes use of dimes and pennies, 27 being represented by 2 dimes and 7 pennies, etc. Abacus illustrations are still more abstract and hence usually of less value in the early learning stages. However, the vertical wire form of line abacus shown in Figure 1-5 may be effectively employed, provided the wires extend high enough to accommodate 18 beads, so that the sums may be shown directly without immediate regrouping.

2. ADDITION: GENERAL

Addition procedures involve (1) the separate summing of the values of digits representing units, tens, hundreds, etc., and (2) the rearrangement of the results in standard numeral form.

To carry out (1), a pupil must know how to add the value of a digit to any number. Assuming that he knows how to add the values of two digits, how may he mentally add the value of a digit to the value of a two-digit numeral? Consider the case: 25 + 3. He mentally adds the 3 to the 5 of the 25, and stays in the twenties: "Twenty-(five plus three) = twenty-eight." Consider 25 + 7. Adding the 7 to the 5 gives him twelve, which is 2 over ten, so he advances to the thirties. These examples are typical of the two principal cases. Some textbooks on arithmetic refer to *bridging the tens* in cases like 25 + 7.

Let us see what addition looks like without regrouping. Consider the sum of the four numbers 27631, 5917, 232, 14826. Abbreviate units by U, tens by T, etc. Then we have Table 5-1. Note that the order of adding within columns is irrelevant—right to left, left to right, or higgledy-piggledy. But regrouping takes place from right to left. The surplus 10

Table 5-1

TTH	TH	H	T	U
2	7	6	3	1
	5	9	1	7
		2	3	2
1	4	8	2	6
3	16	25	9	16

in the units column, for example, must eventually be regrouped as 1 ten and joined to the tens column. The successive steps of regrouping for the example above are as in Table 5-2.

Table 5-2

STEP	TTH	TH	H	T	U
1	3	16	25	9	16
2	3	16	25	10	6
3	3	16	26	0	6
4	3	18	6	0	6
5	4	8	6	0	6

With our common adding scheme, the regrouping is effected along with the summing. As each column is summed, the units of the sum are written and the tens annexed to the next column immediately. It would seem that no speedier scheme could be possible.

	2	7	6	3	1
		5	9	1	7
			2	3	2
unwritten results	1	4	8	2	6
of regrouping $\longrightarrow$		(1)	(2)	(1)	(1)
		4	8	6	0	6

Despite the efficiency of our right-to-left regrouping process, the right-to-left order is an unfortunate choice from one important aspect. Not only does it deal with the digits of the numerals in the reverse order to that in which we write them, but it focuses first attention upon the *least important* end of the numeral. An error made in adding units is not as costly as one made in adding thousands, particularly if it should be committed in a checkbook!

It may be interesting and enlightening to the student to experiment with left-to-right procedures. They all involve extra writing, or mental regrouping, which will affect a column sum that is to be recorded:

```
  2 7 6 3 1        2 7 6 3 1        2 7 6 3 1
    5 9 1 7          5 9 1 7          5 9 1 7
      2 3 2            2 3 2            2 3 2
  1 4 8 2 6        1 4 8 2 6        1 4 8 2 6
  ─────────        ─────────        ─────────
  3 2 5 9          3 6 5 9 6        3 6 5 9 6
  1 6   1 6        1 2   1          1 2   1
  ─────────        ─────────        ─────────────────────────
  4 8 5   6        4 8 5 0 6        4 8 6 0 6  (1 mental regrouping)
    1 0              1
  ─────────        ─────────             work direction
  4 8 6 0 6        4 8 6 0 6         ──────────────────►
                                          left to right
```

The Hindus added from left to right. As regrouping called for changes in results already recorded, they adjusted by erasing and rewriting. This was easy for them, since they wrote on a "dust" board (red flour on a white background was common), and an erasure was but a smoothing of the dust. Hence their work took this form at successive stages:

```
  27631      27631      27631      27631      27631
  ·5917       5917       5917       5917       5917
   232        232        232        232        232
  14826      14826      14826      14826      14826
  ─────      ─────      ─────      ─────      ─────
  3          46         485        4859       48606
```

What actually showed on their tiny slates was less than displayed above. They may have summed the ten thousands first, erasing as they worked, ending with the numeral 3 alone on the slate; next the thousands; and so on.

When Europeans took over the Hindu arithmetic, they *crossed out* instead of erasing, this being the easier thing to do when the writing medium was ink on parchment or paper. Then the steps of the work looked like this:

27631	27631	27631	27631	27631
5917	5917	5917	5917	5917
232	232	232	232	232
14826	14826	14826	14826	14826
3	36̸	36̸5̸	36̸5̸9	36̸5̸9̸6̸
	4	48	48	4860

The Europeans called this process a **scratch method**. Naturally there were also scratch methods for the other arithmetic processes. During the sixteenth century, these methods declined in popularity. To print the "scratched" digits, extra type was needed. This led to the printing of some examples without scratches, which made the examples hard for the reader to follow. The upshot was, the methods were changed.

Problem Set 1

1. Perform the following additions by expressing each number as a sum of units, tens, etc., combining and simplifying (23 = 2 tens + 3 units, etc.):

(a)   27
+31

(b)   66
+28

(c)   78
+25

(d)   85
+79

(e)   376
+ 52

(f)   487
+215

(g)   729
+271

(h)   9206
+5728

2. Demonstrate the additions in Problem 1 by using pennies, dimes, dollars and ten-dollar bills to represent units, tens, hundreds and thousands, respectively. ("Play money" bills will do, made by writing $1 or $10 on slips of paper.)
3. Use matchsticks or toothpicks, making bundles of ten with the aid of rubber bands (or use squares of paper and paper clips, etc.), to demonstrate these additions:

(a)   13
+24

(b)   18
+36

(c)   28
+32

(d)   27
+38

4. Can you tell without adding that the following additions will all give the same result? Explain how.

2736	727	323
924	2324	716
6317	6513	2927
+ 523	+ 936	+6534

5. Explain how CPA and APA enter into the answer to Problem 4.

6. Carry out the addition at the left in Problem 4 by the separate column scheme shown in Tables 5-1 and 5-2, with columns headed Th, H, T, U. Show the successive steps of adjusting the answer to the usual numeral form.
7. Carry out the addition at the left in Problem 4 by a left-to-right procedure (no erasing or scratching).
8. Add by the scratch method:

(a)	231	(b)	3718	(c)	2693	(d)	43207
	328		292		371		18928
	67		6		56920		21329
	+1089		+9237		+ 4768		+64718

3. SUBTRACTION

Somehow subtraction never became wholly standardized. Several different methods are currently taught in United States schools. A teacher in the middle grades is likely to find that some pupils who received their earlier schooling elsewhere are accustomed to using a different scheme from that common in her locality.

The methods of performing subtraction are based on the two concepts: (1) subtraction is the inverse of addition, and (2) it is possible to regroup a number.

Illustration of (1)

$$\text{If } 3 + 4 = 7, \text{ then } 7 - 4 = 3.$$

Illustration of (2)

$25(20 + 5 = 2 \text{ tens} + 5 \text{ units})$ can be
regrouped into $10 + 15$ (1 ten + 15 units).

We shall consider two different methods of subtraction. Since we shall need to refer to these methods, we give them names that are suggestive of their nature:

1. Regroup-subtract
2. Regroup-add

Thus, each method involves regrouping, but in the first method we think directly of subtraction, whereas in the second method we think of addition. Examples 1 and 2 show what is meant.

Example 1 Direct subtraction:

(2)	(1)	STEPS	(SAID TO ONESELF)
5	7	(1) $7 - 3 = 4$	"3 from 7 gives 4"
− 2	3	(2) $5 - 2 = 3$	"2 from 5 gives 3"
3	4		

Example 2 Via addition:

(*2*)	(*1*)	STEPS	(SAID TO ONESELF)
5	7	(*1*) 3 + 4 = 7	"3 plus what is 7? 4"
− 2	3	(*2*) 2 + 3 = 5	"2 plus what is 5? 3"
3	4		

Now consider a more complicated example worked out by regroup-subtract and regroup-add methods.

(*4*)	(*3*)	(*2*)	(*1*)
9	8	2	5
− 4	7	6	8
5	0	5	7

1. Regroup-subtract.

(*1*) 15 − 8 = 7   (25 = 10 + 15)
(*2*) 11 − 6 = 5   (810 = 700 + 110; 110 − 60 = 50)
(*3*) 7 − 7 = 0   (700 − 700 = 0; no regrouping necessary)
(*4*) 9 − 4 = 5   (9,000 − 4,000 = 5,000; no regrouping necessary)

The regroup-subtract method may be analyzed in a different way for the example above:

$$9,825 - 4,768$$

is the same as

$$9,000 + 800 + 20 + 5$$
$$-(4,000 + 700 + 60 + 8),$$

which is the same as

$$9,000 + 800 + 10 + 15$$
$$-(4,000 + 700 + 60 + 8),$$

which is the same as

9,000	+ 700	+ 110	+ 15
−(4,000	+ 700	+ 60	+ 8)
5,000	+ 0	+ 50	+ 7

which is the same as 5,057.

2. Regroup-add

(*1*) 8 + 7 = 15   (25 = 10 + 15)
(*2*) 6 + 5 = 11   (810 = 700 + 110; 60 + 50 = 110)
(*3*) 7 + 0 = 7   (no regrouping necessary)
(*4*) 4 + 5 = 9   (no regrouping necessary)

The written analysis of the regroup-add method would be the same as that for regroup-subtract, except for the questions we would ask ourselves in the last step:

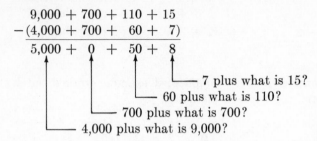

$$9,000 + 700 + 110 + 15$$
$$-(4,000 + 700 + 60 + 7)$$
$$\overline{5,000 + 0 + 50 + 8}$$

7 plus what is 15?
60 plus what is 110?
700 plus what is 700?
4,000 plus what is 9,000?

Which method is best? A variety of experiments have been made pitting one method against another. Generally speaking, the results have been inconclusive—as might have been anticipated at the outset. The manipulative procedures are similar in each method so that a child could be expected to become skilled in using one of them about as readily as in using the other. The crucial test might therefore be: Which method is most easily explained by the teacher and clearly understood by the pupil? This kind of criterion calls more for subjective agreement on the part of "master teachers" than for elaborate experimentation. There being little such agreement, perhaps there is no point in disputing the relative merits of the methods, except as follows: By choosing a method and arguing for it, a teacher will be stimulated toward devising effective ways of teaching it.

There is little point here in presenting a systematic treatment of the logic or meaning underlying each method. As the student actually teaches a method, he will discover for himself various ways of helping his students see the "why" of the process.

Matchsticks can be used to demonstrate the regroup-subtract method to young children. In doing

$$\begin{array}{r} 32 \\ -9 \\ \hline \end{array}$$

the child will begin with 3 bundles of ten sticks each and 2 loose sticks to represent 32. Now he unties one bundle of ten sticks, giving him 2 bundles of ten sticks and 12 loose sticks. He removes 9 sticks from the 12, obtaining 2 bundles of ten sticks and 3 loose sticks. Thus,

$$\begin{aligned} 32 - 9 &= (20 + 12) - 9 \\ &= 20 + (12 - 9) \\ &= 20 + 3 \\ &= 23, \end{aligned}$$

which can be shown as:

$$\begin{array}{r} 32 \\ -9 \\ \hline \end{array}$$

is the same as

$$\begin{array}{r} 20 + 12 \\ - \qquad 9 \\ \hline 20 + 3 \end{array} \quad \text{or} \quad 23.$$

Problem Set 2

In Problems 1 to 12, carry out the subtractions by each of the two methods presented above. As in the text examples, list each step, keying the number of the step to indices (1), (2), . . . written above each digit column in the sub-traction setup.

1. $\begin{array}{r} 67 \\ -42 \\ \hline \end{array}$ 2. $\begin{array}{r} 62 \\ -48 \\ \hline \end{array}$ 3. $\begin{array}{r} 964 \\ -512 \\ \hline \end{array}$ 4. $\begin{array}{r} 273 \\ -82 \\ \hline \end{array}$

5. $\begin{array}{r} 372 \\ -169 \\ \hline \end{array}$ 6. $\begin{array}{r} 253 \\ -57 \\ \hline \end{array}$ 7. $\begin{array}{r} 681 \\ -298 \\ \hline \end{array}$ 8. $\begin{array}{r} 4192 \\ -2818 \\ \hline \end{array}$

9. $\begin{array}{r} 3046 \\ -2618 \\ \hline \end{array}$ 10. $\begin{array}{r} 5123 \\ -4166 \\ \hline \end{array}$ 11. $\begin{array}{r} 60918 \\ -27374 \\ \hline \end{array}$ 12. $\begin{array}{r} 21231 \\ -18749 \\ \hline \end{array}$

13. Demonstrate the following subtractions according to the regroup-subtract procedure, using matchsticks and bundles of ten sticks held by rubber bands:

(a) $\begin{array}{r} 48 \\ -12 \\ \hline \end{array}$ (b) $\begin{array}{r} 32 \\ -8 \\ \hline \end{array}$ (c) $\begin{array}{r} 43 \\ -35 \\ \hline \end{array}$ (d) $\begin{array}{r} 51 \\ -18 \\ \hline \end{array}$

14. Explain each step in the following:

$$\begin{aligned} 342 - 178 &= (300 + 40 + 2) - (100 + 70 + 8) \\ &= (300 + 30 + 12) - (100 + 70 + 8) \\ &= (200 + 130 + 12) - (100 + 70 + 8) \\ &= (200 - 100) + (130 - 70) + (12 - 8) \\ &= 100 + 60 + 4 \\ &= 164. \end{aligned}$$

15. (*1*) $215 = 200 + 10 + 5$

(*2*) $= (300 - 100) + (90 - 80) + (9 - 4)$
(*3*) $= (300 + 90 + 9) - (100 + 80 + 4)$
(*4*) $= 399 - 184.$

In step (*2*) use different pairs of numbers within parentheses, thus showing 215 as the difference of two numbers, not 399 and 184.

16. If a, b, c, a', b', c' are digits and $a > a'$ (a is greater than a'), then

$$(100a + 10b + c) - (100a' + 10b' + c')$$
$$= 100(a - a') + 10(b - b') + (c - c').$$

Replace a by 9, b by 3, c by 1, a' by 3, b' by 7, c' by 8 in the equation above and complete the problem.

17. Use pennies and dimes in place of matchsticks to demonstrate the subtractions in Problem 13.
18. Explain each step in the following:

$$1,000 - 364 = 1,000 - (300 + 60 + 4)$$
$$= (990 + 0 + 10) - (300 + 60 + 4)$$
$$= (900 + 90 + 10) - (300 + 60 + 4)$$
$$= (900 - 300) + (90 - 60) + (10 - 4)$$
$$= 600 + 30 + 6$$
$$= 636.$$

19. Following the scheme of problem 18, write out similar steps in $10,000 - 8,175$.

4. SIGNED DIGITS

Our numeration system is *additive*, the value of a numeral being the sum of the values associated with the digits by virtue of their position in the numeral.

As with Roman numerals, suppose we introduce a *subtractive* concept. To indicate that a digit value is to be subtracted, we shall place a bar (minus sign) over the digit. Thus:

$$2\bar{3} = 20 - 3 = 17; \qquad 5\bar{3}6\bar{2} = 5000 - 300 - 60 + 2 = 4642.$$

We will refer to this concept as one of using **signed digits.**

In 1726, J. Colson advocated a "negativo-affirmative arithmetick" based on the use of signed digits.[1] The aim of the presentation of this and of other *curiosa* is to broaden the student's outlook and to stimulate his mathematical imagination. If he intends to teach arithmetic, he should early realize that the subject is not cut and dried, not fixed immutably in its current form, that it is a fertile field for research of a sort or even just for playful toying.

A numeral written with signed digits may speedily be converted into standard numeral form by proceeding from left to right and converting only two-digit sections at a time (except when a zero digit is followed by a negative digit). Thus if the sequence $2\bar{3}$ appears anywhere in a numeral it may be replaced by 17. *Example:*

$4\ \bar{3}\ 7\ \bar{2}\ \bar{8}\ 0\ \bar{4}$	*Reasons*
$= 3\ 7\ 7\ \bar{2}\ \bar{8}\ 0\ \bar{4}$	$4\ \bar{3} = \quad 40 - 3 = \quad 37$
$= 3\ 7\ 6\ 8\ \bar{8}\ 0\ \bar{4}$	$7\ \bar{2} = \quad 70 - 2 = \quad 68$
$= 3\ 7\ 6\ 7\ 2\ 0\ \bar{4}$	$8\ \bar{8} = \quad 80 - 8 = \quad 72$
$= 3\ 7\ 6\ 7\ 1\ 9\ 6$	$2\ 0\ \bar{4} = 200 - 4 = 196$

With a little practice the converted result can be written at once.

[1] The scheme is fully described in Cedric Smith, *Biomathematics* (New York: Hafner, 1954), Ch. 22.

Several positive and negative numbers (representing amounts taken in and paid out, for example) may be represented in a single column and added in one operation if signed digits are used. To carry out the work, the student must have some facility in the handling of negative numbers. The signed-digit idea will be referred to later in several connections. Here we use it as the basis of a novel scheme of subtraction.

To subtract a number from another, proceed in either left-to-right or right-to-left order. When the value of a lower digit is less than that of an upper digit, subtract it. When the upper is less, *take that from the lower instead,* but put a bar over the answer digit to show that it is negative. Thus:

$$
\begin{array}{r}
7\ 4\ 6\ 5\ 8\ 0 \\
-4\ 8\ 9\ 1\ 3\ 7 \\
\hline
3\ \bar{4}\ \bar{3}\ 4\ 5\ \bar{7} = 257443.
\end{array}
$$

5. COMPLEMENTS

A *complementary* method of subtraction was taught in many United States schools in the nineteenth century. Such methods have been known at least since medieval times. They arose because of the ease with which a number can be subtracted from the power of ten next greater than the number. Call this result the **complement** of the number.

The complement of 297 is 703, because $1,000 - 297 = 703$. The complement of 32 is 68, because $100 - 32 = 68$. That of 3 is 7, since $10 - 3 = 7$.

If 1 is subtracted from any power of ten, the result is "all nines": $10,000 - 1 = 9,999$; $100 - 1 = 99$, etc. Hence to find a number's complement, proceed from left to right along its digits, subtracting the value of each digit from 9 and writing down the result. But take the last (units) digit from 10, so as to restore the previously subtracted 1:

$$
\begin{array}{ccccc}
\begin{array}{r} 100,000 \\ -\ 57,218 \\ \hline 42,782 \end{array}
& = &
\begin{array}{r} 9\ 9\ 9\ 9\ 10 \\ -5\ 7\ 2\ 1\ \ 8 \\ \hline 4\ 2\ 7\ 8\ \ 2 \end{array}
& \text{because} &
\begin{array}{r} 99,999 \\ +\ \ \ \ \ \ 1 \\ \hline 100,000 \end{array}
\end{array}
$$

Using complements speeds number work in many special instances. Anyone who does much computing or mental arithmetic learns to recognize the possibilities as they turn up. No formal drill or rule memorizing is needed. Most people when asked to subtract 38 from 104 "in their heads" will do it by thinking: "38 from 100 is 62, and 4 is 66." (Some will insert an intermediate step of complementary type: "38 from 40 is 2, and 60 is 62 . . . .")

A complementary type of method is ordinarily used by clerks in returning change to customers. In this usage, complements are taken with respect to the next higher monetary denomination instead of the next higher power of ten. When a dollar bill is tendered for a 23¢ purchase, the clerk usually returns two pennies, then a quarter and a half-dollar, saying "23, and 2 makes 25, and 25 makes 50, and 50 makes one (100)."

To subtract 4,768 from 9,825, one may use the complement of 4,768, add this to 9,825, then deduct the appropriate power of ten (10,000). It is especially convenient just to write the signed digit $\bar{1}$ in front of the complement of 4,768, as this will automatically provide for the deduction:

$$
\begin{array}{r}
9\ 8\ 2\ 5 \\
-4\ 7\ 6\ 8 \\
\hline
\end{array}
\quad = \quad
\begin{array}{r}
9\ 8\ 2\ 5 \\
+\bar{1}\ 5\ 2\ 3\ 2 \\
\hline
5\ 0\ 5\ 7
\end{array}
$$

To show what has been done, we write this example in a different form:

$$
\begin{aligned}
9{,}825 - 4{,}768 &= 9{,}825 - (10{,}000 - 5{,}232) \\
&= 9{,}825 - 10{,}000 + 5{,}232 \\
&= (9{,}825 + 5{,}232) - 10{,}000 \\
&= (9{,}825 + 5{,}232) + \bar{1}0{,}000 \\
&= 9{,}825 + \bar{1}5{,}232.
\end{aligned}
$$

Problem Set 3

1. Give the complement of each of the following numbers:

   (a)   3   (b)   26   (c)   98   (d)   999
   (e) 20   (f) 723   (g) 2006   (h) 3276

2. Convert the following signed-digit numerals to ordinary numerals:

   (a) $4\bar{3}$ (b) $7\bar{8}$ (c) $4\bar{3}2$ (d) $4\bar{3}26$
   (e) $5\bar{2}4$ (f) $30\bar{2}$ (g) $4\bar{2}3\bar{8}$ (h) $5\bar{4}3\bar{2}$
   (i) $7\bar{2}3480\bar{4}$ (j) $6\bar{3}4\bar{2}78\bar{3}$ (k) $1\bar{2}00\bar{3}$ (l) $100\bar{5}$

3. Subtract by the signed-digit method:

   Example 1 $\begin{array}{r} 75 \\ -49 \\ \hline 3\bar{4} = 26 \end{array}$ **Example 2** $\begin{array}{r} 2053 \\ -\ \ 97 \\ \hline 20\bar{4}\bar{4} = 1956 \end{array}$

   (a) $\begin{array}{r} 62 \\ -48 \\ \hline \end{array}$ (b) $\begin{array}{r} 273 \\ -\ 82 \\ \hline \end{array}$ (c) $\begin{array}{r} 372 \\ -169 \\ \hline \end{array}$ (d) $\begin{array}{r} 253 \\ -\ 57 \\ \hline \end{array}$

   (e) $\begin{array}{r} 681 \\ -298 \\ \hline \end{array}$ (f) $\begin{array}{r} 4192 \\ -2818 \\ \hline \end{array}$ (g) $\begin{array}{r} 60918 \\ -27374 \\ \hline \end{array}$ (h) $\begin{array}{r} 21231 \\ -18749 \\ \hline \end{array}$

4. Subtract by adding the complement and using the appropriate signed digit.

Example 1   423   423   **Example 2**   36001   36001

           $=$ $=$

        $- 95$ $+\bar{1}05$ $- 562$ $+ \bar{1}438$
                    328   35439

(a)   8   (b)   64   (c)   125
      -3 -26 $- 98$

(d)   20342   (e)   8761   (f)   11823
      $- 723$ -2006 $- 3276$

5. At the right, it is shown
   how a column of posi-
   tive and negative num-
   bers can be added di-
   rectly by using signed
   digits. Try this out on
   the problems below:

	(3)	*(2)*	*(1)*
	2	1	8
	−	6	7
		5	2
	1	0	5
	−	4	3
	3	4	5 = 265

(1) $-3 + 5 + 2 - 7 + 8 = 5$
(2) $-4 + 0 + 5 - 6 + 1 = -4$
(3) $1 + 2 = 3$

(a)   507   (b)   21   (c)   320   (d)   2631
      $- 23$ $- 368$ -166 507
        37   2013 $- 19$ -1182
      -158 $- 187$ 285   19
        29             $- 96$ 36 $- 72$

BIBLIOGRAPHY

Asimov, Isaac, *Realm of Numbers*. Boston: Houghton Mifflin Co., 1959.
Branford, Benchara, *A Study of Mathematical Education, Including the Teaching of Arithmetic*. Oxford: Clarendon Press, 1908.
Conant, L. L., *The Number Concept*. New York: The Macmillan Company, 1896.
Deans, Edwina, "Algebraic Approaches to Developmental Work with the Operations," *The Arithmetic Teacher* (April 1964), pp. 266–269.
Flournoy, Frances, "Applying Basic Mathematical Ideas in Arithmetic," *The Arithmetic Teacher* (February 1964), pp. 105–108.
Haggerty, John B., "Kalak—an Ancient Game of Mathematical Skill," *The Arithmetic Teacher* (May 1964), pp. 326–330.
Karpinski, Louis C., *The History of Arithmetic*. New York: Rand McNally & Co., 1925.
The National Council of Teachers of Mathematics, *Tenth Yearbook, Arithmetic in General Education*. Washington, D.C.: The Council, 1935.
——, *Sixteenth Yearbook, The Teaching of Arithmetic*. Washington, D.C.: The Council, 1941.
——, *Twenty-fifth Yearbook, Instruction in Arithmetic*. Washington, D.C.: The Council, 1960.
——, *Twenty-seventh Yearbook, Enrichment Mathematics for the Grades*. Washington, D.C.: The Council, 1963.
Piaget, Jean, *The Child's Conception of Number*. London: Routledge & Paul, 1952.

Smith, Thyra, *Number* (An Account of Work in Number with Children throughout the Primary School Stage). Oxford: Basil Blackwell, 1954.

Spencer, P. L., and M. Brydegaard, *Building Mathematical Concepts in the Elementary School.* New York: Holt, Rinehart and Winston, Inc., 1952.

Spross, Patricia, guest ed., "Considerations in the Selection of Learning Aids," *The Arithmetic Teacher* (May 1964), pp. 350–353.

Wernick, William, "An Experiment in Teaching Mathematics to Children," *The Arithmetic Teacher* (March 1964), pp. 150–156.

6

MULTIPLICATION
AND
DIVISION

1. MULTIPLYING BY DOUBLING

The Egyptians used a multiplication process that we shall call **doubling and summing.** Figure 6-1 shows the Egyptian scheme.

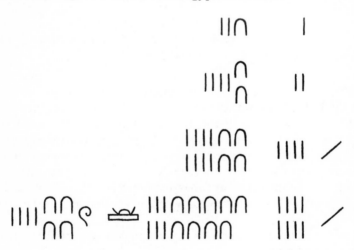

Fig. 6-1   An Egyptian Multiplication: 12 × 12 = 144

It is easy to express any number as a sum of powers of 2. Keep in mind the way these powers ascend:

$$1, \ 2, \ 4, \ 8, \ 16, \ 32, \ 64, \ \ldots$$
$$\uparrow \ \uparrow \ \uparrow \ \uparrow \ \ \uparrow \ \ \ \uparrow \ \ \ \uparrow$$
$$2^0, 2^1, 2^2, 2^3, \ 2^4, \ 2^5, \ 2^6, \ldots$$

Consider the number 27. Run along the sequence above to find the largest power of 2 that is less than 27. This is 16. Taking 16 from 27 leaves 11. Note that this remainder 11 *must* be less than the power of 2 taken off (16). Otherwise a higher power of 2 could have been subtracted. The largest power of 2 less than 11 is 8, and this is deducted, leaving 3. When 2 is taken from this, 1 remains. Hence,

$$27 = 16 + 8 + 2 + 1.$$

To multiply a number by 27, therefore, one may multiply it by 1, 2, 8, 16 and then sum the results. But these multiplications may be done by successive *doublings*.

Example 1 Find 27 × 31 by doubling and summing.

Step 1		Step 2	
27	* 1	31	31
− 16 *	* 2	62	62
11	4	124	
− 8 *	* 8	248	248
3	* 16	496	496
− 2 *			837 (*Answer*)
1 *			

Justification: $27 \times 31 = (1 + 2 + 8 + 16) \times 31$
$$= (1 \times 31) + (2 \times 31) + (8 \times 31) + (16 \times 31)$$
$$= 31 + 62 + 248 + 496$$
$$= 837.$$

What property of multiplication and addition is used?

This kind of multiplication process continued in use century by century, not disappearing until the Hindu-Arabic arithmetic quite routed the older ways. The doubling was easily performed with any type of abacus as well as with Egyptian or Roman numerals: It amounted merely to matching each numeral or abacus counter with one of the same value. Textbooks on the history of arithmetic refer to the above method by the term *duplation*. They call the variation next described *duplation and mediation*.

In medieval Europe the process usually took a form that we shall call **doubling and halving.**

Example 2 Find 27 × 31 by doubling and halving.

Halve on this side	*27	31	31	*Double on this side*
Discard remainders.	*13	62	62	Add where the stars
Star (*) each numeral	6	124		are.
naming an odd	* 3	248	248	
number.	* 1	496	496	
			837	

This method is based upon the principle that, if one factor of a product is halved while the other is doubled, the result is unchanged. In the above work, for example, $6 \times 124 = 3 \times 248$. It would be true that $27 \times 31 = 1 \times 496 = 496$ were it not that there are losses along the way. Because 27 is an odd number, in proceeding from 27×31 to 13×62, 31 is lost. 62 is lost in passing from 13×62 to 6×124. The rule of starring the numerals for odd numbers (on the left) and adding where the stars are (on the right) restores the lost parts of the product.

Using the right distributive property, we can display the successive steps in the example above as:

$$
\begin{aligned}
27 \times 31 &= (13 + \tfrac{1}{2}) \times 62 \\
&= (13 \times 62) + 31 \\
&= (6 + \tfrac{1}{2}) \times 124 + 31 \\
&= 6 \times 124 + 62 + 31 \\
&= 3 \times 248 + 62 + 31 \\
&= (2 + 1) \times 248 + 62 + 31 \\
&= 496 + 248 + 62 + 31.
\end{aligned}
$$

Russian peasants were still using the doubling and halving scheme at the time of World War I.

Problem Set 1

1. Perform each multiplication: first by "doubling and summing," and second by "doubling and halving."

(a) 6×13 (b) 12×27 (c) 36×52
(d) 7×13 (e) 15×35 (f) 219×405

2. Use the right distributive property of multiplication over addition to justify the "doubling and summing" method, and "doubling and halving" method for:

(a) 5×13 (b) 12×27 (c) 15×35

2. SCRATCH METHOD

Indian and European *scratch* methods of multiplying came in various arrangements. We show here successive stages in the multiplication of 2,417 by 362. The order of work is always from left to right. In the first stage the value of each digit of 2,417 is multiplied by 3, and the result continuously cumulated:

In the above, the units place is over the 2 of the 362, so that in actuality 2,417 has been multiplied by 300, with the result 725,100. Next comes the multiplication by 60. To get the partial products in their correct place-value positions, the 2,417 is written one place further to the right.

```
                                                            7 0 1
            8             8 6 9         8 6 9 7         8 6 9 7
7   5 1     7 4 5 1       7 4 5 1       7 4 5 1         7 4 5 1 2
6 2 3 3 6 2 6 2 3 3 6 2   6 2 3 3 6 2   6 2 3 3 6 2     6 2 3 3 6 2
2 4 1 7 7   2 4 1 7 7     2 4 1 7 7     2 4 1 7 7       2 4 1 7 7
2 4 1       2 4 1         2 4 1         2 4 1           2 4 1
```

Another shift of the 2,417, and we are ready to multiply by 2.

```
            4             4 9           4 9             4 9
7 0 1       7 0 1         7 0 1         7 0 1           7 0 1 5
8 6 9 7     8 6 9 7       8 6 9 7       8 6 9 7 4       8 6 9 7 4
7 4 5 1 2   7 4 5 1 2     7 4 5 1 2     7 4 5 1 2       7 4 5 1 2 4
6 2 3 3 6 2 6 2 3 3 6 2   6 2 3 3 6 2   6 2 3 3 6 2     6 2 3 3 6 2
2 4 1 7 7 7 2 4 1 7 7 7   2 4 1 7 7 7   2 4 1 7 7 7     2 4 1 7 7 7
2 4 1 1     2 4 1 1       2 4 1 1       2 4 1 1         2 4 1 1
2 4         2 4           2 4           2 4             2 4
```

The final answer is read over the top of the completed work: 874,954.

Although this scratch multiplication process appears formidable at first glance, it is really not difficult and is reasonably rapid. The reader will recall that the European scratches correspond to Hindu *erasures*. When a Hindu finished the multiplication exercise above, the *only* figures showing on his dust board were the answer digits 874954. He *had* to keep a cumulative result in order to accommodate the work on his tiny board.

Problem Set 2

Perform each multiplication by the scratch method.

1. 23 × 31   2. 67 × 528   3. 412 × 3,526

3. GRATING METHOD

In sharp contrast to the scratch method, with its cumulative progress toward the product, stands the **grating** method, in which the products of the values of digits are separately set down, then added to give the answer. The method received its name because the computation was done in a framework resembling a window grating, *gelosia* in Italian (French, *jalousie*).

The grating is a rectangle ruled into cells by evenly spaced vertical and horizontal lines. A set of diagonals is drawn dividing the cells in two. The number to be multiplied is shown across the top and the multiplier down the right side, as in Figure 6-2 for the example 362 × 2,417. Each

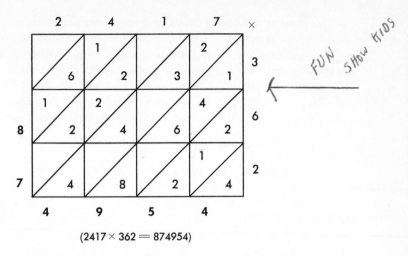

(2417 × 362 = 874954)

Fig. 6-2   2,417 × 362 = 874,954

digital product is written in a cell, with the units in the lower portion, and the tens, if any, in the upper. Addition takes place along diagonal strips from right to left, just as though the strips were vertical columns.

The following shows a different display of what is the same as the grating method for the example above:

$$2,417 \times 362$$

$$14 = 2 \times 7$$
$$20 = 2 \times 10$$
$$800 = 2 \times 400$$
$$4,000 = 2 \times 2,000$$
$$420 = 60 \times 7$$
$$600 = 60 \times 10$$
$$24,000 = 60 \times 400$$
$$120,000 = 60 \times 2,000$$
$$2,100 = 300 \times 7$$
$$3,000 = 300 \times 10$$
$$120,000 = 300 \times 400$$
$$600,000 = 300 \times 2,000$$

$$4 = 4$$
$$1 + 2 + 2 = 5$$
$$8 + 4 + 6 + 1 = 19$$
$$4 + 4 + 2 + 3 = 13$$
$$2 + 2 + 2 = 6$$
$$1 + 1 + 6 = 8$$

874954

The grating method is quick and easy once the grating is drawn. But for this last handicap, it might have become our present process.

Besides those we have described, many other multiplication methods have been used in Europe and in other parts of the world. Our modern process first appeared in print in an Italian text dated 1470. Its general adoption was not rapid, as may be judged by the fact that an American text published in 1710 treated multiplication by a scratch method.

4. MULTIPLICATION: ANALYSIS

In multiplying 2,417 by 362, all "partial" products were shown. In attempting to shed further light on why the grating and scratch methods work, we can show the partial products by resorting to indicating the place-values of digits by U for units, T for tens, and so on.

Consider 23×456. Write 23 in the form $2T + 3U$. Applying the commutative, associative, and distributive properties as needed, we find:

$$
\begin{aligned}
23 \times 456 &= (2T + 3U) \times 456 \\
&= 2T \times 456 + 3U \times 456 \\
&= 2T \times (4H + 5T + 6U) + 3U \times (4H + 5T + 6U) \\
&= (2 \times 4)(T \times H) + (2 \times 5)(T \times T) + (2 \times 6)(T \times U) \\
&\quad + (3 \times 4)(U \times H) + (3 \times 5)(U \times T) + (3 \times 6)(U \times U).
\end{aligned}
$$

The product can be found by adding all products of digit values, provided each of these is given an appropriate place value. It is left to the student to show how the geometry of the grating framework ensures the correct placement. (The analysis will be simpler if the cells are not split by diagonals.) To display the work in a clearer scheme, we present Table 6-1.

Table 6-1
$23 \times 456 = 10,488$

STEP		TTH	TH	H	T	U
(U × U)	3 × 6					18
(T × U)	2 × 6				12	
(U × T)	3 × 5				15	
(U × H)	3 × 4			12		
(T × T)	2 × 5			10		
(T × H)	2 × 4		8			
			8	22	27	18
		1	0	4	8	8

Performing multiplication according to some systematic scheme reduces the possibility of error, especially the error of omitting some digital product or placing it wrongly, and may avoid readjustments in cases of regrouping. However, it may be worth while for a student to try out a few "disorderly multiplications," as this will help him remember what is essential, and what is not, to multiplication procedures.

In the disorderly multiplication of 23×456 in Table 6-2, the digital product 2×5 was put down first, its position determined by noting that the 2 and the 5 are both in T (tens) position, so that their product will be in $T \times T = H$ (hundreds) position.

Table 6-2
$23 \times 456 = 10488$

STEP	TTH	TH	H	T	U
2×5			10		
3×6					18
3×5				15	
2×6				12	
3×4			12		
2×4		8			
		8	22	27	18
	1	0	4	8	8

Problem Set 3

1. Perform each multiplication by the grating method.

(a) 23×31 (b) 67×528 (c) $412 \times 3,526$

(d) 43×302 (e) 322×794 (f) $5,218 \times 32,764$

2. Analyze the following multiplications as was done at the beginning of Section 4, decomposing each product into digital products to which are assigned appropriate place values. [In (b), begin by replacing 43 by $4T + 3U$, etc.]

(a) 8×324 (b) 43×87 (c) 24×563

3. Carry out a disorderly multiplication in these cases:

(a) 43×87 (b) 24×563

4. Carry out a grating multiplication of 563 by 24 without drawing the diagonals through the cells. Explain how, by the geometry of the cell array, the digital products receive their proper place values (when added along diagonal directions).

5. Using the example of Problem 4 (24 × 563) but now putting in the diagonals, explain how this modification simplifies the work and still produces a correct result.

6.* Prepare a brief report on Napier's Bones, a computational device based on the grating scheme.

5. MODERN MULTIPLICATION

All multiplication procedures with Hindu-Arabic numerals involve the multiplication of the values of the digits of one number by those of the other. So the child's primary task is that of learning a *multiplication table*. Ideally, this learning is not a matter of rote memory, but a lengthy cumulative process during which every multiplication "fact," like 3 × 4 = 12, is engraved upon the child's mind by his own initiative following many "discoveries" or verifications of the "fact" by counting or adding (3 × 4 = 4 + 4 + 4) as well as applications of the "fact" in a variety of situations.

The next step is that of learning how to multiply a number by the value of a digit. Let us use 4 × 372 as an illustration. According to the distributive and associative properties,

$$4 \times 372 = 4 \times (3 \text{ hundreds} + 7 \text{ tens} + 2 \text{ units})$$
$$= (4 \times 3) \text{ hundreds} + (4 \times 7) \text{ tens} + (4 \times 2) \text{ units}$$

Thus to multiply a number by 4, it is only necessary to multiply its units, tens, hundreds, etc., separately by 4, and add. There are many ways in which this may be made obvious on a concrete level. With a two-digit example, like 3 × 24, if 24 is represented by 2 bundles of ten and 4 loose matchsticks, it is plain that the tripling of the bundles and loose sticks separately results in the tripling of the whole group.

The basic idea of multiplying by the value of one digit is therefore as in Table 6-3.

Table 6-3
4 × 372

	TH	H	T	U
		3	7	2
		12	28	8
	1	4	8	8

×4

or

$$\begin{array}{r} 372 \\ \times \quad 4 \\ \hline 8 \\ 28 \\ 12 \\ \hline 1488 \end{array}$$

With the exhibit shown as a basis, various ways of arranging a single-digit multiplication may be devised. Selecting a left-to-right direction of work leads to a scratch method. Recording the digital products as shown, then simplifying by regrouping in a right-to-left direction of work, produces a grating method. If the digital products are not recorded until the regrouping is mentally done, then the scheme becomes our common one:

(4) *(3)* *(2)* *(1)*	STEPS
3 7 2	*(1)* 4 × 2 = 8. Write 8.
× 4	*(2)* 4 × 7 = 28. Write 8, remember ②.
1 4 8 8	*(3)* 4 × 3 = 12. And ② gives 14.
	Write 4, remember ①.
	(4) And ①. Write 1.

Once multiplication by a digit value is mastered, the step to general multiplication is easy. For with our present-day method of multiplying, general multiplication is simply adding of *partial products* found by single digit-value multiplication. To keep place values straight, we shift these partial products so that their units digits line up (vertically) with the digit of the multiplier to which they belong:

```
   2 4 1 7              2 4 1 7            2 4 1 7
     3 6 2              3 6 2                3 6 2
   ───────      or    ───────      or    ───────
   4 8 3 4          1 4 5 0 2            7 2 5 1
 1 4 5 0 2            4 8 3 4          1 4 5 0 2
 7 2 5 1           7 2 5 1                4 8 3 4
 ─────────         ─────────            ─────────
 8 7 4 9 5 4       8 7 4 9 5 4          8 7 4 9 5 4
```

Our common method, shown at the left above, possesses the virtue that all work directions, including the direction of "shift" of the partial products, are from right to left. With the method at the right, the digits of the multiplier are used in the left-to-right order, giving an arrangement useful in some special ways, as in connection with "abridged" multiplication schemes occasionally taught in upper grade or in high school courses. (See Chapter 11.) The middle arrangement is simply disorderly.

It is easy to explain any of these arrangements by filling in zeros and taking into account the numeral structure of the multiplier, as follows:

```
          2 4 1 7
        × 3 6 2
        4 8 3 4 =     2 × 2 4 1 7
      1 4 5 0 2 0 =   6 0 × 2 4 1 7
    7 2 5 1 0 0 = 3 0 0 × 2 4 1 7
    ─────────────────────────────
    8 7 4 9 5 4 = 3 6 2 × 2 4 1 7
```

To multiply 2,417 by 362 on an abacus, use the partial-product scheme set forth earlier and modified as follows:

$$2 \times 2\ 4\ 1\ 7 = 2 \times \quad\quad 2\ 4\ 1\ 7$$
$$6\ 0 \times 2\ 4\ 1\ 7 = 6 \times \quad 2\ 4\ 1\ 7\ 0$$
$$3\ 0\ 0 \times 2\ 4\ 1\ 7 = 3 \times 2\ 4\ 1\ 7\ 0\ 0$$
$$\overline{3\ 6\ 2 \times 2\ 4\ 1\ 7}$$

ADD

$$\left.\begin{array}{l} 2\ 4\ 1\ 7 \\ 2\ 4\ 1\ 7 \end{array}\right\} 2$$

The right-hand products are found by repeated additions. That is, 2 4 1 7 is put on the abacus twice, 2 4 1 7 0 six times, and 2 4 1 7 0 0 three times, the addition being cumulative. The work scheme to the right is thus a guide for the abacus operation. Electric calculating machines of the type used in business offices multiply according to this abacus scheme.

$$\left.\begin{array}{l} 2\ 4\ 1\ 7\ 0 \\ 2\ 4\ 1\ 7\ 0 \\ 2\ 4\ 1\ 7\ 0 \\ 2\ 4\ 1\ 7\ 0 \\ 2\ 4\ 1\ 7\ 0 \\ 2\ 4\ 1\ 7\ 0 \end{array}\right\} 6$$

$$\left.\begin{array}{l} 2\ 4\ 1\ 7\ 0\ 0 \\ 2\ 4\ 1\ 7\ 0\ 0 \\ 2\ 4\ 1\ 7\ 0\ 0 \end{array}\right\} 3$$

$$\overline{8\ 7\ 4\ 9\ 5\ 4}$$

Problem Set 4

1. Use matchsticks and bundles to demonstrate these multiplications:

   (a) 2×24 (b) 3×24 (c) 4×13 (d) 5×14

2. Use pennies, dimes, and "play money" one- and ten-dollar bills (or use slips of paper with 1, 10, 100, 1000 written on them) to demonstrate these multiplications:

   (a) 2×368 (b) 3×572 (c) 7×486 (d) 3×1628

3. In each case of Problem 2, multiply according to the U, T, H, Th column scheme shown in Section 5, then convert to ordinary numeral form by both a left-to-right and a right-to-left procedure.

4. In each case of Problem 2, multiply according to our usual procedure and list the steps of the work, as shown in Section 5.

5. In multiplying by a several-digit multiplier, why do we place the units digit of each partial product below the corresponding multiplier digit?

6. Multiply in the usual way, then multiply again, this time using the digits of the multiplier in left-to-right order:

   (a) 26×304 (b) 203×451 (c) 427×5136

7. Explain the multiplications in Problem 6 by filling out the partial products with zeros, etc., as shown in the text.

8. Set up abacus work schemes for each multiplication in Problem 6. Carry out the work on a line abacus.

9. The multiplication of 2,417 by 362 may be displayed in a way demonstrating the use of distributivity:

$$2,417 \times 362 = 2,417 \times (300 + 60 + 2)$$
$$= (2,417 \times 300) + (2,417 \times 60) + (2,417 \times 2)$$
$$= 725,100 + 145,020 + 4,834$$
$$= 874,954$$

It can also be shown as:

$$2,417 \times 362 = (2,000 + 400 + 10 + 7) \times 362$$
$$= (2,000 \times 362) + (400 \times 362) + (10 \times 362) + (7 \times 362)$$
$$= 724,000 + 144,800 + 3,620 + 2,534$$
$$= 874,954$$

Or as:

$$2,417 \times 362 = (2,000 + 400 + 10 + 7) \times (300 + 60 + 2)$$
$$= (2,000 \times 300) + (2,000 \times 60) + (2,000 \times 2)$$
$$+ (400 \times 300) + (400 \times 60) + (400 \times 2)$$
$$+ (10 \times 300) + (10 \times 60) + (10 \times 2)$$
$$+ (7 \times 300) + (7 \times 60) + 7 \times 2$$
$$= 600,000 + 120,000 + 4,000$$
$$+ 120,000 + 24,000 + 800$$
$$+ 3,000 + 600 + 20$$
$$+ 2,100 + 420 + 14$$
$$= 874,954$$

Do each of the following in the three ways shown above:

(a) 25×17 (b) 351×78 (c) $139 \times 1,217$

6. DIVISION

Division is related to multiplication in the same way that subtraction is related to addition. For example,

$$18 \div 6 = 3 \quad \text{means} \quad 3 \times 6 = 18.$$

In general, $a \div b = c$ means $c \times b = a$. We say that division is an inverse of multiplication.

Another way of showing this relation between division and multiplication is

$$\forall_n \forall_m (n \times m) \div m = n.$$

That is, multiplying any number n by m, then dividing the product by m, results in a quotient that is the original number n.

In doing arithmetic involving division of whole numbers, we conceive of division as related to subtraction.

How many times does 3 "go into" 19? We may take away 3's one at a time and count the number of times, as shown at the right. This number, 6, is called the **quotient**. With the six 3's taken away, what is left of the 19 is 1, and this is called the **remainder**. By our work we have shown:

$$19 = 3 \times 6 + 1.$$

In words,

$$\text{dividend} = \text{divisor} \times \text{quotient} + \text{remainder}.$$

```
TAKE
AWAY   19
   / 3   16
   | 3   13
 6 ) 3   10
   | 3    7
   | 3    4
   \ 3    1
```

This will be referred to as the **basic division relation.**

The remainder may be zero, in which case the dividend is said to be **divisible** by the divisor. Or, the divisor is said to be a **factor** of the dividend. The remainder is always less than the divisor, simply because we keep subtracting the divisor as long as possible:

$$0 \leq \text{remainder} < \text{divisor}.$$

In practice the result of a division is often stated in fractional form:

$$\frac{19}{3} = 6 + \frac{1}{3} = 6\frac{1}{3}.$$

In words,

$$\frac{\text{dividend}}{\text{divisor}} = \text{quotient} + \frac{\text{remainder}}{\text{divisor}}.$$

How many times does 3 go into 1,900? It would be absurd to take away 3's one at a time. Why not ten at a time, or a hundred, or a thousand, . . . ? Write down some of these multiples of 3:

$$3; 30; 300; 3,000; \ldots$$

Since 3,000 exceeds 1,900, a thousand 3's at once is too big a lump. But 300 is under, and we proceed to deduct 300's as long as we can, as shown in the work scheme at the right. With six 300's, or six hundred 3's, taken away, we can next take away 3's ten at a time, finally one at a time. In all, the number of 3's taken away is $600 + 30 + 3 = 633$. Hence the basic division relation reads:

$$1,900 = 3 \times 633 + 1.$$

```
 TAKE
 AWAY   1900
    / 300  1,600
    | 300  1,300
  6 ) 300  1,000
    | 300    700
    | 300    400
    \ 300    100
    --------------
    / 30     70
  3 | 30     40
    \ 30     10
    --------------
    /  3      7
  3 |  3      4
    \  3      1
    --------------
 Quotient:   633
 Remainder:    1
```

This *continued subtraction* method of division is an entirely feasible general process, simpler and more efficient than many division schemes used in medieval times. The subtractions are readily made on an abacus, the count of their number being kept on unused rods. This is the method used with electric calculating machines; on all but the cheapest machines the whole process is automatic.

If a bright grade-school pupil were taught this method of division, he would soon of his own accord begin to shorten the procedure. Why should he take away 300's one by one when it is apparent that six of them can be removed at one fell swoop?

At first his work might take the form shown at the left in the next example. It should not be difficult to guide him toward the rearrangement of the work as shown in the middle, then toward the form at the right, which is the one in common use.

$$
\begin{array}{ccc}
1900 \div 3 & 633 & 633 \\
\hline
1900 & 3)\overline{1900} & 3)\overline{1900} \\
6\ -1800 & 1800 & 18 \\
\hline
100 & 100 & 10 \\
3\ -\ 90 & 90 & 9 \\
\hline
10 & 10 & 10 \\
3\ -\ 9 & 9 & 9 \\
\hline
1 & 1 & 1
\end{array}
$$

Our common arrangement is superior on several counts. Not only is unnecessary writing eliminated, but *place values of quotient digits are taken care of automatically.* In the case of 1,900 ÷ 3, for example, the pupil's thinking need not be in terms of 3 into 1,900, but only of 3 into 19, and next of 3 into 10 instead of 3 into 100.

The analysis applies as well when the divisor is named by a two or more digit numeral. Consider the division of 7,707 by 24:

$$
\begin{array}{ccc}
7{,}707 \div 24 & 321 & 321 \\
\hline
7707 & 24)\overline{7707} & 24)\overline{7707} \\
300 \times 24 = 7200 & 7200 & 72 \\
\hline
507 & 507 & 50 \\
20 \times 24 = 480 & 480 & 48 \\
\hline
27 & 27 & 27 \\
1 \times 24 = 24 & 24 & 24 \\
\hline
3 & 3 & 3
\end{array}
$$

Basic division relation: $7{,}707 = 24 \times 321 + 3$.

In carrying out the work, one complication enters. To see that 3 goes into 19 six times is easy—it is a matter of mentally scanning the multiples of 3: . . . $5 \times 3 = 15, 6 \times 3 = 18, 7 \times 3 = 21,$ . . . . But who can rattle off the multiples of 24?

The pupil can avoid this difficulty by listing the multiples of the divisor (found by cumulative addition) before he begins the division. First he wishes to know how many times 24 goes into 77:

$$
\begin{array}{c}
? \\
24)\overline{7707}
\end{array}
$$

Reading down the list of multiples he sees that 72 is less

MULTIPLES OF 24	
1	24
2	48
3	72
4	96
5	120
6	144
7	168
8	192
9	216

and 96 greater than 77, so that "24 goes 3 times." He writes:

$$
\begin{array}{r}
3 \\
24)\overline{7707} \\
72 \\
\hline
50
\end{array}
$$

Reading down the list again, he spots 48 as the greatest multiple less than the partial remainder of 50. So 2 is his next quotient digit.

Yet the tabulation of multiples is a cumbersome "crutch" that most pupils will hasten to discard even for nothing better than sheer guessing and the frequent correcting that will then be necessary. In the next section we shall take up rules that help pupils make good guesses, or estimates, of their "trial quotient digits."

Problem Set 5

1. Perform the following divisions "physically," i.e., in the case of $19 \div 3$, lay out 19 pennies or other objects, then remove 3 at a time, counting the number of removals to get the quotient and calling the final number left the remainder. Write the basic division relation for each case.

   (a) $19 \div 3$ (b) $24 \div 4$ (c) $32 \div 5$ (d) $41 \div 7$ (e) $30 \div 11$

2. For each division in Problem 1, show the "continued subtraction form" as displayed for $19 \div 3$ at the beginning of Section 6.

3. For each division in Problem 1, use the continued subtraction form obtained in Problem 2 as an abacus work scheme.

4. Perform these divisions as continued subtractions. Show the basic division relations found in each case.

   (a) $300 \div 13$ (b) $736 \div 32$ (c) $5681 \div 13$
   (d) $14864 \div 64$ (e) $9774 \div 362$ (f) $9900 \div 362$

5. Carry out the divisions in Problem 4 in the usual way. Fill in zeros and show that the work is essentially the same as with the continued subtraction scheme.

6. Observe that $20 \div 3 = (18 + 2) \div 3 = (18 \div 3) + (2 \div 3) = 6 + \frac{2}{3} = 6\frac{2}{3}$. This is an example of the distributive property of division over addition. More generally, $(a + b) \div c = (a \div c) + (b \div c)$ or $\dfrac{a + b}{c} = \dfrac{a}{c} + \dfrac{b}{c}.$ An extension of this is:

$$
(a_1 + a_2 + \cdots + a_n) \div b = \frac{a_1}{b} + \frac{a_2}{b} + \cdots + \frac{a_n}{b}.
$$

Example $176 \div 25 = (100 \div 25) + (75 \div 25) + (1 \div 25)$

$$
= 4 + 3 + \frac{1}{25}
$$

$$
= 7\frac{1}{25}
$$

Find the quotients by representing the dividends as sums of convenient addends.

(a) $277 \div 15$ (b) $968 \div 32$ (c) $2678 \div 42$

7. ESTIMATING QUOTIENTS

After the meaning of division and its relation to multiplication is understood and after some preliminary exploration of distributive properties in relation to division, the student is ready to develop a division algorithm that will equip him to carry out divisions in a brief and systematic way. For this, we resort to estimation of quotients, which we illustrate by examples.

Consider the division of 184 by 4.

One 4 in 184: $1 \times 4 = 4$ and $4 < 184$, 1 is too small.

Ten 4's in 184: $10 \times 4 = 40$ and $40 < 184$, 10 is too small.

Hundred 4's in 184: $100 \times 4 = 400$ and $400 > 184$, 100 is too large. The quotient $184 \div 4$ is in the interval between 10 and 100. We proceed to obtain an estimate of the quotient to the nearest 10.

Ten 4's in 184: $10 \times 4 = 40$ and $40 < 184$, 10 is too small.

Twenty 4's in 184: $20 \times 4 = 80$ and $80 < 184$, 20 is too small.

Thirty 4's in 184: $30 \times 4 = 120$ and $120 < 184$, 30 is too small.

Forty 4's in 184: $40 \times 4 = 160$ and $160 < 184$, 40 is too small.

Fifty 4's in 184: $50 \times 4 = 200$ and $200 > 184$, 50 is too large.

Thus, the quotient, $184 \div 4$, is in the interval between 40 and 50. It does not take a child long to learn that he need not begin with 10 and try all successive multiples of 10. He soon makes intelligent guesses and tries 40 first.

The next step is to estimate the ones place in the quotient. Exactly the same procedure is applied again.

Forty-one 4's in 184: $41 \times 4 = 164$ and $164 < 184$, 41 is too small.

Forty-two 4's in 184: $42 \times 4 = 168$ and $168 < 184$: 42 is too small.

Forty-three 4's in 184: $43 \times 4 = 172$ and $172 < 184$, 43 is too small.

Forty-four 4's in 184: $44 \times 4 = 176$ and $176 < 184$, 44 is too small.

Forty-five 4's in 184: $45 \times 4 = 180$ and $180 < 184$, 45 is too small.

Forty-six 4's in 184: $46 \times 4 = 184$ and $184 = 184$, 46 is the quotient.

Thus, $184 \div 4 = 46$, since $46 \times 4 = 184$.

The above estimates may be recorded in the following manner:

$$
\begin{array}{r}
6 \\
40 \\
4\overline{)184} \\
160 \\
\hline
24 \\
24 \\
\hline
0
\end{array}
$$

The next step to obtain the usual form of recording division is simple: We write 4 in the quotient numeral above the tens and do not write 0 to its right, rather we leave space for the estimate of ones. Hence,

$$
\begin{array}{r}
46 \leftarrow \text{quotient} \\
\text{divisor} \rightarrow 4\overline{)184} \leftarrow \text{dividend} \\
16 \\
\hline
24 \\
24 \\
\hline
0
\end{array}
$$

The procedure illustrated in dividing 184 by 4 can be generalized to any division problem involving natural numbers.

We illustrate the same procedure in showing the initial steps in dividing 7,707 by 24.

Ten 24's in 7,707: $10 \times 24 = 240$ and $240 < 7,707$; 10 is too small.

One hundred 24's in 7,707: $100 \times 24 = 2,400$ and $2,400 < 7,707$; 100 is too small.

One thousand 24's in 7,707: $1,000 \times 24 = 24,000$ and $24,000 > 7,707$; 1,000 is too large.

The quotient, therefore, is in the interval between 100 and 1,000. Next we estimate the quotient to the nearest hundred.

Two hundred 24's in 7,707: $200 \times 24 = 4,800$ and $4,800 < 7,707$; 200 is too small.

Three hundred 24's in 7,707: $300 \times 24 = 7,200$ and $7,200 < 7,707$; 300 is too small.

Four hundred 24's in 7,707: $400 \times 24 = 9,600$ and $9,600 > 7,707$; 400 is too large.

Thus, the quotient is in the interval between 300 and 400.

The student should complete the problem by estimating tens and ones. The completed procedure can be summarized in the following form:

(a)
$$
\begin{array}{r}
1 \\
20 \\
300 \\
\hline
24\overline{)7707} \\
7200 \\
\hline
507 \\
480 \\
\hline
27 \\
24 \\
\hline
3
\end{array}
$$

which is next abbreviated to:

(b)

$$\begin{array}{r} 321 \\ 24\overline{)7707} \\ 7200 \\ \hline 507 \\ 480 \\ \hline 27 \\ 24 \\ \hline 3 \end{array}$$

We obtained the quotient 321 and remainder 3. Thus,

$$7707 = 321 \times 24 + 3.$$

A somewhat more mature and abbreviated sequence of steps to yield scheme (a) above is:

estimate of hundreds: 24 into 7,707—300.
estimate of tens: 24 into 507—20.
estimate of ones: 24 into 27—1.

This procedure brings the elementary school child to the adult level of handling division of natural numbers.

8. DIVISION MISCELLANY

In practical application, it is sometimes the "under," sometimes the "over," and sometimes the "nearest" result of a division that furnishes the appropriate answer. The next examples illustrate this.

If rolls cost 5¢ each, and a customer has only 33¢, then he can buy only 6. This is an "under" result, with remainder 3, associated with the *basic* division relation:

$$\begin{array}{r} 6 \\ 5\overline{)33} \\ 30 \\ \hline 3 \end{array} \qquad 33 = 5 \times 6 + 3$$

If rolls are 5 for 33¢, and a customer wishes only one, he must pay 7¢. This is an "over" result. The remainder is *negative*, -2. The division relation is:

$$\begin{array}{r} 7 \\ 5\overline{)33} \\ 35 \\ \hline -2 \end{array} \qquad 33 = 5 \times 7 - 2$$

When the "nearest" result is needed, either the "under" or the "over" result must be chosen, whichever one involves the remainder of least **absolute value.**

Absolute value of a positive number is that number, that is, $\forall_{x>0}|x| = 0$ (read $|x|$: *the absolute value of x*). For example, $|2| = 2$.

Absolute value of 0 is 0: $|0| = 0$.

Absolute value of a negative number is the positive number that is the opposite of the given negative number, that is, $\forall_{x<0}|x| = -x$. For example, $|-2| = 2$, because 2 is the opposite of -2. Thus, $|2| = |-2| = 2$, that is, 2 and -2 have the same absolute value.

For $33 \div 5$, the "nearest" result is 7, since $33 = 5 \times ⑥ + 3$ and $33 = 5 \times ⑦ + (-2)$. When 6 is taken as the quotient, the remainder is 3. For the quotient 7, the remainder is -2, and $|-2| < |3|$.

Until a few hundred years ago, division was considered a very difficult art, and its mastery was sought only by "specialists" who needed to become skilled in computation for professional or business purposes. (In still older eras, to be sure, only the priests were adept at mathematical skills.) Today, all who are literate learn to divide. Yet we may be thankful that we need not struggle to comprehend some of the involved and complicated division techniques that were employed in medieval times in Europe. Texts on the history of mathematics describe a variety of curious historical processes.

A scratch method of division was commonly used in Europe for several centuries preceding the seventeenth. Even some American texts, one of date 1719, show the method. It was often called the "galley" method because the arrangement suggested the form of a ship. After successfully navigating the treacherous course of a problem like $297,603,942,163 \div 753,218$, a sixteenth-century pupil frequently spent the next half-hour in decorating his work, supplying as embellishments flags, masts, and so on, even as a schoolboy may today—but with a difference: the teachers in those times often required it!

These are the successive steps in the galley division of 7,704 by 24 to get the quotient 321:

		1	1̸5
7704 (	7704 (3	7704 (3	7704 (3
24	24	2̸4	2̸4̸

		1	1̸
1̸5	1̸5	1̸5̸	1̸5̸2
7704 (3	7704 (32	7704 (32	77̸0̸4 (32
2̸4̸4	2̸4̸4	2̸4̸4	2̸4̸4̸
2	2	2̸	2

$$
\begin{array}{llll}
\cancel{1} & \cancel{1} & \cancel{1} & \cancel{1} \\
\cancel{152} & \cancel{152} & \cancel{152} & \cancel{152} \\
77\cancel{0}4 \quad (32 & 77\cancel{0}4 \quad (321 & 77\cancel{0}4 \quad (321 & 77\cancel{0}4 \quad (321 \\
2\cancel{444} & 2\cancel{444} & 2\cancel{444} & 2\cancel{444} \\
22 & 22 & 22 & 22
\end{array}
$$

On the first row, $3 \times 24(00)$ is subtracted from 7,704, leaving 504. This is done by first subtracting $3 \times 2(000)$, leaving 1,704, then taking off $3 \times 4(00)$ more, leaving 504. On the second row, $2 \times 24(0)$ is subtracted from 504, leaving 24. On the third row, 1×24 is subtracted from 24, leaving a remainder of 0. Despite the unusual arrangement, the general scheme of the galley method is therefore much like our own.

Problem Set 6

1. Carry out each division showing each estimate as in the examples of Section 7. Then check the answers by multiplying.

   (a) $300 \div 13$ (b) $736 \div 32$ (c) $5,681 \div 13$
   (d) $14,864 \div 64$ (e) $9,774 \div 362$ (f) $9,900 \div 362$

2. Show how you used multiplication in Problem 1(a).
3. Give the absolute value of each of the following numbers:

   (a) 5   (b) -23 (c) 0
   (d) 365   (e) -987 (f) -1

4. (a) Make up an illustrative verbal problem to which $40 \div 11$ would furnish the "under" result.
   (b) The same as for (a), but to obtain the "over" result.
   (c) To obtain the "nearest" result.
5. Do the problem $6,657 \div 21$ by the scratch method.

BIBLIOGRAPHY

Banks, J. Houston, *Learning and Teaching Arithmetic*, 2nd ed. Boston: Allyn and Bacon, Inc., 1964, pp. 181–290.

Bell, Clifford, Clela D. Hammond, and Robert B. Herrera, *Fundamentals of Arithmetic for Teachers*. New York: John Wiley and Sons, Inc., 1962, pp. 59–77, 91–109.

Bell, E. T., *Development of Mathematics*, 2d ed. New York: McGraw-Hill Book Company, Inc., 1945.

Boole, Mary E., *Lectures in the Logic of Arithmetic*. Oxford: Clarendon Press, 1903.

Davis, Robert B., *Discovery in Mathematics: A Text for Teachers*. Reading, Mass.: Addison-Wesley Publishing Company, Inc., 1964, pp. 130–132.

Dubitsky, Pauline, "Multiplication: Using Equations and Postulates in Patterned Form," *The Arithmetic Teacher* (December 1963), pp. 509–513.

Grossnickle, Foster E., and Leo J. Brueckner, *Discovering Meanings in Elementary School Mathematics*, 4th ed. New York: Holt, Rinehart and Winston, 1963, pp. 160–211.

Lung, Clarence, "Division Made Easy," *The Arithmetic Teacher* (November 1963), pp. 453–454.

Mueller, Francis J., *Arithmetic: Its Structure and Concepts*, 2d ed. Englewood Cliffs, N.J.: Prentice-Hall, Inc., 1964, pp. 163–188.

Peck, Lyman C., and Niswonger, Dan, "Measurement and Partition—Commutativity of Multiplication," *The Arithmetic Teacher* (April 1964), pp. 258–259.

School Mathematics Study Group, *Studies in Mathematics, Vol. IX: A Brief Course in Mathematics for Elementary School Teachers*, rev. ed. Stanford, Calif.: Leland Stanford Junior University, 1963, pp. 77–126.

Stern, Catherine, and Margaret B. Stern, "Comments on Ancient Egyptian Multiplication," *The Arithmetic Teacher* (April 1964), pp. 254–257.

Swenson, Esther J., *Teaching Arithmetic To Children.* New York: The Macmillan Company, 1964, pp. 191–291.

Ward, Morgan, and Clarence Ethel Hardgrove, *Modern Elementary Mathematics.* Reading, Mass.: Addison-Wesley Publishing Company, Inc., 1964, pp. 145–158.

Wirtz, Robert W., Morton Botel, and B. G. Nunley, *Discovery in Elementary School Mathematics.* New York: Encyclopedia Britannica, Inc., 1963, Unit 11.

Youse, Bevan K., *Arithmetic: A Modern Approach.* Englewood Cliffs, N.J.: Prentice-Hall, Inc., 1963, pp. 49–57.

7

RATIONAL NUMBERS
OF ARITHMETIC:

Names of the Form $\frac{a}{b}$ $(b \neq 0)$

1. TERMINOLOGY

In this book we shall use the terms *rational number of arithmetic*, *fractional number*, and *fraction* to mean the same thing—a number that has a name of the form a/b, where a and b are whole numbers and $b \neq 0$. We shall call a name of such form a **fractional numeral**.

Thus, $\frac{4}{5}$ is a fractional number. Also 6 is a fractional number, because it can be named by a fractional numeral $\frac{6}{1}$, which is of the required form. Also, .65 is a fractional number, because it has a name of the form a/b, for example, 65/100.

Each fractional number has many names of the form a/b. For example, some of the fractional numerals for 0.2 are

$$\frac{1}{5}, \frac{2}{10}, \frac{20}{100}, \text{ and } \frac{50}{250}.$$

2. AN ANCIENT BUGABOO

In past eras, eminent scholars quailed before fractions even as the school children of today.

Unit fractional numerals—those with numerators 1, such as $\frac{1}{2}, \frac{1}{3}, \frac{1}{4}$—were used almost exclusively for centuries, even after notations had been developed for representing other fractions.

Perhaps it was difficult for our forebears to conceive of operating with a *pair* of numbers as though the pair were a single number. Yet in avoiding this conceptual difficulty, they had to resort to computational techniques of forbidding complexity. In the famed mathematical compendium of the Egyptians, the *Rhind papyrus*, the ratio of 2 to 43 is expressed in the form

$$\frac{1}{42} + \frac{1}{86} + \frac{1}{129} + \frac{1}{301}.$$

The papyrus gives a list of such decompositions, from 2/5 to 2/101. (These quotients are the *doubles* of fractions that can be named by unit fractional numerals and were needed to facilitate multiplication and division by numbers represented by mixed numerals according to the Egyptian doubling and summing scheme.)

The Greeks finally developed an adequate notation for all fractions, similar to our own. But their early mathematicians had found repugnant the notion of taking parts of a unit, *unity* being for them a true numerical "atom," even a Deity symbol. So before Archimedes' time, only *ratios* of integers were treated, and great stress was laid upon the idea of proportion. Greek merchants were less particular, using fractions without troubling themselves over philosophical or theological objections.

The Romans side-stepped fraction difficulties by creating submultiples (twelfths, twenty-fourths, etc.) of their common units of money, weights, and measures—even as today we use inches instead of twelfths of feet, ounces instead of sixteenths of pounds, cents instead of hundredths of dollars.

The use of unit fractional numerals carried over into medieval times, leading to many awkward situations and computational errors. The ordinary mercantile calculations did not suffer, since they were usually carried out on the abacus or counting table, with the Roman subunits playing whatever fractional roles were required.

In early Renaissance times, the use of fractions became widespread. The rules we use today for adding, subtracting, multiplying, and simplifying fractions were set down in more or less their present forms. The last of our modern rules to appear was that for dividing by a fraction. Surprisingly enough, this simple rule did not come into common use until the seventeenth century, although a Hindu writer had cited it a thousand years earlier.

Note on Egyptian Techniques of Handling Fractions

The Egyptian techniques for handling fractions are explained in detail in pages 19–30 of Van Der Waerden, *Science Awakening*. Also, see pages 73–78 of Neugebauer, *The Exact Sciences in Antiquity*. Apparently the Egyptians put down a few obvious relations between simple unit fractions, then applied these to derive other relations. This is a true example of deductive technique, perhaps the closest approach made by the Egyptians to the concept of mathematical and scientific derivation or "proof."

Let us write $\tilde{2}$ for $\frac{1}{2}$, $\tilde{3}$ for $\frac{1}{3}$, etc., so that our unit fractional numeral will be structurally similar to the Egyptians'. Also, $\tilde{\tilde{3}}$ for $\frac{2}{3}$. Note that multiplying the number named under the "wave" by an integer actually divides the fraction by that integer: $\tilde{6}$ is *half* of $\tilde{3}$, etc. The following relations are obvious:

$$(1) \qquad \tilde{2} + \tilde{2} = 1 \qquad\qquad (\tfrac{1}{2} + \tfrac{1}{2} = 1)$$
$$(2) \qquad \tilde{3} + \tilde{3} = \tilde{\tilde{3}} \qquad\qquad (\tfrac{1}{3} + \tfrac{1}{3} = \tfrac{2}{3})$$
$$(3) \quad \tilde{3} + \tilde{3} + \tilde{3} = 1 \qquad (\tfrac{1}{3} + \tfrac{1}{3} + \tfrac{1}{3} = 1)$$

Halving relations (2) and (3), we get

$$\tilde{6} + \tilde{6} = \tilde{3} \qquad \text{and} \qquad \tilde{6} + \tilde{6} + \tilde{6} = \tilde{2}.$$

These combine, giving $\tilde{3} + \tilde{6} = \tilde{2}$. Using the addition property of equations and adding $\tilde{6}$, we obtain

$$\tilde{3} + \tilde{6} + \tilde{6} = \tilde{2} + \tilde{6}, \quad \text{or} \quad \tilde{3} + \tilde{3} = \tilde{2} + \tilde{6}, \quad \text{or} \quad \tilde{\tilde{3}} = \tilde{2} + \tilde{6}.$$

Halving this gives $\tilde{3} = \tilde{4} + \widetilde{12}$. This procedure of deriving new relations can be carried on indefinitely.

One method of finding quotients was to build up the dividend in terms of successive halves of the divisor: $1, \tilde{2}, \tilde{4}, \tilde{8}, \ldots$. To find $\frac{2}{7}$, for example, we proceed by halving:

$$1 \times 7 = 7 \qquad\qquad (= 6 + 1)$$
$$\tilde{2} \times 7 = 3 + \tilde{2} \qquad\quad (= 2 + 1 + \tilde{2})$$
$$\tilde{4} \times 7 = 1 + \tilde{2} + \tilde{4}$$

At this stage, we need to add $\tilde{4}$ to $1 + \tilde{2} + \tilde{4}$ to get 2. But $\tilde{4} = \widetilde{28} \times 7$. Hence $2 = (\tilde{4} + \widetilde{28}) \times 7$, so that

$$2 \div 7 = \tilde{4} + \widetilde{28}.$$

3. COMPARING SETS

The *meaning* of a natural number may be described in various ways. The number 3 may be used ordinally, to designate a counted position: "3rd shelf from bottom." It may be used as an integer, to characterize a net outcome: "3 up" (golf). It may be used as a scale number, "3 ft. long," an interpretation we have not yet explored. It may be used in a cardinal sense to tell the size of a set: "3 eggs." It is, in fact, only this last interpretation which we have fully exploited, to the extent that it has been our basic theme. The relationship of other interpretations to the set, or cardinal, concept is generally apparent, so that it would scarcely be worth while to develop them all in detail.

Fractions likewise have various interpretations. We may describe their meaning in terms of *ratio, partition, division,* or concretely through *length, area,* etc. The Greeks conceived of a fraction as picturing a ratio. In theory, the ratio approach is perhaps the simplest. But the idea of a ratio is more abstract than, say, the idea of partition. Hence we shall not fix upon any one interpretation as basic to the development but shall use several. Such a procedure is contrary to the mathematician's idea of how a subject ought to be treated, but is in accordance with historical patterns of development (also with "learning" patterns), whereby concepts may evolve in several directions simultaneously.

We ordinarily compare the sizes of two sets in one of two ways. We may ask: *How many more* objects are there in one set than in the other? To answer this question we usually perform the operation of subtraction. Or we may ask the question: The number of objects in one set is *how many times* as great as the number of objects in the other set? To answer that, we usually resort to division.

Suppose that John has 6 apples, while Bill has only 2. To make the comparison between the sets in the "how many more" sense, we *subtract* the number of one from the number of the other. We say, "John has 4 *more* apples than Bill."

To make the comparison in the "how many times" sense, we divide one number by the other. We say, "John has 3 *times as many* apples as Bill."

If we are limited to natural numbers, our comparisons in the *how many times* sense will be restricted. Suppose that Ted has 3 apples, while Bill has 2. In natural numbers, we can only make "proportional" or "ratio" statements: "Ted's number of apples is to Bill's number as 3 is to 2."

We now introduce new numbers, called **rational numbers of arithmetic** or **fractional numbers,** or **fractions,** which permit us to make comparisons in the *how many times* sense between any two sets. The notation is

$$\frac{a}{b} \qquad (\text{``}a \text{ over } b\text{''}),$$

where a and b are the numbers of the sets. The number named by a is the **numerator,** the number named by b is the **denominator,** and $b \neq 0$.

In place of saying, "Bill's number of apples is to Ted's number as 2 is to 3," we can say, "Bill has $\frac{2}{3}$ (two-thirds) as many apples as Ted." Or we may say, "Ted has $\frac{3}{2}$ (three-halves) as many apples as Bill."

Returning to John and Bill, with 6 and 2 apples, respectively, we note that the statement "John has 3 times as many apples as Bill" implies a multiplication. The number of the second set (John's) is obtained from the number of the first (Bill's) by multiplying by 3, the quotient of 6 by 2:

$$②\overset{\times 3}{\longrightarrow}⑥$$

We take the statement "Bill has $\frac{2}{3}$ as many apples as Ted" as also implying a multiplication. We regard $\frac{2}{3}$ as the quotient of 2 and 3:

$$\frac{2}{3} = 2 \div 3.$$

And we say that when 3 is multiplied by $\frac{2}{3}$, the result is 2:

$$\frac{2}{3} \times 3 = 2.$$

$$\textcircled{3} \xrightarrow{\times \frac{2}{3}} \textcircled{2}$$

4. MULTIPLYING FRACTIONAL NUMBERS

You have seen that $\frac{2}{3} \cdot 3 = 2$. Similarly, $\frac{5}{7} \cdot 7 = 5$, $\frac{11}{3} \cdot 3 = 11$, and $\frac{12}{5} \cdot 5 = 12$. In general,

$$\frac{a}{b} \cdot b = a \qquad (b \neq 0).$$

What is $\frac{4}{5} \cdot 6$ equal to? Let us say that $x = \frac{4}{5} \cdot 6$. Then it follows by the multiplication property of equations that

$$5 \cdot x = 5 \cdot \left(\frac{4}{5} \cdot 6 \right).$$

By associativity

$$5 \cdot \left(\frac{4}{5} \cdot 6 \right) = \left(5 \cdot \frac{4}{5} \right) \cdot 6,$$

and therefore

$$5 \cdot x = \left(5 \cdot \frac{4}{5} \right) \cdot 6$$
$$= 4 \cdot 6.$$

If $5 \cdot x = 4 \cdot 6$, then $x = \dfrac{4 \cdot 6}{5}$.

We stated at the outset that $x = \dfrac{4}{5} \cdot 6$ and have shown that $x = \dfrac{4 \cdot 6}{5}$. Therefore,

$$\frac{4}{5} \cdot 6 = \frac{4 \cdot 6}{5}.$$

In general,

$$\frac{a}{b} \cdot c = \frac{ac}{b} \qquad (b \neq 0).$$

We have developed a way for multiplying a fractional number by a whole number:

$$\forall_a \forall_b \forall_c \frac{a}{b} \cdot c = \frac{ac}{b} \qquad (a, b, c \text{ natural numbers})$$

If we seek to extend these properties to whole numbers (zero as well as the natural numbers), we find that the extension does not work out in the case of a zero denominator. The fraction candidate $\frac{5}{0}$, for example, would have to mean $5 \div 0$, a number which when multiplied by 0 gives 5:

$$\frac{5}{0} \times 0 = 5 \qquad (?)$$

$\frac{5}{0}$ cannot denote a whole number, because the product of a whole number and zero is zero. Further, if we try to define $\frac{5}{0}$ as some new kind of fraction, we meet with trouble. For assuming the above relation, $(\frac{5}{0}) \times 0 = 5$, and supposing that the associative property is to be maintained, we find:

$$25 = 5 \times 5 = \left(\frac{5}{0} \times 0\right) \times 5 = \frac{5}{0} \times (0 \times 5) = \frac{5}{0} \times 0 = 5.$$

It is therefore impossible to define $\frac{5}{0}$ in any satisfactory way. We must rule out the concept of a fraction with a zero denominator, as well as the equivalent concept of dividing by zero.

The matter of dividing 0 by 0 is somewhat different. Consistent with the inverse relation between multiplication and division, if $\frac{0}{0} = x$, then $x \cdot 0 = 0$. But the latter is true for every number x. Thus, for example, $\frac{0}{0} = 5$ and $\frac{0}{0} = 8$. We could not accept, however, these two statements and have a consistent arithmetic, since, according to the transitive property of equality, if $5 = \frac{0}{0}$ and $\frac{0}{0} = 8$, then $5 = 8$. For this reason, we rule out division of 0 by 0.

A zero *numerator* is allowable. The number 0 can be obtained by multiplying 0 by 5. The inverse operation, dividing by 5, when applied to the result 0, therefore gives 0 again. So $0 \div 5 = 0$, and $\frac{0}{5} = 0$, as shown in

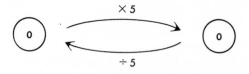

Fig. 7-1

Figure 7-1. Also $\frac{2}{3} \times 0 = 0 \times \frac{2}{3} = 0$, etc. For $\frac{2}{3} \times 0 = 2 \times \frac{0}{3} = 2 \times 0 = 0$, or

$$0 \times \frac{2}{3} = \frac{0 \times 2}{3} = \frac{0}{3} = 0.$$

Now to find the product of two fractional numbers $\frac{a}{b} \cdot \frac{c}{d}$, we consider the example $\frac{3}{4} \cdot \frac{5}{7}$.

Let us say that $x = \frac{3}{4} \cdot \frac{5}{7}$. Then, as above, it follows that $4 \cdot x = 4 \cdot \left(\frac{3}{4} \cdot \frac{5}{7} \right)$ or

$$4 \cdot x = \left(4 \cdot \frac{3}{4} \right) \cdot \frac{5}{7} \qquad \text{(Why?)}$$

$$= 3 \cdot \frac{5}{7}$$

$$= \frac{3 \cdot 5}{7}$$

If $4 \cdot x = \frac{3 \cdot 5}{7}$, then $(7 \cdot 4) \cdot x = 3 \cdot 5$ and $x = \frac{3 \cdot 5}{7 \cdot 4}$. Since $x = \frac{3}{4} \cdot \frac{5}{7}$ and $x = \frac{3 \cdot 5}{4 \cdot 7}$, it follows that $\frac{3}{4} \cdot \frac{5}{7} = \frac{3 \cdot 5}{4 \cdot 7}$. In general,

$$\forall_a \forall_{b \neq 0} \forall_c \forall_{d \neq 0} \quad \frac{a}{b} \cdot \frac{c}{d} = \frac{ac}{bd} \qquad (a,\, b,\, c,\, d \text{ whole numbers}).$$

The quotient of two fractional numbers may be defined in essentially the same way in which we defined the quotient of two natural numbers. Given the fractions f_1 and f_2, by $f_1 \div f_2$ is meant the number f such that $f \times f_2 = f_1$. So with $f_1 = \frac{a}{b}$ and $f_2 = \frac{c}{d}$ we have:

$$f \times \frac{c}{d} = \frac{a}{b}, \qquad \text{where } f = \frac{a}{b} \div \frac{c}{d}.$$

But to get from $\frac{c}{d}$ to $\frac{a}{b}$, we may multiply by d and divide by c to get 1, then multiply by $\frac{a}{b}$. Hence:

$$f = \frac{a}{b} \times \frac{d}{c}.$$

Thus,

$$\forall_a \forall_{b \neq 0} \forall_{c \neq 0} \forall_{d \neq 0} \quad \frac{a}{b} \div \frac{c}{d} = \frac{a}{b} \times \frac{d}{c}.$$

For example, $\frac{2}{3} \div \frac{5}{7} = \frac{2}{3} \times \frac{7}{5} = \frac{14}{15}$.

In application, the use of the word "of" following a fraction is a signal to multiply: "$\frac{2}{3}$ of 6" means "$\frac{2}{3} \times 6$." A person may be instructed to take two-thirds *of* a group of 6 apples, upon which he takes $\frac{2}{3} \times 6$, or 4 of them. A taxpayer complains that $\frac{2}{5}$ *of* his salary goes for taxes. If his salary is \$25,000, he is claiming that $\frac{2}{5} \times \$25,000$, or \$10,000, is paid out in taxes.

Problems involving successive multiplication by fractions may be treated as such, or may be handled by first multiplying the fractions. If a worker "takes home" $\frac{4}{5}$ of his gross pay, and his wife uses $\frac{3}{4}$ of this in her household budget, then the amount used by his wife is $\frac{3}{4} \times \frac{4}{5}$, or $\frac{12}{20}$ ($= \frac{3}{5}$) of his gross pay. [For if the gross pay is P, we have $\frac{3}{4} \times (\frac{4}{5} \times P)$ $= (\frac{3}{4} \times \frac{4}{5}) \times P = \frac{3}{5} \times P$.]

Division applications occur now and then in everyday arithmetic. If a man walks $\frac{4}{5}$ of a mile in 16 minutes, then his speed in miles per hour is

$$\frac{4}{5} \div \frac{16}{60} = \frac{4}{5} \times \frac{60}{16} = \frac{4 \times 60}{5 \times 16} = 3.$$

If there are equal numbers of men, women, and children in a group and there are 150 adults, then the whole group numbers $150 \div \frac{2}{3}$ or $150 \times \frac{3}{2}$ or 225. (But this last problem would undoubtedly be worked in practice without using fractions explicitly—by dividing 150 by 2 to get the common number of the groups of men, women, children, then multiplying by 3 to get the total. The walking-rate problem can also be worked by considering that the walker traveled each $\frac{1}{5}$ mile in $\frac{4}{60}$ of an hour, hence 1 mile in $5 \times \frac{4}{60} = \frac{1}{3}$ of an hour, hence 3 miles in 1 hour.)

Yet the "invert, then multiply" rule is used more frequently than many teachers and educators realize. When the housewife cuts three grapefruit into halves, she knows at once that she will get *twice* three servings. In cases of this sort the division concept is applied, even though the problem is not explicitly formulated as one involving division by a fraction.

Problem Set 1

1. Given that George has 8 pencils, while Ben has 2, compare the sets in "how many more" and "how many times" senses.

2. Given sets A and B with a and b elements, respectively, B compares with A as b to a. We get b from a by multiplying:

$$a \xrightarrow{\times \frac{b}{a}} b$$

Show how this relationship works out in each of the following cases:

$a = n(A)$	2	3	3	6	4	8
$b = n(B)$	6	12	1	2	3	6

3. The statement "$\frac{1}{2} = \frac{2}{4}$" means that $\frac{1}{2}$ and $\frac{2}{4}$ are two fractional numerals naming the same fractional number. What does the statement "$\frac{1}{3} \neq \frac{1}{2}$" mean?

4. Explain why 10 is a rational number.
5. Give two fractional numerals for 0.7.
6. Explain why 0.31 is a rational number.
7. Compute the products.

   (a) $\frac{1}{3} \times 2$ (b) $\frac{2}{3} \times 6$ (c) $\frac{3}{4} \times 5$ (d) $\frac{3}{5} \times 15$

8. Show that, if $\frac{3}{0}$ is regarded as a meaningful expression, with $\frac{3}{0} \times 0 = 3$, then it follows that $9 = 3$.
9. Show that $\frac{0}{3} = 0$.
10. Using the transitive property of equality, prove that if $\frac{0}{0} = 3$ and $\frac{0}{0} = 76$, then $3 = 76$.
11. Compute the products:

    (a) $\frac{2}{3} \times \frac{3}{8}$ (b) $\frac{1}{2} \times \frac{4}{3}$ (c) $\frac{2}{5} \times \frac{4}{3}$ (d) $\frac{3}{4} \times \frac{4}{3}$ (e) $\frac{12}{5} \times \frac{5}{12}$

12. Compute the quotients:

    (a) $\frac{2}{3} \div \frac{5}{2}$ (b) $\frac{3}{5} \div \frac{3}{4}$ (c) $\frac{5}{1} \div \frac{1}{2}$ (d) $\frac{5}{7} \div \frac{5}{7}$ (e) $\frac{1}{2} \div \frac{1}{3}$

13. If plums are selling at 3 for 10¢, (a) how much will 2 dozen cost? (b) how many can be bought for 50¢? (Do these in terms of fractions.)
14. If a person pays an income tax of $\frac{1}{5}$ of his salary, and $\frac{3}{5}$ of this tax is used for defense expenditures, what fractional part of his salary goes toward defense?
15. What is a person's reading rate in words per minute if he reads 100 words in 8 sec.?

5. DIFFERENT NUMERALS FOR THE SAME FRACTIONAL NUMBER

The two entries in each row of the table at the right give the numbers of elements in set A and set B. When A and B have 1 and 3 elements, respectively, then set B contains 3 *times as many* elements as A, and the fraction associated with the comparison is $\frac{3}{1} = 3$. Likewise, when sets A and B have 4 and 12 elements, the set B contains 3 times as many elements as A, and the associated fraction is $\frac{12}{4} = 3$. *In these and in the other listed cases, the associated fraction is always the same number.*

NUMBER IN SET	
Set A	*Set B*
1	3
2	6
3	9
4	12
5	15
6	18

The fractional numerals $\frac{3}{1}$, $\frac{6}{2}$, $\frac{9}{3}$, etc. are thus merely different ways of denoting the same number:

$$\frac{3}{1} = \frac{6}{2} = \frac{9}{3} = \frac{12}{4} = \cdots .$$

The second tabular exhibit brings out the same facts with reference to a pair of sets with numbers in the ratio of 2 to 3. Set B has $\frac{2}{3}$ as many elements as set A. This associated fraction can be named in many ways:

$$\frac{2}{3} = \frac{4}{6} = \frac{6}{9} = \frac{8}{12} = \frac{10}{15} = \cdots .$$

NUMBER IN SET	
Set A	*Set B*
3	2
6	4
9	6
12	8
15	10

The numeral $\frac{2}{3}$ is the simplest, and such a numeral is said to be **in lowest terms**. Note that 2 and 3 are relatively prime, that is, they have 1 as their only common factor. We can obtain different numerals for $\frac{2}{3}$ by multiplying 2 and 3 by some natural number. For example,

$$\frac{2}{3} = \frac{2 \cdot 2}{3 \cdot 2} = \frac{4}{6}$$
$$= \frac{2 \cdot 3}{3 \cdot 3} = \frac{6}{9}$$
$$= \frac{2 \cdot 4}{3 \cdot 4} = \frac{8}{12}$$

and so on.

The truth of these statements is based on the property that, for every number x, $x \cdot 1 = x$. To show how this property enters into consideration, examine the following:

$$\frac{2}{3} = \frac{2}{3} \cdot 1 = \frac{2}{3} \cdot \frac{2}{2} = \frac{2 \cdot 2}{3 \cdot 2} = \frac{4}{6}.$$

Denoting by N the set of natural numbers, we can state this in general form:

$$\forall_{x \in N} \frac{2}{3} = \frac{2x}{3x}$$

And more generally still,

$$\forall_{x \in N} \forall_{a \in N} \forall_{b \in N} \frac{a}{b} = \frac{ax}{bx}.$$

Let us now observe a pattern that leads from more complicated to less complicated names.

$$\frac{18}{24} = \frac{18}{24} \div 1 = \frac{18}{24} \div \frac{6}{6} = \frac{18 \div 6}{24 \div 6} = \frac{3}{4}.$$

Observe that $\frac{3}{4}$ is in lowest terms. Furthermore, observe that 6 is the **Greatest Common Divisor** of 18 and 24. Now consider another example:

$$\frac{8}{20} = \frac{8}{20} \div 1 = \frac{8}{20} \div \frac{4}{4} = \frac{8 \div 4}{20 \div 4} = \frac{2}{5}.$$

Here again $\frac{2}{5}$ is in lowest terms and $4 = \text{GCD } (8,20)$. To generalize,

$$\forall_{x \in N} \forall_{a \in N} \forall_{b \in N} \frac{ax}{bx} = \frac{a}{b}.$$

We may compare two fractions by dividing one into the other, but it is more direct to express them both with the same denominator, then to compare their numerators. According as one numerator is less than, equal to, or greater than the other, so are the fractions. Thus,

$$\frac{11}{24} > \frac{7}{24} \quad \text{and} \quad \frac{2}{9} < \frac{3}{9}.$$

Two or more fractions may be named by numerals having as their *common denominator* the LCM of the denominators of the given fractions. (The **Lowest Common Multiple** of the denominators is occasionally called the *lowest common denominator*.) Suppose we wish to compare $\frac{3}{8}$ and $\frac{5}{12}$. We find:

$$\text{LCM } (8,12) = 24 \qquad \frac{3}{8} = \frac{3 \cdot 3}{8 \cdot 3} = \frac{9}{24}$$

$$\frac{5}{12} = \frac{5 \cdot 2}{12 \cdot 2} = \frac{10}{24}$$

Since $\frac{10}{24} > \frac{9}{24}$, it is true that $\frac{5}{12} > \frac{3}{8}$.

In multiplying or dividing fractions, we may look for simpler names piecemeal or all at once. The piecemeal scheme is usually easier. Using the fact that GCD (48,300) = 12, we have:

$$\frac{6}{20} \times \frac{8}{15} = \frac{6 \times 8}{20 \times 15} = \frac{48}{300} = \frac{12 \times 4}{12 \times 25} = \frac{4}{25}.$$

However, we may first completely factor, then apply commutative and associative properties as needed to obtain the product in simplest form. This procedure is illustrated:

$$\frac{6}{20} \times \frac{8}{15} = \frac{2 \times 3}{2 \times 2 \times 5} \times \frac{2 \times 2 \times 2}{3 \times 5} = \frac{2}{2} \times \frac{2}{2} \times \frac{3}{3} \times \frac{2 \times 2}{5 \times 5} = \frac{4}{25}.$$

Another way to obtain this product is to factor the numerator and denominator of each fraction separately. Observe that

$$\text{GCD } (6,20) = 2 \text{ and GCD } (8,15) = 1.$$

$$\frac{6}{20} \times \frac{8}{15} = \frac{3 \times 2}{10 \times 2} \times \frac{8}{15} = \frac{3}{10} \times \frac{8}{15}$$

$$= \frac{3 \times 2 \times 2 \times 2}{2 \times 5 \times 3 \times 5}$$

$$= \frac{2}{2} \times \frac{3}{3} \times \frac{2 \times 2}{5 \times 5}$$

$$= \frac{4}{25}$$

"Cancellation" is a physical, not a mathematical, operation. Any procedure involving a cancellation must therefore be justified in terms of whatever mathematical operation was performed: addition, subtraction, multiplication, or division. In the previous example, if the work should be shown as

$$\frac{6}{20} \times \frac{8}{15} = \frac{2}{20} \times \frac{8}{5} = \frac{2 \times 2}{5 \times 5} = \frac{4}{25}$$

then the mathematical operations that were performed are the following:

$$\frac{6}{20} \times \frac{8}{15} = \frac{6 \times 8}{20 \times 15} = \frac{(6 \times 8) \div 3}{(20 \times 15) \div 3} \qquad \text{(divide numerator and denominator by 3)}$$

$$= \frac{2 \times 8}{20 \times 5}$$

$$= \frac{(2 \times 8) \div 4}{(20 \times 5) \div 4} \qquad \text{(divide numerator and denominator by 4)}$$

$$= \frac{2 \times 2}{5 \times 5}$$

$$= \frac{4}{25}$$

The various rules and techniques for handling fractions that we have discussed in the last few pages all stem from the multiple ways that exist of expressing a number in fractional form. It is of paramount importance that one should maintain in his mind the clear-cut distinction between a *number* and the fractional numerals by which it may be designated: $\frac{1}{2}, \frac{2}{4}, \frac{3}{6}, \frac{4}{8}$, for example. These fractional numerals are merely different names for the same number. It is not just the scientist and the engineer who must heed this lesson in the basic semantics of symbolic usage. So must the housewife, as she indulges in painful number juggling while trying to transform a recipe serving 6 into one serving 4.

Confusion between the number and numeral is the common source of error in operating with fractions. Even many college students cling to the delusion that fractions are "special" numbers characterized by a superior kind of invariance: "Whatever you do to them, you don't change the value." This blithe attitude records itself in ghastly muscle work like:

$$\frac{3}{4} = \frac{3-1}{4-1} = \frac{2}{3}, \qquad \frac{4}{5} + \frac{3}{4} = \frac{3}{5}, \qquad \frac{22}{32} = \frac{2}{3}.$$

It is difficult to shatter the delusion and restore the student to mathematical sanity by convincing him that a fraction as a number possesses no special property—that adding to it any number except 0 changes it, that multiplying it by any number except 1 changes it, etc.

Problem Set 2

In Problems 1 to 4, write fractional numerals in lowest terms. (Find the GCD of numerator and denominator, and divide the numerator and denominator by it.)

1. (a) $\dfrac{12}{16}$ (b) $\dfrac{20}{25}$ (c) $\dfrac{6}{4}$ (d) $\dfrac{3}{111}$ (e) $\dfrac{32}{48}$

2. (a) $\dfrac{35}{60}$ (b) $\dfrac{200}{75}$ (c) $\dfrac{63}{84}$ (d) $\dfrac{60}{100}$ (e) $\dfrac{45}{72}$

3. (a) $\dfrac{127}{195}$ (b) $\dfrac{32}{200}$ (c) $\dfrac{105}{168}$ (d) $\dfrac{84}{270}$ (e) $\dfrac{120}{347}$

4. (a) $\dfrac{315}{445}$ (b) $\dfrac{264}{480}$ (c) $\dfrac{323}{437}$ (d) $\dfrac{391}{667}$ (e) $\dfrac{851}{1073}$

5. True or false?

   (a) $\dfrac{6}{15} = \dfrac{74}{185}$ (b) $\dfrac{6}{15} = \dfrac{50}{124}$ (c) $\dfrac{9}{12} = \dfrac{35}{44}$

   (d) $\dfrac{70}{112} = \dfrac{45}{72}$ (e) $\dfrac{6}{14} = \dfrac{11}{24}$ (f) $\dfrac{216}{126} = \dfrac{284}{161}$

   (g) $\dfrac{33}{88} = \dfrac{2223}{5848}$ (h) $\dfrac{17}{60} = \dfrac{8}{35}$ (i) $\dfrac{13}{42} = \dfrac{17}{56}$

   (j) $\dfrac{3}{4} > \dfrac{4}{5}$ (k) $\dfrac{10}{11} < \dfrac{11}{12}$ (l) $\dfrac{4}{7} = \dfrac{5}{8}$

   (m) $\dfrac{1}{4} < \dfrac{1}{3}$ (n) $\dfrac{4}{3} < \dfrac{5}{4}$ (o) $\dfrac{1}{9} < \dfrac{2}{17}$

6. Compute the products. Before multiplying, factor each numerator and denominator completely.

   (a) $\dfrac{12}{35} \times \dfrac{21}{24}$ (b) $\dfrac{15}{32} \times \dfrac{56}{105}$ (c) $\dfrac{6}{10} \times \dfrac{4}{27} \times \dfrac{9}{15}$

7. Are there any conditions under which 1 can be added to both numerator and denominator without changing the value of a fractional numeral? (*Hint:* Set $(a + 1)/(b + 1) = a/b$, and consider the implications.)

6. ADDING FRACTIONAL NUMBERS

A comparison of a part of a group with the entire group is simpler to conceive and to talk about than is a comparison between just any two groups. In initially discussing the addition of fractions, we shall use the part-whole concept, even though it temporarily restricts us to fractions that are less than 1.

Consider the set of a dozen blocks in Figure 7-2. Several fractions can be represented concretely as subsets of this given **base set**. To represent $\frac{1}{2}$,

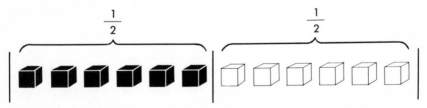

Fig. 7-2

for example, we **partition** the given set into two mutually matching subsets—6 blocks in each. Either subset then *represents* $\frac{1}{2}$. Since the representation is by 6 objects out of 12, we choose the numeral $\frac{6}{12}$ for $\frac{1}{2}$. To represent $\frac{2}{3}$, we partition the set of 12 into 3 mutually matching subsets, then take any 2 of the subsets, Figure 7-3. Since 8 blocks are chosen from 12, we choose the numeral $\frac{8}{12}$ for $\frac{2}{3}$.

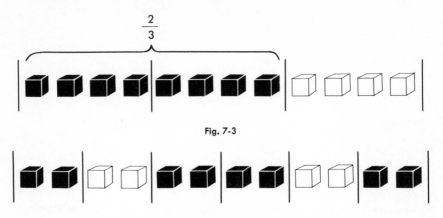

Fig. 7-3

Fig. 7-4

To reflect another concrete representation of $\frac{2}{3}$, we may choose $\frac{4}{6}$ as a numeral for $\frac{2}{3}$. In this case, we partition the set of 12 into 6 mutually matching subsets, then take any 4 of the subsets (Fig. 7-4). To correspond with the numeral $\frac{8}{12}$ for $\frac{2}{3}$, we choose 8 blocks from the 12 blocks, Figure 7-5.

Fig. 7-5

Should we wish to represent $\frac{2}{3}$ by $\frac{16}{24}$, our dozen blocks would be inadequate. We would have to use a new base set of 24 blocks (or some multiple of 24).

Let us now consider the addition of two fractions, $\frac{1}{3}$ and $\frac{1}{2}$, for example. Since $\frac{1}{3}$ can be represented by any 4 blocks and $\frac{1}{2}$ by any 6 blocks, the sum should be represented by $4 + 6$ or 10 blocks. But 10 blocks out of 12 correspond to a representation of $\frac{10}{12} = \frac{5}{6}$. Thus:

$$\frac{1}{3} + \frac{1}{2} = \frac{4}{12} + \frac{6}{12} = \frac{10}{12} = \frac{5}{6}.$$

What we have done above is to associate the *addition of two fractional numbers* with the *union of two sets that correspond to their representatives* (Fig. 7-6).

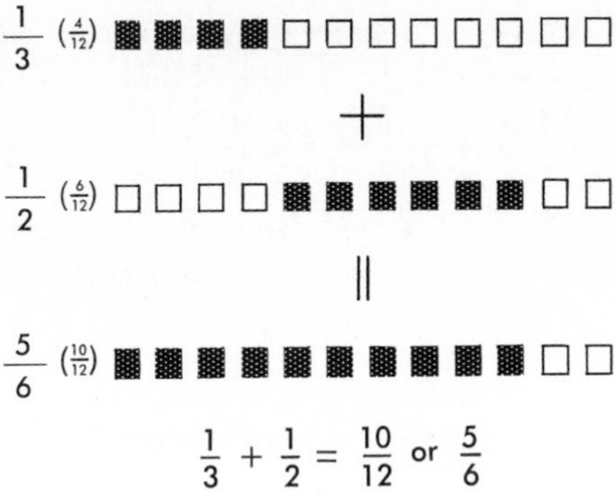

$\dfrac{1}{3}$ $(\tfrac{4}{12})$ ■ ■ ■ ■ □ □ □ □ □ □ □ □

$+$

$\dfrac{1}{2}$ $(\tfrac{6}{12})$ □ □ □ □ ■ ■ ■ ■ ■ ■ □ □

$\parallel$

$\dfrac{5}{6}$ $(\tfrac{10}{12})$ ■ ■ ■ ■ ■ ■ ■ ■ ■ ■ □ □

$$\frac{1}{3} + \frac{1}{2} = \frac{10}{12} \text{ or } \frac{5}{6}$$

Fig. 7-6 $\tfrac{1}{3} + \tfrac{1}{2} = \tfrac{10}{12}$ or $\tfrac{5}{6}$

Consider the sum

$$\frac{1}{4} + \frac{3}{10}.$$

In order to picture this addition, we need a base set of blocks large enough for both $\tfrac{1}{4}$ and $\tfrac{3}{10}$ to be represented. A number of blocks equal to the product of denominators, 4×10 or 40, will do. The least choice, however, is given by the LCM: LCM $(4,10) = 20$. With 20 blocks we have Figure 7-7.

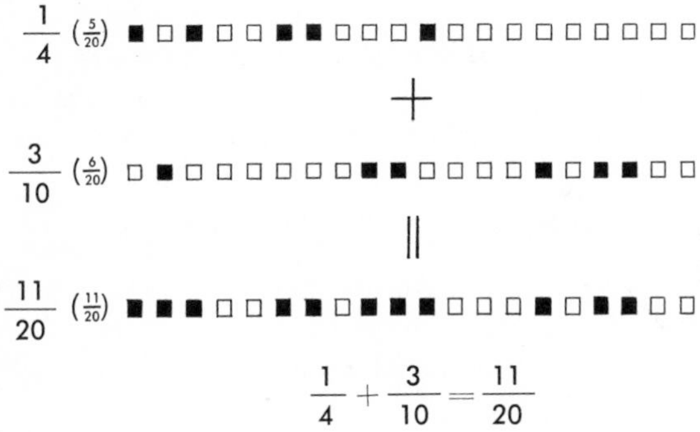

$\dfrac{1}{4}$ $(\tfrac{5}{20})$ ■ □ ■ □ □ ■ ■ □ □ □ ■ □ □ □ □ □ □ □ □ □

$+$

$\dfrac{3}{10}$ $(\tfrac{6}{20})$ □ ■ □ □ □ □ □ □ ■ ■ □ □ □ □ ■ □ ■ ■ □ □

$\parallel$

$\dfrac{11}{20}$ $(\tfrac{11}{20})$ ■ ■ ■ □ □ ■ ■ □ ■ ■ ■ □ □ □ ■ □ ■ ■ □ □

$$\frac{1}{4} + \frac{3}{10} = \frac{11}{20}$$

Fig. 7-7 $\tfrac{1}{4} + \tfrac{3}{10} = \tfrac{11}{20}$

On the basis of our discussion, we may frame a simple procedure for adding fractions: *Express both fractions by names having the same denominator* (the LCM of the given denominators being the best choice). *Add the numerators. Place this result over the common denominator.* This may be stated as

$$\forall_a \forall_b \forall_n \; \frac{a}{n} + \frac{b}{n} = \frac{a+b}{n} \qquad (a, b, n \text{ natural numbers}).$$

In this discussion, $a + b \leq n$.

Note that the above is a consequence of one of the distributive properties:

$$\frac{a}{n} + \frac{b}{n} = \frac{1}{n} \times a + \frac{1}{n} \times b = \frac{1}{n} \times (a + b) = \frac{a + b}{n}.$$

The subtraction of one fraction from another can be pictured as a take-away procedure with the blocks, the procedure being

$$\frac{a}{n} - \frac{b}{n} = \frac{a - b}{n}.$$

This procedure may be extended to fractions greater than 1. For example,

$$\frac{11}{4} + \frac{3}{2} = \frac{11}{4} + \frac{6}{4} = \frac{17}{4}.$$

If the numerator is greater than the denominator, as is the case in $\frac{17}{4}$, we can name the rational number by a *mixed numeral* or a whole-number name:

$$\frac{17}{4} = \frac{4 \times 4 + 1}{4} = \frac{4 \times 4}{4} + \frac{1}{4} = 4 + \frac{1}{4} = 4\frac{1}{4}.$$

$$\frac{16}{4} = \frac{4 \times 4}{4} = \frac{4}{1} = 4.$$

For another example, consider

$$\frac{207}{5} = \frac{5 \times 41 + 2}{5} = \frac{5 \times 41}{5} + \frac{2}{5} = 41 + \frac{2}{5} = 41\frac{2}{5}.$$

The expression $41\frac{2}{5}$ is an abbreviation for the sum $41 + \frac{2}{5}$. In practice, the procedure for finding a mixed numeral is carried out by dividing and using the pattern (obtained from the basic division relation):

$$\frac{\text{dividend}}{\text{divisor}} = \text{quotient} + \frac{\text{remainder}}{\text{divisor}}.$$

To reverse the procedure, we reverse the steps. (Many pupils are taught to follow a special rule, which enables them to do the work quickly but which, like all purely mechanical procedures, heightens the possibility of error.)

$$41\frac{2}{5} = 41 + \frac{2}{5} = \frac{205}{5} + \frac{2}{5} = \frac{207}{5}.$$

7. REMARKS ON TEACHING

In the work with fractions in the early school grades, pictorial representations using blocks or other objects are a major teaching aid. Twelve blocks make a good group to work with because the three most common fractional types, halves, thirds, and fourths, can be represented, compared, and added or subtracted. Rectangular lengths can also be used. "Pie slices" are among the common devices, $\frac{1}{2} + \frac{1}{4}$ being shown in Figure 7-8. Disks of cardboard or heavier materials are available com-

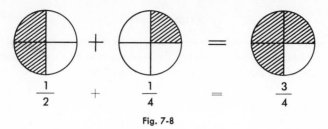

Fig. 7-8

mercially, cut up into sectors of different sizes, so that fractions can be represented. Thinner divided disks, with special backings, can be placed on flannel boards.

It is usual to introduce multiplication by first considering the multiplication of a fraction by a natural number:

$$4 \times \frac{1}{2} = \frac{1}{2} + \frac{1}{2} + \frac{1}{2} + \frac{1}{2} = \frac{1+1+1+1}{2} = \frac{4}{2} = 2.$$

The idea of $\frac{1}{2}$ *of* 4 is usually separately introduced as a partitioning concept (Fig. 7-9). It may then be suggested that, since $4 \times \frac{1}{2} = 2$, it is

Fig. 7-9

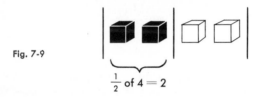

$\frac{1}{2}$ of 4 = 2

reasonable to assume that $\frac{1}{2} \times 4 = 2$. Hence $\frac{1}{2}$ of 4 can be taken as meaning $\frac{1}{2} \times 4$. The concept of the general case of multiplication of fractions can then be gradually built up.

After a pupil has learned the "area" or "two-way array" representation of natural number multiplication, as discussed in Chapter 4, he can be shown a similar representation for the multiplication of fractions. (See Fig. 7-10.)

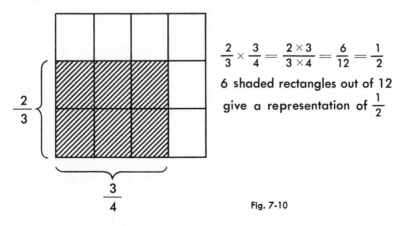

$$\frac{2}{3} \times \frac{3}{4} = \frac{2 \times 3}{3 \times 4} = \frac{6}{12} = \frac{1}{2}$$

6 shaded rectangles out of 12

give a representation of $\frac{1}{2}$

Fig. 7-10

Problem Set 3

In problem work involving fractional representation, sketch squares instead of three-dimensional blocks, shading the squares that form the representation. The following, for example, is a representation of $\frac{3}{4}$ as $\frac{6}{8}$:

In Problems 1 to 20, represent each fraction by the name requested. Vary your choice of "blocks," sometimes picking a consecutive group and at other times spotting them here and there.

	FRACTION TO BE REPRESENTED	FORM		FRACTION TO BE REPRESENTED	FORM
1.	$\frac{1}{2}$	$\frac{1}{2}$	2.	$\frac{1}{2}$	$\frac{2}{4}$
3.	$\frac{1}{2}$	$\frac{3}{6}$	4.	$\frac{1}{2}$	$\frac{4}{8}$
5.	$\frac{1}{2}$	$\frac{6}{12}$	6.	$\frac{1}{3}$	$\frac{1}{3}$
7.	$\frac{1}{3}$	$\frac{2}{6}$	8.	$\frac{1}{3}$	$\frac{3}{9}$
9.	$\frac{1}{3}$	$\frac{4}{12}$	10.	$\frac{1}{3}$	$\frac{8}{24}$
11.	$\frac{2}{3}$	$\frac{4}{6}$	12.	$\frac{2}{3}$	$\frac{8}{12}$
13.	$\frac{3}{4}$	$\frac{6}{8}$	14.	$\frac{3}{4}$	$\frac{9}{12}$
15.	$\frac{5}{6}$	$\frac{10}{12}$	16.	$\frac{3}{5}$	$\frac{6}{10}$
17.	$\frac{3}{8}$	$\frac{3}{8}$	18.	$\frac{3}{8}$	$\frac{6}{16}$
19.	$\frac{5}{8}$	$\frac{15}{24}$	20.	1	$\frac{4}{4}$

In Problems 21 to 29, picture each addition or subtraction in terms of fractional representations as was done in Section 6. Use the smallest possible base set in each case (LCM).

21. $\dfrac{1}{5} + \dfrac{2}{5}$ 22. $\dfrac{1}{2} + \dfrac{1}{4}$ 23. $\dfrac{1}{2} + \dfrac{1}{3}$

24. $\dfrac{3}{4} + \dfrac{1}{6}$ 25. $\dfrac{1}{4} + \dfrac{3}{8}$ 26. $\dfrac{3}{8} + \dfrac{5}{12}$

27. $\dfrac{4}{5} - \dfrac{1}{5}$ 28. $\dfrac{5}{8} - \dfrac{1}{4}$ 29. $\dfrac{5}{6} - \dfrac{3}{8}$

30. Picture the operation of Problem 22 in terms of pie slices.
31. Picture the operation of Problem 25 in terms of pie slices.
32. Picture the operation of Problem 28 in terms of pie slices.
33. Picture the operation of Problem 23 in terms of pie slices.
34. Picture the operation of Problem 24 in terms of pie slices.
35. Picture the following multiplications on a rectangular grid as shown at the end of Section 7:

$\qquad$ (a) $\dfrac{1}{2} \times \dfrac{3}{4}$ $\quad$ (b) $\dfrac{2}{3} \times \dfrac{3}{8}$ $\quad$ (c) $\dfrac{2}{3} \times \dfrac{2}{5}$ $\quad$ (d) $\dfrac{3}{4} \times \dfrac{5}{7}$

36. We can show addition of $\frac{2}{3}$ and $\frac{4}{7}$ as

$$\frac{2}{3} + \frac{4}{7} = \frac{2}{3} \times \frac{7}{7} + \frac{4}{7} \times \frac{3}{3} = \frac{14}{21} + \frac{12}{21} = \frac{14 + 12}{21} = \frac{26}{21}.$$

Show the same pattern for

$$\frac{a}{b} + \frac{c}{d}.$$

37. Show the pattern of problem 36 for

$$\frac{a}{b} - \frac{c}{d} \quad \left(\frac{a}{b} > \frac{c}{d}\right).$$

8. PROCEDURES FOR OPERATING WITH FRACTIONAL NUMBERS

We collect here the various procedures needed for handling fractions, most of which were developed during the preceding discussion. Taken in conjunction with the earlier procedures for operating with whole numbers, the listed procedures suffice for all manipulations with fractions (powers and roots excepted).

The Procedures for Fractions

In Groups **A** and **B**, the numbers n, a, b, c, d, are whole numbers and no number appearing in a denominator is zero.

A. Special   1. $n = \dfrac{n}{1}$ 2. $\dfrac{a}{b} = a \div b$ 3. $\dfrac{a}{b} = \dfrac{na}{nb}$

B. Operations*   1. $\dfrac{a}{n} + \dfrac{b}{n} = \dfrac{a+b}{n}$ 3. $\dfrac{a}{b} \times \dfrac{c}{d} = \dfrac{ac}{bd}$

   2. $\dfrac{a}{n} - \dfrac{b}{n} = \dfrac{a-b}{n}$ 4. $\dfrac{a}{b} \div \dfrac{c}{d} = \dfrac{a}{b} \times \dfrac{d}{c}$

C. Manipulation   The above patterns hold when the various numerators and denominators are themselves fractions.

D. Properties   The basic properties of appropriate operations, commutative, associative, and distributive, hold for fractions.

* These generalize, in the obvious ways, to cases of three or more fractions.

To show how these procedures are used, we give several typical numerical examples, and cite the procedure used at each step. Thus A3 signifies that the step is justified by Procedure A3: $\dfrac{a}{b} = \dfrac{na}{nb}$. CA3 refers to a manipulation of type $\dfrac{f_1}{f_2} = \dfrac{ff_1}{ff_2}$, fractions f, f_1, f_2 replacing the whole numbers n, a, b of the original Procedure A3. Some steps shown in the examples would ordinarily be omitted or performed mentally.

Example 1 Name in lowest terms: (a) $\dfrac{28}{35}$; (b) $\dfrac{561}{935}$.

(a) $\dfrac{28}{35} = \dfrac{4 \times 7}{5 \times 7} = \dfrac{4}{5}$; (A3)

(b) $\dfrac{561}{935} = \dfrac{3 \times 187}{5 \times 187} = \dfrac{3}{5}$. (A3)

Example 2 Multiply: $5 \times \dfrac{2}{3}$.

By (A1), $5 = \dfrac{5}{1}$. By (B3), $\dfrac{5}{1} \times \dfrac{2}{3} = \dfrac{10}{3}$.

Example 3 Express in the form of a single fractional numeral: $4\dfrac{2}{3}$.

$$4\dfrac{2}{3} = 4 + \dfrac{2}{3} = \dfrac{4}{1} \times \dfrac{3}{3} + \dfrac{2}{3} = \dfrac{12}{3} + \dfrac{2}{3} = \dfrac{14}{3}.$$ (A1, A3, B1)

Example 4 Express $\dfrac{384}{65}$ in the form of a mixed numeral.

$$\dfrac{384}{65} = \dfrac{5 \times 65 + 59}{65} = 5 + \dfrac{59}{65} = 5\dfrac{59}{65}.$$ (B1, A3, A1)

$$\begin{array}{r} 5 \\ 65\overline{)384} \\ 325 \\ \hline 59 \end{array}$$

(In practice, the answer is written at once by inspection of the division work.)

Example 5 Subtract: $\dfrac{5}{8} - \dfrac{3}{20}$.

LCM (8,20) = 40.

$$\dfrac{5}{8} - \dfrac{3}{20} = \dfrac{25}{40} - \dfrac{6}{40} = \dfrac{19}{40}.$$ (A3, B2)

$$\begin{aligned} 8 &= 2 \times 2 \times 2 \\ 20 &= 2 \times 2 \times 5 \\ \hline \text{LCM} &= 2 \times 2 \times 2 \times 5 \end{aligned}$$

Example 6 Divide: $\dfrac{35}{16} \div \dfrac{49}{24}$.

$$\dfrac{35}{16} \div \dfrac{49}{24} = \dfrac{35}{16} \times \dfrac{24}{49} = \dfrac{35 \times 24}{16 \times 49}$$

$$= \dfrac{5 \times 7 \times 2 \times 2 \times 2 \times 3}{2 \times 2 \times 2 \times 2 \times 7 \times 7} = \dfrac{5 \times 3}{2 \times 7} = \dfrac{15}{14}.$$ (B4, B3, A3)

In practice, factors are divided out at once:

$$\dfrac{\overset{5}{\cancel{35}}}{\underset{2}{\cancel{16}}} \times \dfrac{\overset{3}{\cancel{24}}}{\underset{7}{\cancel{49}}} = \dfrac{15}{14} \quad \left(\text{i.e., } \dfrac{35}{16} \times \dfrac{24}{49} = \dfrac{5}{16} \times \dfrac{24}{7} = \dfrac{5}{2} \times \dfrac{3}{7} = \dfrac{15}{14} \right)$$

Example 7 Divide: $25\dfrac{3}{5} \div 4\dfrac{1}{3}$.

METHOD A

$$25\tfrac{3}{5} \div 4\tfrac{1}{3} = \frac{25\tfrac{3}{5}}{4\tfrac{1}{3}} = \frac{25 + \tfrac{3}{5}}{4 + \tfrac{1}{3}} \quad \text{(CA2)}$$

$$= \frac{15 \times (25 + \tfrac{3}{5})}{15 \times (4 + \tfrac{1}{3})} \quad \text{(CA3)} \qquad \begin{array}{l}\text{Note that}\\ \text{LCM }(3,5) = 15.\end{array}$$

$$= \frac{375 + 9}{60 + 5} \quad \text{(D; also Example 2)}$$

$$= \frac{384}{65} = 5\frac{59}{65} \quad \text{(Example 4)}$$

METHOD B

$$25 + \frac{3}{5} = \frac{125}{5} + \frac{3}{5} = \frac{128}{5}; \qquad 4 + \frac{1}{3} = \frac{12}{3} + \frac{1}{3} = \frac{13}{3} \quad \text{(Example 3)}$$

$$\frac{128}{5} \div \frac{13}{3} = \frac{128}{5} \times \frac{3}{13} = \frac{128 \times 3}{5 \times 13} = \frac{384}{65} = 5\frac{59}{65} \quad \text{(CA2; Examples 6, 4)}$$

Example 8 Multiply: $25\dfrac{3}{5} \times 4\dfrac{1}{3}$.

METHOD A

Use the scheme of Example 7B:

$$25\frac{3}{5} \times 4\frac{1}{3} = \frac{128}{5} \times \frac{13}{3} = \frac{128 \times 13}{5 \times 3} = \frac{1664}{15} = 110\frac{14}{15}.$$

METHOD B

$$25\frac{3}{5} \times 4\frac{1}{3} = \left(25 + \frac{3}{5}\right)\left(4 + \frac{1}{3}\right)$$

$$= 25 \times 4 + \frac{3}{5} \times 4 + 25 \times \frac{1}{3} + \frac{3}{5} \times \frac{1}{3} \quad \text{(D)}$$

$$= 100 + \frac{12}{5} + \frac{25}{3} + \frac{1}{5} \quad \text{(A1, B3, A3)}$$

$$= 100 + 2 + 8 + \frac{3}{5} + \frac{1}{3} \quad \text{(B1, A3, A1, B1)}$$

$$= 110 + \left(\frac{9}{15} + \frac{5}{15}\right) = 110\frac{14}{15} \quad \text{(A3, B1).}$$

Example 9 Simplify: $\dfrac{2}{3} - \dfrac{1}{10} + \dfrac{4}{45}$.

LCM $(3,10,45) = 90$.

$$\frac{2}{3} - \frac{1}{10} + \frac{4}{45} = \frac{60}{90} - \frac{9}{90} + \frac{8}{90} = \frac{59}{90}$$

$$\begin{array}{l}3 = 3\\ 10 = 2 \times 5\\ \underline{45 = 3 \times 3 \times 5}\\ \text{LCM} = 2 \times 3 \times 3 \times 5\end{array}$$

(A3, B2, B1)

Problem Set 4

Work each problem in the manner of the illustrative Examples 1 to 9 above, at each step citing the procedure that justifies the work.

1. Name in lowest terms:

   (a) $\frac{42}{56}$ (b) $\frac{36}{84}$ (c) $\frac{286}{598}$ (d) $\frac{437}{943}$

2. Multiply:

   (a) $3 \times \frac{4}{7}$ (b) $\frac{3}{4} \times 5$ (c) $20 \times \frac{5}{8}$ (d) $\frac{2}{3} \times 6$

3. Express as fractional numerals:

   (a) $2\frac{2}{5}$ (b) $10\frac{1}{2}$ (c) $63\frac{3}{4}$ (d) $111\frac{1}{9}$

4. Express as mixed numerals:

   (a) $\frac{11}{3}$ (b) $\frac{59}{8}$ (c) $\frac{303}{10}$ (d) $\frac{1190}{73}$

5. Add and simplify:

   (a) $\frac{2}{3} + \frac{1}{6}$ (b) $\frac{3}{12} + \frac{3}{20}$ (c) $\frac{7}{24} + \frac{5}{16}$

6. Subtract and simplify:

   (a) $\frac{2}{3} - \frac{1}{6}$ (b) $\frac{7}{8} - \frac{5}{12}$ (c) $\frac{13}{20} - \frac{7}{20}$

7. Perform the indicated operations and simplify:

   (a) $\frac{1}{2} - \frac{1}{6} + \frac{1}{9}$ (b) $\frac{7}{8} - \frac{1}{12} + \frac{5}{6}$

8. Divide and simplify:

   (a) $\frac{20}{33} \div \frac{35}{12}$ (b) $\frac{18}{35} \div \frac{24}{49}$

9. Divide, using two methods: $4\frac{3}{4} \div 5\frac{1}{6}$.
10. Multiply, using two methods: $8\frac{1}{4} \times 5\frac{1}{3}$.

Bibliography

Brumfiel, Charles F., Robert E. Eicholz, Merrill E. Shanks, and P. G. O'Daffer, *Principles of Arithmetic*. Reading, Mass.: Addison-Wesley Publishing Company, Inc., 1963, pp. 139–204.

Corle, Clyde G., *Teaching Mathematics in the Elementary School*. New York: The Ronald Press Company, 1964, pp. 163–202.

Crouch, Ralph, and George Baldwin, *Mathematics for Elementary Teachers*. New York: John Wiley & Sons, Inc., 1964, pp. 127–202.

Montague, Harriet F., and Mabel D. Montgomery, *The Significance of Mathematics*. Columbus, Ohio: Charles E. Merrill Books, Inc., 1963, pp. 47–51.

Nichols, Eugene D., *Pre-Algebra Mathematics*. New York: Holt, Rinehart and Winston, Inc., 1965, Chap. 5.

Peterson, John A., and Joseph Hashisaki, *Theory of Arithmetic*. New York: John Wiley & Sons, Inc., 1963, pp. 151–191.

Schaaf, William L., *Basic Concepts of Elementary Mathematics*. New York: John Wiley & Sons, Inc., 1960, pp. 130–137.

School Mathematics Study Group, *Studies in Mathematics, Vol. IX: A Brief Course for Elementary School Teachers*. rev. ed. Stanford, Calif.: Leland Stanford University, 1963, pp. 219–291.

————, *Studies in Mathematics, Vol. VI: Number Systems*, prelim. ed. New Haven: Yale University Press, 1961, pp. 95–165.

8

RATIONAL NUMBERS
OF ARITHMETIC:
DECIMALS

1. BACKGROUND

Old European textbooks display horrendous problems involving fractions like

$$\frac{231,976}{50,872,371}.$$

As future clerks and tradesmen labored with these monstrosities, their schoolroom frustrations must have grown so intense as to dwarf those that plague the pupils of today and are so much the concern of our educational specialists.

Why did the old-time schoolmen foist such numerical complexities upon their pupils? They may have felt that work tedium was good for the mind—or for the soul. Yet actually they had no other choice. Before decimals were invented, the practical computer had no way to avoid dealing with cumbersome fractions.

A Belgian, Simon Stevin, introduced the idea of **decimals** in the book *La Disme*, published in 1585. We have seen that the Babylonians had the first notions of this sort, making particular use of the "sexagesimal" fractions $\frac{1}{60}$ and $\frac{1}{3600}$. But Stevin combined the idea of using fractional numerals whose denominators are powers of the number base (10) with the modern place value concept. The combination was a brilliant stroke.

Merchants, artisans, and others were slow to accept the new form. It was hard to agree on a standard notation. The following notations, shown for the number $\frac{314}{100}$ were among those tried and discarded:

$$3①1①4②; \qquad 3,1'4''; \qquad 3/\overset{1\ 2}{\overline{1\ 4}}; \qquad 3/\overset{.}{1}\ \overset{.}{4}; \qquad 3/\underline{14}.$$

150 /

At present, the decimal point (dot .) is used as the "separatrix" in the United States and in England, but the English write it higher up than we do. In Belgium, France, Germany, Italy, and the Scandinavian countries, a comma is used instead. Scandinavians also print the fractional part in smaller type than the integral part:

U. S.,   3.14   France, etc., 3,14

England, 3·14   Scandinavia, 3,14

We use a still different notation when writing checks, $3\frac{14}{100}$ instead of 3.14, having found this is a greater protection against misreading or alteration.

2. DECIMALS

The following are examples of decimal numerals:

3.14,   .017,   176.26901.

The number of digits following the point is called the number of **decimal places** in the decimal numeral. For example, 3.14 is given to two decimal places; .017 is given to three decimal places; and 176.26901 is given to five decimal places.

If a rational number is named by a fractional numeral with the denominator a power of 10, then it is very easy to find a corresponding decimal numeral. Observe the pattern suggested by these examples:

$$\frac{3}{10} = \frac{3}{10^1} = .3$$

$$\frac{7}{100} = \frac{7}{10^2} = .07$$

$$\frac{39}{1,000} = \frac{39}{10^3} = .039$$

$$\frac{11}{10,000} = \frac{11}{10^4} = .0011$$

The term $1/10^n$ ($n \geq 1$), given as a decimal numeral, would have n digits to the right of the decimal point.

When a number is named in decimal form, its *place-value structure* may be seen to be as in Fig. 8-1, the numeral 204.3708 being used in the illustration. Sometimes the place names are used in reading the numeral: "two hundred four *and* three thousand seven hundred eight ten-thousandths." (The "and" signifies the addition of the whole number portion and the fractional portion.) The more usual way of reading is: "two-zero-four point three-seven-zero-eight."

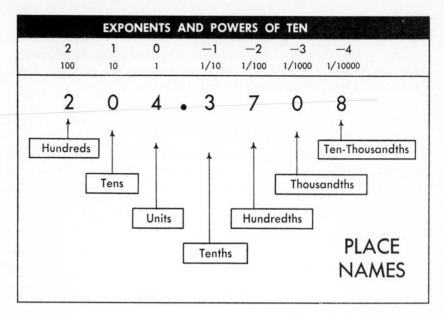

Fig. 8-1   Place-Value of a Decimal Numeral

The decimal form helps us to compare numbers. Only a glance is needed to tell which of two numbers is the greater. The decimal form simplifies computation enormously: Handling decimals is much like handling whole numbers; the complications of fractions are by-passed.

It is very easy to find fractional numerals corresponding to some decimal numerals. For example,

$$.47 = \frac{47}{100}, \qquad .109 = \frac{109}{1000}, \qquad .365901 = \frac{365,901}{1,000,000}.$$

In general,

$$.a_1a_2 \cdots a_n = \frac{a_1a_2a_3 \cdots a_n}{\underbrace{100 \cdots 0}_{n \text{ zeros}}} \qquad (n \geq 1),$$

where a_1, a_2, a_3, $\cdots$, a_n are replaceable by digits chosen from 0, 1, 2, 3, 4, 5, 6, 7, 8, 9.

We have observed that it is rather easy to find a decimal numeral corresponding to a fractional numeral with a denominator a power of 10. What about fractional numerals with denominators that are not powers of 10? Let us examine some of these:

$$\frac{1}{2} = \frac{5}{10} = .5$$

Since 2 can be multiplied by a whole number to obtain a power of 10, there is no difficulty in finding the decimal numeral for $\frac{1}{2}$.

What about $\frac{1}{3}$? There is no whole number to be multiplied by 3 to result in a power of 10. Thus, finding a decimal numeral for $\frac{1}{3}$ is more difficult. We shall discuss it in more detail in the next chapter.

$$\frac{1}{4} = \frac{25}{100} = .25$$

$$\frac{1}{5} = \frac{2}{10} = .2$$

The problem with $\frac{1}{6}$ and $\frac{1}{7}$ is similar to that which we had with $\frac{1}{3}$. Explain.

Thus, we see that for some fractional numerals it is rather easy to find corresponding decimal numerals, for others it is not easy. We shall explore this problem in greater depth in the next chapter.

3. OPERATIONS WITH DECIMALS

Shifting the decimal point one place in a decimal numeral multiplies or divides a number by ten (Why?). Shifting it several places therefore multiplies or divides a number by the power of ten equal to the places shifted. Thus, 21,470 is 1,000 or 10^3 times as large as 21.47, whereas .2147 is 100 or 10^2 times smaller than 21.47.

Addition and Subtraction

Arrange the numerals in a column with decimal points lined up vertically. Add or subtract as though the numerals named whole numbers. Insert a decimal point in the answer in position below the others:

7.14	Add as though	7140
306.008	the numbers were:	306008
2150.		2150000
2463.148		2463148

The following analysis shows why the scheme works:

$$7.14 + 306.008 + 2150 = 7.140 + 306.008 + 2150.000$$
$$= \frac{7140}{1000} + \frac{306008}{1000} + \frac{2150000}{1000}$$
$$= \frac{2463148}{1000} = 2463.148$$

See the scheme of Figure 8-2.

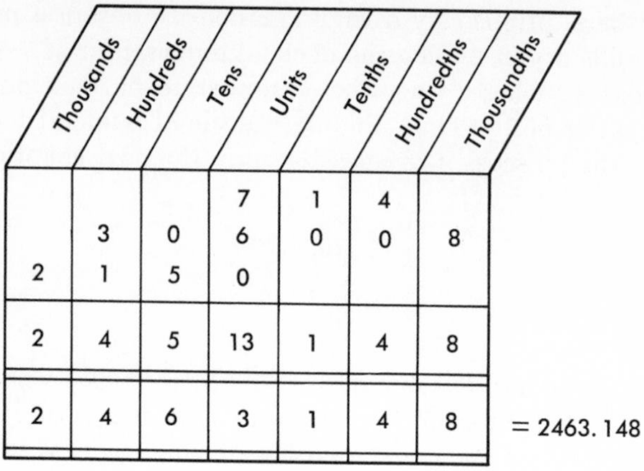

Thousands	Hundreds	Tens	Units	Tenths	Hundredths	Thousandths
			7	1	4	
	3	0	6	0	0	8
2	1	5	0			
2	4	5	13	1	4	8
2	4	6	3	1	4	8

= 2463.148

Fig. 8-2

Multiplication

Multiply as though the numbers were whole numbers. The sum of the numbers of decimal places in the given numerals gives the number of decimal places in the answer. Study the justification for this procedure under *Reason*.

$$
\begin{array}{r}
46.52 \\
\times \quad 2.3 \\
\hline
13956 \\
9304 \\
\hline
106.996
\end{array}
$$

2 places
1 place

3 places

Reason

$$2.3 \times 46.52 = \frac{23}{10} \times \frac{4652}{10 \times 10}$$

$$= \frac{23 \times 4652}{10 \times 10 \times 10}$$

Division

Before dividing, multiply both divisor and dividend by as many tens as needed to produce a whole-number divisor. This will not change the quotient. Place the decimal point for the quotient above its new position in the dividend. In the following examples, crosses ($\times$) indicate the new positions of the decimal points after the multiplication by 100.

$$29.6 \div 2.28$$

$$
\begin{array}{r}
12. \\
2.28_\times \overline{)29.60_\times} \\
22\,8 \\
\hline
6\,80 \\
4\,56 \\
\hline
2\,24
\end{array}
$$

$$
\begin{array}{r}
12.982 \\
2.28_\times \overline{)29.60_\times 000} \\
22\,8 \\
\hline
6\,80 \\
4\,56 \\
\hline
2\,240 \\
2\,052 \\
\hline
1880 \\
1824 \\
\hline
560 \\
456 \\
\hline
104
\end{array}
$$

If the division process does not terminate at some stage with a zero remainder, then it may be continued as far as is wished. The work at the left above corresponds to the whole-number division of 2960 by 228:

$$\frac{29.6}{2.28} = \frac{2960}{228} = 12 + \frac{224}{228} = 12\,\frac{224}{228}.$$

The work at the right corresponds to:

$$\frac{29.6}{2.28} = \frac{2960}{228} = \frac{1}{1000} \times \frac{2960000}{228}$$

$$= \frac{1}{1000}\left(12982 + \frac{104}{228}\right)$$

$$= 12.982 + \frac{\frac{104}{228}}{1000}.$$

This result could be written as $12.982\,\frac{104}{228}$, the fractional numeral $\frac{104}{228}$ being understood to be in the same decimal place as the 2 to its left, *thousandths*. But such a form is confusing. The division should be carried out to a point at which the error term, 104/228000 in this case, may for the purpose at hand be disregarded. The question of how the error term may be expressed then becomes irrelevant.

General Computation

In calculating the value of an expression involving the multiplication and/or division of several decimals, computers sometimes disregard all decimal points, then place the point in the final answer by making a crude estimate. This scheme is especially useful when calculations are made upon instruments or machines, such as the slide rule, which have no built-in provision for handling decimal points.

Consider the problem

$$x = \frac{93.6 \times 2.346}{.0718}.$$

This might be worked as follows:

936 × 2346 $\doteq$ 2196 . . . , (actually 2195856)   ($\doteq$ means is *approxi-*
2196 ÷ 718 $\doteq$ 306 . . . .   *mately* equal to)

But

$$x \doteq \frac{100 \times 2}{.07} = \frac{200}{.07} = \frac{20000}{7} \doteq \frac{21000}{7} = 3000$$

Hence

$$x \doteq 3060 \quad \text{(approximate answer)}.$$

The idea of making crude estimates of an answer is of considerable importance. Pupils should be taught to make such estimates in connection with most of their computational work. Not only are estimates valuable as gross checks, but making them serves to focus the attention of pupils upon the sizes of the numbers being dealt with. This keeps them closer to the realities behind the "paper" problems.

Problem Set 1

1. Give the corresponding decimal numeral for each of the following:

   (a) $\frac{1}{8}$ (b) $\frac{13}{8}$ (c) $\frac{7}{40}$ (d) $\frac{11}{25}$

   (e) $\frac{9}{125}$ (f) $\frac{87}{50}$ (g) $\frac{3}{625}$ (h) $\frac{1}{200}$

2. Compute the difference between

   (a) $\frac{1}{3}$ and .3   (b) $\frac{2}{3}$ and .67

   (c) $\frac{1}{6}$ and .17   (d) $\frac{1}{9}$ and .1

3. Give the corresponding simplest fractional numeral for each of the following:

   (a) .4   (b) 12.4   (c) .035   (d) .101

4. (a) Divide 1 by 6, carrying out the division to three decimal places.
   (b) What would each successive digit be should you continue the process in (a)?

5. (a) Divide 1 by 7, carrying out the division to seven decimal places.
   (b) Write down the "block" of digits that repeats on and on should you continue the process in (a).
   *(c) Explain why, in dividing by 7, the largest possible block of digits that will repeat contains six digits.

6. Multiply: 80.43 × 1371.2.
7. Multiply: .0036 × 27.2.
8. Carry out the division of 21.4 by 3.5 to two decimal places and use the resulting remainder to express the difference between your answer and the exact quotient of 21.4 by 3.5.

4. SCIENTIFIC NOTATION

When very large or very small numbers are to be dealt with, various devices can be used to avoid writing long strings of 0's.

The 1964 *Britannica Book of the Year* cites the national budget receipts of the United States for the fiscal year 1963 as $86,357,000,000. In a news story, it might be felt that $86,000,000,000 would be a sufficiently accurate figure to use. But rather than having to write nine 0's, the reporter would likely write "86 billion dollars." In similar fashion, a technician working with radar or with a high-speed electronic computing machine might speak of a time interval of 35 microseconds instead of .000035 seconds.

A general mathematical device is that of expressing numbers in **scientific notation.** The first step is to find the number between 1 and 10 that "corresponds" to the given number. This is found by placing the decimal point in a position just to the right of the first nonzero digit (reading from left to right) of the given numeral. It is suggested that this corresponding number between 1 and 10 may be named the **dekapart** ("ten-part").

GIVEN NUMBER	CORRESPONDING NUMBER BETWEEN 1 AND 10 (dekapart)
214	2.14
21,400	2.14
5.63	5.63
30.8	3.08
.6	6.
.00083	8.3

"Moving" the decimal point in a numeral either multiplies or divides the number by the power of 10 equal to the number of places the decimal point is moved. Hence:

$$214 = 2.14 \times 10^2 \quad \text{(moved 2 places to left)}$$
$$21{,}400 = 2.14 \times 10^4 \quad \text{(moved 4 places to left)}$$
$$5.63 = 5.63 \times 10^0 \quad \text{(moved 0 places)}$$
$$30.8 = 3.08 \times 10^1 \quad \text{(moved 1 place to left)}$$
$$.6 = 6 \times \frac{1}{10^1} \quad \text{(moved 1 place to right)}$$
$$.00083 = 8.3 \times \frac{1}{10^4} \quad \text{(moved 4 places to right)}$$

In Chapter 2 we developed the following concerning the powers of 10:

$$10^0 = 1, \quad 10^{-1} = \frac{1}{10^1}; \quad 10^{-2} = \frac{1}{10^2}; \quad 10^{-3} = \frac{1}{10^3}; \quad 10^{-4} = \frac{1}{10^4}; \quad \text{etc.}$$

Then we may write:

$$.6 = 6 \times 10^{-1} \quad \text{(moved 1 place to right)}$$
$$.00083 = 8.3 \times 10^{-4} \quad \text{(moved 4 places to right)}$$

It is apparent that a negative exponent will appear *only when the given number is less than one.*

The forms listed at the right in our examples are in scientific notation. The exponent of 10 is called the *characteristic* of the given number. If the corresponding number between 1 and 10 is called the dekapart, as suggested, we have:

$$\text{number} = \text{dekapart} \times 10^{\text{characteristic}}$$

In computing with numbers given in scientific notation, we make use of simple rules for multiplying and dividing powers of ten. The product or quotient of two powers of ten is again a power of ten. For the product, the exponent is the *sum* of the two exponents. For the quotient, it is the *difference:*

$$10^2 \times 10^3 = 10^5,$$

because

$$(10 \times 10) \times (10 \times 10 \times 10) = 10 \times 10 \times 10 \times 10 \times 10.$$

$$\frac{10^5}{10^2} = 10^3,$$

because

$$\frac{10 \times 10 \times 10 \times 10 \times 10}{10 \times 10} = 10 \times 10 \times 10.$$

Example Compute $(295,000) \times (.00621)$ using scientific notation.

$$
\begin{aligned}
(295,000) \times (.00621) &= (2.95 \times 10^5) \times (6.21 \times 10^{-3}) \\
&= (2.95) \times (6.21) \times 10^5 \times 10^{-3} \\
&= 2.95 \times 6.21 \times 10^2 \\
&\doteq 18.3 \times 10^2 \\
&= 1.83 \times 10^3 \quad \text{(scientific notation)} \\
&= 1830 \quad \text{(approximate answer)}
\end{aligned}
$$

Tables of logarithms list *logarithms* of numbers between 1 and 10. The logarithms of numbers outside this range may be found with the aid of scientific notation:

$$
\begin{aligned}
\log 243 &= \log (2.43 \times 10^2) = \log 2.43 + \log 10^2 \\
&= \log 2.43 + 2 = .386 + 2.
\end{aligned}
$$

$$\log .0076 = \log (7.6 \times 10^{-3}) = \log 7.6 - 3 = .881 - 3 = .881 + (-3)$$

In general, log of number = log of dekapart + characteristic.

Problem Set 2

1. Write in scientific notation:

  (a) 820
  (c) 82,000
  (e) .82
  (g) .0082

  (b) 373,000,000
  (d) 52.4
  (f) .00000029
  (h) .000000009

2. Write in ordinary form:

   (a) 2.6×10^3 (b) 5.081×10^1 (c) 2.81×10^{-1}
   (d) 3.62×10^5 (e) 7.2×10^{12} (f) 3.7×10^{-3}

3. The sun is about 9.3×10^7 miles away. Light travels at about 1.86×10^5 miles per second. How long does it take for the light from the sun to reach the earth?

4. A radio station is broadcasting on 1,000 kilocycles (marked either 10 or 100 on your AM band). This means that $1,000 \times 1,000 = 10^6$ waves pass your antenna each second. Their velocity is the same as that of light, about 1.86×10^5 miles per second. How long is one wave, in feet? How long is one wave from an FM station broadcasting on 100 megacycles (1 megacycle = 1 million cycles)?

5. The sun's mass is about 2.2×10^{27} tons. The mass of a hydrogen atom is about 3.7×10^{-21} pounds. If the sun were all hydrogen (which it isn't, quite), about how many atoms would it contain?

6. If a plant grows 2 inches per day, what is its average rate of growth per second? Give the answer in scientific notation.

7. One light-year is approximately 6,000,000,000,000 miles. State this relation using scientific notation.

8. The sun emits, every second, 3,900,000,000,000,000,000,000,000,000,000 ergs of electromagnetic radiation. Give this number in scientific notation.

5. RATIO

In introducing the concept of a fraction, we considered the notion of a ratio of one number to another, as of 3 to 2. This at first provided no more than a way of stating how one set compared with another. Within the enlarged number system, however, such ratios may be interpreted to be fractional numbers.

Definition   The ratio of the number a to the number b is the fractional number $\dfrac{a}{b}$.

In common usage, some ratios are referred to as such, and others are called *rates*. The latter term is often used when "dissimilar units" are involved. If an auto travels 120 miles in 3 hours, for example, we compute its average *rate* of speed by forming the ratio of 120 to 3, $120/3 = 40$, and we cite the result as "40 miles per hour." Similarly a price *rate:* "$4\frac{1}{2}$¢ per pound." Or a production *rate:* "2,000 widgets per day." However, if 8 of 10 members attend a club meeting, then the *ratio* of attendance is $\frac{8}{10}$ or .8. A car with standard transmission may have a gear ratio of 3.70, meaning that in high gear the motor makes 370 revolutions for each 100 revolutions of the wheels.

A statement that two ratios are equal is called a **proportion**. Thus,

$$\frac{3}{2} = \frac{12}{8}.$$

In fractional terms this reads awkwardly: "Three halves equals twelve eighths." The language of proportion is more expressive: *3 is to 2 as 12 is to 8*. In older days, the notation 3:2::12:8 was often used, a form that has now happily vanished.

Noting that he has traveled 12 miles during the last 30 minutes and that he still has 8 miles to go, a motorist may ask himself how long this will take at the same rate. In effect, he is trying to solve for x the following proportion:

$$\frac{x}{30} = \frac{8}{12}.$$

Before doing this, let us observe the following:

$$\frac{3}{2} = \frac{12}{8} \quad \text{and} \quad 3 \times 8 = 2 \times 12 \quad (24 = 24)$$

$$\frac{4}{7} = \frac{8}{14} \quad \text{and} \quad 4 \times 14 = 7 \times 8 \quad (56 = 56)$$

In general:

$$\text{If } \frac{a}{b} = \frac{c}{d}, \text{ then } ad = bc.$$

Returning to the proportion

$$\frac{x}{30} = \frac{8}{12}$$

and applying the pattern we just stated, we have:

$$x \cdot 12 = 30 \cdot 8$$
$$= 240$$
$$x = 20$$

So the driver may anticipate that the rest of the trip will require 20 min.

Much mental juggling of this sort goes on during the normal round of daily activities, as we compare prices of cans of different sizes in the supermarket, as we revamp to the family's needs recipes designed to serve different numbers, as we "build it ourselves" in the basement workshop, as we scan the multitudes of comparative figures scattered through the newspaper.

We also spend a great deal of time reflecting upon things that may or may not happen. Often we ascribe numerical *probabilities* to these uncertain events. A coin can fall in two ways, each as "likely" as the other. The number of ways that it can fall heads is 1. The number of ways it can fall tails is 1. Hence we say the *odds* for heads are equal (1 to 1). The total number of ways the coin can fall is $1 + 1$, or 2. The *probability* or "chance" of the coin's falling heads is $\frac{1}{2}$, the ratio of the ways for heads to the total ways. Similarly, if it is known that of 24,386 people who have contracted the dread disease "mathophilia," 5,476 have died, we estimate the probability that a person who contracts the disease will die as the ratio 5476/24386, or .22 (approximately). In less clear-cut circumstances, we still make probability estimates and back them with hard cash: "I will put up \$5 to your \$3 that Senator Phogbound is re-elected." The tacit hypothesis here is that the probability of the Senator's election is at least $\frac{5}{8}$.

The usefulness of maps and diagrams depends upon the geometric similarity between these representations and the real objects (in projection), that is, upon the maintenance of a proportion: The ratio between two measurements on the map must equal the ratio between corresponding measurements on the object. This relationship is also the basis of the sense of reality which we get from photographs.

Example 1 One store sells potatoes at 29¢ for 6 lb., another store at 36¢ for 8 lb. Compare these prices.

The ratios giving the prices per pound are

$$\frac{29}{6} \quad \text{and} \quad \frac{36}{8}.$$

These may be compared by finding a common denominator:

$$\frac{29}{6} = \frac{116}{24}; \quad \frac{36}{8} = \frac{108}{24}$$

Since $\frac{116}{24} > \frac{108}{24}$, we have $\frac{29}{6} > \frac{36}{8}$. Therefore, 36¢ for 8 lb. represents a lower price per pound. It is of course also feasible to express each ratio as a decimal numeral, then compare:

$$\frac{29}{6} \doteq 4.83; \quad \frac{36}{8} = 4.50$$

and

$$4.83 > 4.50,$$

resulting in $\frac{29}{6} > \frac{36}{8}$.

Example 2 On a house plan, 2 in. represents 5 ft. A room length measures $7\frac{3}{16}$ in. on the plan. What is its actual length?

We have these proportions:

$$\frac{\text{length in feet}}{5} = \frac{7\frac{3}{16}}{2} \quad \text{or} \quad \frac{\text{length in feet}}{7\frac{3}{16}} = \frac{5}{2}.$$

Either may be solved by multiplying on both sides by the denominator of the ratio at the left:

$$\text{length} = \frac{5 \times 7\frac{3}{16}}{2} = \frac{35\frac{15}{16}}{2} = \frac{34\frac{31}{16}}{2} = 17\frac{31}{32} \text{ (ft.)}.$$

Another scheme is to observe successively:

2 in.	represents	5 ft.,
1 in.	represents	$\frac{5}{2}$ ft.,
$7\frac{3}{16}$ in.	represents	$7\frac{3}{16} \times \frac{5}{2}$, or $17\frac{31}{32}$ ft.

6. PERCENT

Many ratios or rates represent comparisons of a "part with a whole," hence of a smaller number with a larger. In these as well as in a great many more general comparisons, the rates are fractional numbers less than 1 but usually more than $\frac{1}{100}$. It is convenient to express such rates as **multiples of** $\frac{1}{100}$.

We write the symbol % as an abbreviation for multiplying by $\frac{1}{100}$, reading it "percent" (Latin: per centum, out of a hundred): $1\% = \frac{1}{100}$. Thus twenty percent or 20% means

$$20 \times \frac{1}{100} = 0.2.$$

Examine the following examples and decide on the correct way to use the "percent names" for numbers:

$$0.24 = 24\%; \qquad 0.436 = 43.6\%; \qquad 6\% = 0.06; \qquad 75\% = 0.75.$$

In dealing with fractional names, it is usually simpler to multiply by 100 before dividing:

$$\frac{2}{9} = \frac{200}{9}\% = 22\frac{2}{9}\%; \qquad \frac{1}{3} = \frac{100}{3}\% = 33\frac{1}{3}\%.$$

Though the percent notion is most useful with numbers in the 0.01 to 1 range, it may be used with any number:

$$0.00032 = 0.032\%; \qquad 0.005 = 0.5\%; \qquad 2.3 = 230\%; \qquad 75 = 7500\%.$$

If a city increases its population from 4 million to 5 million in a decade, then the absolute increase is 1 million, whereas the relative increase is the ratio of 1 million to 4 million, that is, $\frac{1}{4}$ or 0.25. The percent increase is 25%. If an auto weighs 4,000 lb., of which 2,200 is on the front wheels and 1,800 on the rear, the percent weight on the rear is 45% ($\frac{1800}{4000} = \frac{9}{20} = \frac{45}{100}$). If a firm sells $200,000 worth of goods and makes a profit of $12,000, then the percent profit (based on sales) is 6%. If a man pays $80 in taxes on a house valued at $12,000, the percent tax is $\frac{2}{3}\%$ (of the value of the house).

Proportions can be used to good advantage in solving problems involving percent. Before making such use of proportions, let us observe a few patterns.

1. $\frac{2}{3} = \frac{4}{6}$;　　also $\frac{3}{2} = \frac{6}{4}$.

　$\frac{5}{3} = \frac{15}{9}$;　　also $\frac{3}{5} = \frac{9}{15}$.

Pattern: If $\dfrac{a}{b} = \dfrac{c}{d}$, then $\dfrac{b}{a} = \dfrac{d}{c}$.

2. $\dfrac{2}{5} = \dfrac{8}{20}$;　　also $2 = \dfrac{8}{20} \times 5 \left(\dfrac{8}{20} \times 5 = \dfrac{8 \times 5}{20} = \dfrac{40}{20} = 2 \right)$.

　$\dfrac{12}{30} = \dfrac{4}{10}$;　　also $12 = \dfrac{4}{10} \times 30 \left(\dfrac{4}{10} \times 30 = \dfrac{4 \times 30}{10} = \dfrac{120}{10} = 12 \right)$.

Pattern: If $\dfrac{a}{b} = \dfrac{c}{d}$, then $a = \dfrac{c}{d} \times b$.

We now illustrate the use of proportions in solving problems involving percent.

Example 1 Enrollment in a course dropped from 396 to 351. What was the percent of decline?

The drop was $396 - 351$ or 45. We must find what percent 45 is of 396.

$$\frac{x}{100} = \frac{45}{396}$$

According to Pattern 2, $x = \frac{45}{396} \times 100 = \frac{4500}{396} \doteq 11.4\%$. Thus, the drop was about 11.4%.

Example 2 A merchant advertises "30% off" on every item in the store. What will be the sale price on an item regularly sold for $2.96?

The sale price x will be 70% of $2.96:

$$\frac{x}{2.96} = \frac{70}{100}$$

$$x = \frac{70}{100} \times 2.96 = \frac{7 \times 2.96}{10} = \frac{20.72}{10} = 2.07.$$

Thus, the sale price is $2.07.

Example 3 Invested at 6%, a sum of money earns $42 in interest in a year. What was the sum?

6% of the sum x is $42. What is the sum x?

$$\frac{6}{100} = \frac{42}{x}$$

$$\frac{100}{6} = \frac{x}{42}$$

$$x = \frac{100}{6} \times 42$$

$$= 700.$$

Thus, the sum of $700 was invested.

Example 4 John Jones' yearly income is $5,000. He expects to pay out: $700 for income taxes; $900 for rent; $1,500 for food; $400 for transportation (auto); $300 for clothes; $550 for household equipment, TV, furnishings, and repairs; $300 for recreation and miscellaneous; $350 for insurance and savings. Construct a table showing the percent distribution of his anticipated expenditures, so that his budget may be compared with others based on different incomes. Display the distribution pictorially by a "pie" chart or circle graph.

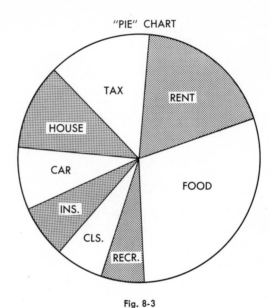

Fig. 8-3

Compute the ratio of each expenditure to Jones' total income and express these ratios as percents. Use a protractor to construct the circle graph. One-hundred percent is to be represented by the full circle, 360°. The 30% expenditure for food is therefore represented by a sector whose central angle is obtained as follows (see Fig. 8-3).

$$\frac{x}{360} = \frac{30}{100}$$

$$x = \frac{30}{100} \times 360$$

$$= \frac{3}{10} \times 360$$

$$= 3 \times 36$$

$$= 108$$

The central angle measures 108°.

JOHN JONES' BUDGET

Item	Amount, dollars	Percent
Food	1,500	30
Rent	900	18
Tax	700	14
Household	550	11
Car	400	8
Insurance	350	7
Clothes	300	6
Recreation	300	6
	5,000	100

Example 5 William Green, salesman, receives a commission of $7\frac{1}{2}\%$ on his sales. He agrees to pay an assistant 30% of his own "take." What net rate will this give him?

He keeps 70% of $7\frac{1}{2}\%$ of his sales. But $70\% \times 7\frac{1}{2}\% = 70\% \times 7.5\% = .7 \times .075 = .0525 = 5.25\%$. His future net earnings will amount to $5\frac{1}{4}\%$ of his sales.

Example 6 If a man's salary is increased by 32%, and at the same time the cost of living goes up 20%, how much is his position improved?

The problem cannot be solved precisely unless it is known just how the general statistical index called "the cost of living" is related to the living habits of the particular man concerned. To simplify the situation, let us suppose that the man spends his whole income on pork chops, the price of which has risen 20%. The same quantity of chops that formerly cost him $100 now cost him $120. Since he now has $132 instead of $100 to spend, he gets $132/120 = 1.1$ times as many chops. His gain is 10%.

Example 7 If two men are precisely similar in their physical structure but one weighs 40% more than the other, how do their heights compare?

On the basis of the improbable hypothesis cited, the weights will compare as the volumes, and these as the *cubes* of the heights. Hence the ratio of the heights will equal the cube root of the ratio of the weights:

$$\sqrt[3]{\frac{140}{100}} = \sqrt[3]{\frac{1400}{1000}} \doteq \frac{11.2}{10} = 1.12 = 112\% \qquad (approximate\ answer)$$

The heavier man is about 12% taller than the other.

Problem Set 3

1. Two cans of tomatoes hold 1 lb. 10 oz. and 1 lb. 2 oz., respectively. What is the ratio of the weight of the contents of the larger can to that of the smaller?
2. If the cans in Problem 1 are of the same brand, and are priced at 38¢ and 27¢, respectively, which is the better buy?

3. The weight of the contents of the smaller can in Problem 1 is what percent of the weight of the contents of the larger can?

4. A $2\frac{1}{4}$ in. by $2\frac{1}{4}$ in. (film size) camera has a 36° angle of view. The angle subtended by the moon is about $\frac{1}{2}$°. What will be the diameter of the image of the moon on a contact print?

5. The owner of the camera in Problem 4 makes an enlargement from a section of his negative in order to get a print on which the moon's image is $\frac{1}{3}$ in. in diameter. What is his enlarging ratio?

6. A model auto is to be made with an 8-in. wheelbase. The full-sized car has a 128-in. wheelbase. What is the scale of the model.

7. If the model in Problem 6 is an *exact* copy, and the full-size car weighs 3600 lb., what does the model weigh?

8. The odds against Kalif. State in its annual grid classic with Oak Ridge U., are estimated at 5 to 4. What is the estimated probability that Kalif. State will win?

9. The probability of your being dealt an aceless bridge hand is about .3. State the odds against your receiving such a hand.

10. The number of possible poker hands is 2,598,960 (number of combinations of 52 things taken 5 at a time). The number of possible "straight flushes" is 40. What are the odds against your being dealt a straight flush?

11. If the cost of living rises 80% while rents rise only 60%, by what percent have rents declined relative to the cost of living?

12. A shopkeeper marks up all his prices 50%. Later he cuts them by 50%. His final prices are what percent of his original prices?

13. As in Problem 12, a markup of 60% is followed by a cut of 40%. These two changes are equivalent to a single markup or cut of what percent?

14. Assume that for each sex taken separately, strength is proportional to weight, but that a woman is 30% weaker than a man of the same weight. How heavy is a woman whose strength equals that of a 140-lb. man?

15. A grocer keeps separate tabs on his sales under these heads: meat, vegetables, tobacco, general. In one day, his receipts under these heads total $48, $40, $8, $64, respectively. Show the percent distribution of his receipts by a table; also by a pie chart.

BIBLIOGRAPHY

Dutton, Wilbur H., and L. J. Adams, *Arithmetic for Teachers*. Englewood Cliffs, N.J.: Prentice-Hall, Inc., 1961, pp. 254–268.

Marks, John L., C. Richard Purdy, and Lucien B. Kinney, *Teaching Arithmetic for Understanding*. New York: McGraw-Hill Book Company, Inc., 1958, pp. 227–250.

Nichols, Eugene D., *Modern Elementary Algebra*. New York: Holt, Rinehart and Winston, Inc., 1965, Chap. 11.

———, *Pre-Algebra Mathematics*. New York: Holt, Rinehart and Winston, Inc., 1965, Chap. 6.

———, R. T. Heimer, and H. Garland, *Modern Intermediate Algebra*. New York: Holt, Rinehart and Winston, Inc., 1965, Chap. 2.

Odom, M. M., and E. D. Nichols (consulting ed.), *Introduction to Exponents* (A Programed Unit). New York: Holt, Rinehart and Winston, Inc., 1964.

Overman, James Robert, *The Teaching of Arithmetic*. Chicago: Lyons and Carnahan, 1961, pp. 197–222.

Smart, James R., *New Understanding in Arithmetic*. Boston: Allyn and Bacon, Inc., 1963, pp. 88–159.

Thorpe, Cleata B., *Teaching Elementary Arithmetic*. New York: Harper & Row, Publishers, 1962.

Webber, G. Cuthbert, and John A. Brown, *Basic Concepts of Mathematics*. Reading, Mass.: Addison-Wesley Publishing Company, Inc., 1963, pp. 146–158.

9

REAL
NUMBERS

1. NEGATIVE NUMBERS

Among primitive peoples living today, some tribes have few words to tell of their needs. Even so, these words include number names. We may from this surmise that *whole numbers* probably played a role in prehistory, before the Great Idea dawned upon man that he might forever freeze his speech and gesture in stone and clay. *Fractions* too were devised in ancient times. The Egyptians used them even in an era when their "written" language still took the picture form.

But the *negative numbers* have few roots in the deep past. All along the course of history, right up to the sixteenth century, we find only scattered instances of anyone daring to entertain the notion that a negative number could be a respectable mathematical concept.

In a manuscript dated 1225, the Italian mathematician Fibonacci obtained a negative answer to a financial problem, and interpreted this to mean a loss, even as we do today. Before Fibonacci, some Hindu mathematicians had used the loss, or debt, notion. Few others followed these leads.

Yet for many centuries computers had manipulated additive and subtractive combinations, using symbols corresponding to our plus and minus signs to link the numbers in them. The Chinese had even used black number rods for the numerals tagged with plus signs, and red rods for those tagged with minus signs. And the "rules of signs" had been worked out. The operation of subtraction essentially implied the "existence" of negative numbers, since the operation was not universally possible without them. The invention of this operation in early times had made it certain that mathematicians would one day seek a larger number system *closed* under the operation, since the systems of whole numbers and rational numbers of arithmetic were not. (A system is closed under an operation

168 /

if performing the operation upon any object or objects of the system again leads to an object of the system. Since 5 cannot be subtracted from 2, the system of the whole numbers is not closed with respect to the operation of subtracting 5.)

But at the time, no one wanted the negative numbers, nor felt they were needed. They were overlooked, or pushed aside as impossible annoyances.

The concept of negative numbers presented itself to the mathematician like a stray kitten on his doorstep, yearning for a home. Distracted by its persistent plaintive mewing, the mathematician at last yielded to the inevitable. With as good grace as he could muster, he quelled the repulsion that seized him at the sight of the unkempt critter, admitted it to his sanctum, and nourished it. Lo! It grew to a sleek beauty, the prize of the household.

Confronted with a numerical form like $2 - 5$, a medieval mathematician could readily reject it as "meaningless" or "absurd" without giving the matter a second thought. But he also dealt with algebraic forms, like $a - b$. He added, subtracted, multiplied, divided, and took powers of such forms, all the while certain that he was accomplishing something useful by his efforts. How frustrating for him to discover at the end of a series of such manipulations that in the particular problem being worked on, the number a was less than the number b! In such a case the form $a - b$, which he had so deftly handled, could mean nothing, so that his work had been sheer nonsense.

In the sixteenth century, mathematicians finally began to accept these new numbers that so clamored for recognition. In 1545, Cardan used them as roots of equations and stated rules for their manipulation. Other prominent mathematicians followed suit. Within a hundred years they were well established.

Cardan called them *false* numbers, revealing his own misgivings about them. Others came to call them *negative* numbers (i.e., "nonnumbers"), stressing the greater legitimacy of the older tried-and-true numbers by reference to the latter as the "affirmative" or *positive* numbers. Other examples of names given new numbers have suggested like distrust: *irrational* ("unreasonable") numbers, *imaginary* ("unreal") numbers, *surds* ("inaudible" or "mute" numbers). No wonder it took a hundred years for the mathematical public to become friendly to them! Modern public relations experts and ad writers would have graced them with adjectives like "super," "cosmic," "stellar," and would have gained quick popular acceptance for them.

As it became apparent that the negatives had useful roles to play and as numerous concrete or practical interpretations of them turned up, the suspicions gradually evaporated. The fantastic became the acceptable and finally the commonplace.

2. THE RATIONAL NUMBER SYSTEM

The system of the fractional numbers embraces all the whole numbers (0, 1, 2, 3, . . .) and all the quotients of pairs of whole numbers ($\frac{2}{3}$, $\frac{51}{8}$, etc.), except that zero may not be the divisor.

Let us tag each such fractional numeral by two labels, $+$ and $-$. The nonzero-valued fractional numerals tagged with $+$ name the **positive** numbers. The nonzero-valued fractional numerals tagged with $-$ name the **negative** numbers. Both $+0$ and -0 are taken to be the same number, **zero** (0).

All these are the rational numbers. The set of rational numbers consists of positive rationals, negative rationals, and 0. It is helpful to picture them as distributed in order of size along the entire line, which then forms a **number line,** as in Figure 9-1. The line extends indefinitely in two

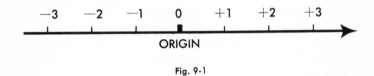

Fig. 9-1

directions. When sketching the number line, we first mark the position of the **origin,** or zero point, and of the point marked $+1$, the **unit point.** With the integers placed, all the other rationals may be located with respect to them. Thus the rational number $-\frac{5}{2}$ is associated with the point lying halfway between the points marked -3 and -2.

Each number and its **opposite,** or **additive inverse,** like $+3$ and -3, are symmetrically located with respect to the origin. They lie at the same distance from the origin, but on opposite sides.

With each rational number we associate the *absolute value* of a number. The symbol for absolute value of $+\frac{1}{2}$ is $|+\frac{1}{2}|$. From the following examples, the student should derive the meaning of the absolute value:

$$|+\tfrac{1}{2}| = +\tfrac{1}{2}; \; |-\tfrac{1}{3}| = +\tfrac{1}{3}; \; |+7| = +7; \; |-32| = +32; \; |0| = 0.$$

Observe that every rational number has an additive inverse: the additive inverse of -3 is $+3$, the additive inverse of $+\frac{1}{4}$ is $-\frac{1}{4}$, and the additive inverse of 0 is 0. The additive inverse of a positive number is a negative number, and the additive inverse of a negative number is a positive number.

From the examples above, used to illustrate the concept of absolute value, we observe that the absolute value of numbers that are additive inverses of each other is the same:

$$|+\tfrac{1}{2}| = |-\tfrac{1}{2}| = +\tfrac{1}{2}.$$

Since the absolute value of any nonzero number is a positive number, we make the following *definition of absolute value:*

$$\forall_{x \geq 0}|x| = x$$
$$\forall_{x < 0}|x| = -x$$

Notice that the last line means that the absolute value of a negative number is a positive number, since $-x$, the additive inverse of a negative number ($x < 0$), is a positive number. For example, if x is -3, we have:

$$|-3| = -(-3) \qquad \text{(read: additive inverse of negative three)}$$
$$= +3$$

There is a rather popular agreement to omit the $+$ when writing numerals for positive numbers. Thus, instead of $+\frac{1}{2}$, we shall write $\frac{1}{2}$.

Today, negative numbers are everywhere with us. Sometimes we use them explicitly, as in citing a temperature reading of $-14°$. More commonly in everyday life we use them implicitly, as when we say that the temperature is "14 below zero." Our language often shows that we have the two-way line in mind, as we distinguish between:

3 miles west—3 miles east
3 hours ago—3 hours hence
3 floors up—3 floors down
left—right
to—fro

And we frequently recognize that we are dealing with the same kind of two-way structure, even though no physical directions may be involved, in the case of opposites like:

profit—loss
credit—debit
export—import
acid—base
excitation—inhibition
extravert—introvert

We may map these variables—economic, chemical, biological, psychological—along the number line, then study their interplay in a precise *quantitative* fashion.

In tackling problems that involve two-way notions, we can sometimes arrange the work in terms of positive numbers alone. It may be possible to break down the work into one-way steps, then combine the separate results by adding and subtracting. But as the number of such stages in a problem increases, this method becomes unwieldy.

In our leisurely perception of everyday life, it may seem satisfactory to picture the separate steps of a to-and-fro motion, as though we were watching a tennis ball pass back and forth across a net.

But as the several billion wheels of our civilization whirl, the points on them move up and down and to and fro many times a second. To try to analyze these motions with the aid only of the one-way positive numbers would seem a hopeless venture.

In describing such processes mathematically, we cannot change the + and − signs in our equations so rapidly. We must have symbols that do their own sign changing automatically, that is, symbols that range in value over the full two-way number line. Without the *directed* (positive and negative) numbers we probably would have no radio sets, much less TV. For Maxwell would then have been unable to carry out the fundamental electrodynamic analysis that he performed around 1870. Without this basic work in pure science, which showed the way, Hertz would scarcely have conceived of producing electric waves, and the notion of an electronic tube in an oscillating circuit would certainly never have materialized. Radio communication would now exist only as a device of the fancy discussed on the pages of our science-fiction magazines.

3. OPERATIONS

As noted in Section 2, we write 3 and +3, etc., interchangeably. That is, we agree to treat the positive rationals just as the fractions or naturals to which they correspond. We agree, for example, that $(+3) + (+2) = +5$ because $3 + 2 = 5$, and that $(+2) \times (+3) = +6$ because $2 \times 3 = 6$. In this way we ensure that the system of the rational numbers will be a true *extension* of the system of the fractional numbers of arithmetic.

What further agreements need we make about ways of operating with rationals? What will be the values of expressions like $(+3) + (-2)$, $(-2) \times (+3)$, $(+3) - (-2)$? In one sense, we may lay down such arbitrary rules as appeal to us; in another sense, our freedom of choice is severely limited. The rules must as a group be consistent, none contradictory with the rest. Furthermore—and this is all-important—the chosen scheme must turn out to be *useful*.

A criterion of utility is often hard to apply. Sometimes the only way to tell which is the most useful of several plans is to try out each over long periods of time. Even then posterity may eventually reverse the decision. In the present case, however, we have already observed the crucial roles played by the commutative, associative, and distributive properties in rendering positive number arithmetic simple and useful. *If possible*, then, let us require that the entire system of the rationals will retain these properties.

In addition, we must in some way explicitly describe the relationship between the negatives and the positives. So far, the two-way symmetric concept on which we have based our approach is only intuitive in our minds. We must translate into mathematical terms our feeling that the negatives are the "mirror images" of the positives. This is not hard to do. We simply require the following:

Property of Additive Inverse [PAI]: If x is any rational number,

$$x + (-x) = 0.$$

The above requirements can be met. When they are, it turns out that we have no further freedom of decision. They wholly determine the structure of the rationals. We shall not carry out a formal development of this theory, but shall cite some numerical examples illustrating how the requirements may be applied to derive familiar rules of operation with directed numbers.

Example 1 Show that $5 + (-2) = 5 - 2 = 3$.

Add 2 to $5 + (-2)$, then simplify by the property of additive inverse:

$$[5 + (-2)] + 2 = 5 + [(-2) + 2] = 5 + 0 = 5.$$

Since $[5 + (-2)] + 2 = 5$,

$$5 + (-2) = 5 - 2.$$

Example 2 Show that $5 - (-2) = 5 + 2 = 7$.

Write $x = 5 - (-2)$. Then

$$x + (-2) = 5.$$

As in Example 1, we may show that $x + (-2) = x - 2$, so that

$$x - 2 = 5 \quad \text{and} \quad x = 5 + 2.$$

Example 3 Show that $(-3) + (-2) = -(3 + 2) = -5$.

Add $(3 + 2)$ to $[(-3) + (-2)]$:

$$[(-3) + (-2)] + (3 + 2) = [(-3) + 3] + [(-2) + 2] = 0.$$

Hence if $x = 3 + 2$, then because $(-x) + x = 0$, we have

$$(-3) + (-2) = -x = -(3 + 2).$$

Example 4 Show that $2 \times (-3) = -(2 \times 3) = -6$.

Add (2×3) to $2 \times (-3)$. Then,

$$2 \times (-3) + (2 \times 3) = 2 \times [(-3) + 3] = 2 \times 0 = 0.$$

Therefore,

$$2 \times (-3) = -(2 \times 3) \qquad \text{[since the sum of } 2 \times (-3) \text{ and } (2 \times 3)$$
is 0, the additive inverse of $2 \times (-3)$ is (2×3)].

Example 5 Show that $(-2) \times (-3) = 2 \times 3 = 6$.

Add $(-2) \times 3$ to $(-2) \times (-3)$:

$$
\begin{aligned}
(-2) \times (-3) \quad + \quad (-2) \times 3 &= (-2) \times [(-3) + 3] \\
&= (-2) \times 0 \\
&= -(2 \times 0) \qquad \text{(show as in Example 4)} \\
&= -0 = 0.
\end{aligned}
$$

Now if $x = 2 \times 3$, then from Example 4, we see that $(-2) \times 3 = -x$. Hence $(-2) \times (-3) = x = 2 \times 3$.

Problem Set 1

1. Draw a line segment a little over 6 in. long, and scale it from -3 to $+3$, as in Figure 9-1. On it mark the approximate positions of the points corresponding to these numbers:

   (a) $\frac{5}{2}$ (b) $-2\frac{1}{2}$ (c) 1.7   (d) 0.5
   (e) $\frac{2}{3}$ (f) $-\frac{2}{3}$ (g) $-.75$ (h) $-\frac{23}{8}$

2. Give the absolute value of each number of Problem 1.
3. Under what conditions is the absolute value of $3 - x$ equal to $x - 3$?
4. Several directional opposites, like "3 miles west–3 miles east" are cited in Section 2. Cite three more such instances.
5. Several opposites, like "acid–base" are cited in Section 2. Cite three more such instances.
6. Which of the following quantities might best be measured by directed numbers and which by nondirected numbers?

   (a) population of countries
   (b) daily change in the price of a stock
   (c) daily minimum temperature at Moscow, U.S.S.R.
   (d) fat content of milk
   (e) monthly net profit of a resort hotel
   (f) yards gained by a football team, down by down
   (g) acceleration of a car during a trip
   (h) level of a river

7. Give the replacements of a and b in $\frac{a}{b}$ ($b \neq 0$) to obtain the set of whole numbers as a subset of the fractional numbers.
8. There is only one rational number that is its own additive inverse. What number is it?

9. $A = \{1, 0, -1\}$ is closed under multiplication because the product of any pair of numbers in A is a member of A:

$$1 \times 1 = 1; \quad 1 \times 0 = 0 \times 1 = 0; \quad 1 \times (-1) = (-1) \times 1 = -1;$$
$$0 \times 0 = 0; \quad 0 \times (-1) = -1 \times 0 = 0; \quad (-1) \times (-1) = 1.$$

(a) Is set A closed under addition?
(b) Is set A closed under division? (Ignore division by 0.)

10. Are the following sets of numbers closed under the operations specified?

(a) whole numbers (0, 1, 2, . . .); under addition
(b) integers; under subtraction
(c) integers; under division
(d) rationals; under division
(e) positive rationals; under division
(f) odd naturals; under addition
(g) positive integers; under multiplication
(h) negative integers; under multiplication
(i) numbers of form $3n/4$ (n a natural number); under addition
(j) same set as in (i); under multiplication

11. Write the instances of the property of additive inverse in these specific cases:

(a) $x = 3$ (b) $x = -3$ (c) $x = 0$ (d) $x = -\frac{5}{3}$

12. As in Example 1 of Section 3, show that $6 + (-4) = 6 - 4$.
13. Show that $2 + (-5) = 2 - 5$. By adding 3 to $[2 + (-5)]$, show that $2 + (-5) = -3$, hence that $2 - 5 = -(5 - 2) = -3$.
14. Show that $2 - (-3) = 5$.
15. Show that $(-4) + (-2) = -6$.
16. Show that $3 \times (-4) = -12$.
17. Show that $(-3) \times (-4) = 12$.
18. Show that $(-12) \div 3 = -4$. (*Hint:* Division is an inverse of multiplication.)
19. Show that $(-12) \div (-3) = 4$.
20. On the basis of the answers to the examples in Section 3 and to Problems 12 to 19, complete the following statements concerning rational numbers:

(a) The sum of two positive numbers is a _____ number.
(b) The sum of two negative numbers is a _____ number.
(c) The sum of a positive number and a negative number is sometimes a _____ and sometimes a _____ number.
(d) The product of two positive numbers is a _____ number.
(e) The product of two negative numbers is a _____ number.
(f) The product of a positive number and a negative number is a _____ number.
(g) The quotient of two positive numbers is a _____ number.
(h) The quotient of two negative numbers is a _____ number.
(i) The quotient of two numbers, one positive and one negative, is a _____ number.

21. Insert "positive" or "negative" to obtain a true statement:

    (a) If $x < 0$, $y > 0$, and $|x| > |y|$, then $x + y$ is a _____ number.
    (b) If $x < 0$, $y > 0$, and $|x| < |y|$, then $x + y$ is a _____ number.

22. Give two examples illustrating each of the following properties of rational numbers:

    (a) $\forall_x \forall_y \; x - y = -(y - x)$.
    (b) $\forall_x \forall_y \; x - y = x + (-y)$.

23. Using the statements in Problem 20 and your knowledge of exponents, explain the truth of each of the following statements:

    (a) $(-2)^4$ is a positive number.
    (b) $(-5)^3$ is a negative number.
    (c) $(-\frac{3}{61})^2$ is a positive number.
    (d) $(-\frac{7}{17})^5$ is a negative number.
    (e) $(-1)^{100}$ is a positive number.
    (f) $(-1)^{101}$ is a negative number.

24. Show that the product of any two rational numbers is a rational number. (*Hint:* Denote two rationals by a/b and c/d, the letters denoting integers. Discuss the product ac/bd.)

25. Show that the sum of any two rational numbers is a rational number.

26. Show that there is a rational number between any two rational numbers. (*Hint:* Find the arithmetic mean of a/b and c/d and show that this mean is between a/b and c/d.)

4. COMPUTATIONS WITH DIRECTED NUMBERS

The statements in Problems 20 to 23 of Problem Set 1 can serve as a guide in computing with directed numbers. Study the examples below.

Example 1 Add 2.34 and -7.80 $[2.34 + (-7.80) = -(7.80 - 2.34)]$.

$$\begin{array}{r} 7.80 \\ -2.34 \\ \hline 5.46 \end{array}$$

$\qquad\qquad$ *Answer:* -5.46

Example 2 Subtract -3.6 from 6.8 $[6.8 - (-3.6) = 6.8 + 3.6]$.

$$\begin{array}{r} 6.8 \\ + \; 3.6 \\ \hline 10.4 \end{array}$$

$\qquad\qquad$ *Answer:* 10.4

Example 3 Subtract 5 from -7 $[-7 - 5 = -7 + (-5)]$.

$$\begin{array}{r} -7 \\ + \; -5 \\ \hline -12 \end{array}$$

$\qquad\qquad$ *Answer:* -12

Example 4 A bank teller lists sums taken in and paid out, tagging the numerals by plus and minus signs, respectively. His list shows ($): $+21$, -59, $+120$, -15, -40. What is his cash increase?

To add the listed numbers, we first rearrange and group them according to associative and commutative properties of addition:

$$[21 + 120] + [(-59) + (-15) + (-40)] = 141 + (-114) = 27.$$
$$\textit{Answer: } \$27$$

Example 5 Is the following a positive or a negative number?

$$\frac{(-29)^3 \times (-7)^2 \times (3.46)}{-5.42}.$$

We find $(-29)^3$ is negative; $(-7)^2$ is positive. Therefore, $(-29)^3 \times (-7)^2 \times (3.46)$ is negative. A negative number divided by -5.42 (negative) is a positive number.

Example 6 The temperature, now $24°$, is falling at the rate of $3°$ per hour. What will it be in 2 hr.?

To illustrate the principle involved, we shall use negatives in place of subtracting. The time rate of *rise* of temperature is $-3°$ per hour. The total rise in 2 hr. is $2 \times (-3) = -6$. Adding this to the present temperature gives $24 + (-6) = 18$. $\textit{Answer: } 18°$

Example 7 The temperature, now $24°$, has been falling at the rate of $3°$ per hour. What was it 4 hr. ago?

The total rise in -4 hr. is $(-4) \times (-3) = +12$, and $24 + (+12) = 36$. $\textit{Answer: } 36°$

5. A PICTORIAL MODEL

The number line furnishes an excellent model for portraying operations with directed numbers. Imagine the line laid along a road running from west to east (positive direction), the origin placed at the center of a town (Fig. 9-2). The numbers $+1$, $+2$, $+3$, . . . designate mileposts to the

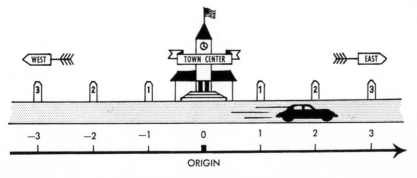

Fig. 9:2 Number Line Laid along a Road

east (E) of the town center; the numbers -1, -2, -3, ... go with mileposts to the west (W).

We now associate numbers with *displacements;* $+5$ corresponds to a displacement or movement of 5 miles toward the east; -2 to a displacement of 2 miles to the west. The sum, $5 + (-2)$, is represented by a displacement of 5 miles to the east, followed by one of 2 miles to the west. The result is a displacement of 3 miles to the east: $5 + (-2) = 3$.

In picturing the displacement operation we may use arrows, as shown in Figure 9-3. The absolute value of a number gives the length of the

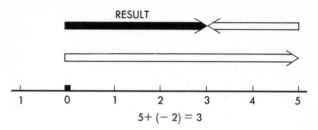

$$5 + (-2) = 3$$

Fig. 9-3   Addition on a Number Line

arrow representing it; the arrow points to the right or left according as the number is positive or negative. To diagram a sum, we draw the first arrow with its tail at the origin, the second with its tail at the head of the first. The student may use such diagrams as aids to his understanding or he may take them as bases for kinaesthetic imagery: He may trace the movements in the air with a finger, or he may pace forward and backward.

Now let us regard a minus sign, whether it designates a negative number or a subtraction, as a *direction-changing operator*. In dealing with both $5 + (-2)$ and $5 - 2$, we think of the positives 5 and 2 as being the numbers involved, and we take the minus sign in front of the 2 in either expression as a signal to reverse the direction of the "2-arrow" before attaching it to the "5-arrow." From this point of view, Figure 9-3 represents both $5 + (-2) = 3$ and $5 - 2 = 3$.

Consider the expression $3 - (-2)$. According to the operator point of view, the two minuses twice reverse the direction of the 2-arrow, giving it a final, positive, right-hand direction. The diagram is shown in Figure 9-4, which also serves for $3 + 2$. Figure 9-5 shows the diagram for $2 + (-5) = 2 - 5$.

The direction-changing idea is also applicable to products and quotients, although arrow diagrams can no longer be used. In the case of the product $(-3) \times (-2)$, the numerical values involved are 3 and 2, whose product is 6. Each minus gives a change of "direction," from $+$ to $-$, then $-$ to $+$.   (*Answer:* $+6$.)

RESULT

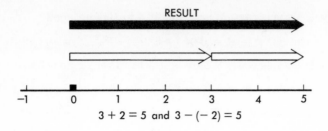

$$3 + 2 = 5 \text{ and } 3 - (-2) = 5$$

Fig. 9-4

RESULT

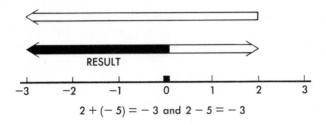

$$2 + (-5) = -3 \text{ and } 2 - 5 = -3$$

Fig. 9-5

Imagine that a bicyclist is traveling along the road of Figure 9-2 at 6 mph and passes the town center (origin) at 12 noon, taken as "time zero."

We can compute the distance traveled in miles from the town center by the relation

$$\text{distance} = \text{speed} \times \text{time}.$$

After 3 hr., the bicycle is 6 × 3 or 18 miles from the town center. *But which way*—east or west?

Were we restricted to positive numbers, we should have to describe these different directional situations by four separate formulas. With directed numbers, one equation does the whole job. We write it

$$d = vt,$$

vt being algebraic shorthand for the product $(v) \times (t)$. In this formula, t denotes the number of hours elapsed from time zero (12 noon), being $+$ for times later than time zero, $-$ for earlier times. The velocity v equals the speed $+6$ if the bicycle is traveling east, but is taken as -6 if the bicycle is traveling west. Similarly, d is $+$ or $-$ according as the bicycle is east or west of the town center.

We illustrate each of the four directional situations:

1. Bicycle travels east. Where is it 3 hr. after 12 noon?

Formula: $d = vt = 6 \times 3 = 18$.   *Answer:* 18 miles east

2. Bicycle travels east. Where was it 3 hr. before noon?

   Formula: $d = vt = 6 \times (-3) = -18$. *Answer:* 18 miles west

3. Bicycle travels west. Where is it 3 hr. after 12 noon?

   Formula: $d = vt = (-6) \times 3 = -18$. *Answer:* 18 miles west

4. Bicycle travels west. Where was it 3 hr. before 12 noon?

   Formula: $d = vt = (-6) \times (-3) = 18$. *Answer:* 18 miles east

These illustrations suggest that the rules we use for multiplying directed numbers are the ones naturally suited to the handling of simple problems involving motion. In more complex engineering and dynamic situations, the rules are indispensable.

Problem Set 2

In Problems 1 to 20, compute the answers.

1. $36.3 + (-8.7)$
2. $21.2 + (-57.6)$
3. $-63 + 120$
4. $(-12.3) + (-25.6)$
5. $\frac{3}{4} + (-\frac{9}{4})$
6. $39 - (-7)$
7. $2.63 - (-3.37)$
8. $-20 - 8$
9. $-14.2 - (-40.2)$
10. $10\frac{1}{2} - (-8\frac{1}{3})$
11. $2 - 8 - 9 + 20 - 6$
12. $-6 - 7 - 15 + 20$
13. $5 \times (-3)$
14. $(-7) \times 4$
15. $(-20) \div 5$
16. $(-24) \div (-8)$
17. $8 - [2 \times (-3)]$
18. $(-1)^{62}$
19. $2 \times (-2) \times (-1) \times (-1) \times 2 \times 2$
20. $[(-4) \times 5] \div [(-2) \times (-3)]$

21. The nurse in charge of a blood bank lists numbers of pints coming in from donors ($+$) and going out for transfusions ($-$). Her list runs: $-3, +1, -4, +2, +2, -2, -6, -4, +1$. What is the net increase in pints of blood?
22. Over a period of a week the daily changes in a stock quotation were $+\frac{3}{4}, -\frac{1}{8}, -1\frac{1}{8}, +2, +\frac{1}{2}, -3\frac{3}{8}, 0$. What was the net increase?
23. Demonstrate in detail how the associative and commutative properties are used to effect the following: $7 - 4 - 2 + 5 = (7 + 5) - (4 + 2)$. [*Hint:* $7 - 4 = 7 + (-4)$.]
24. Now 60°, the temperature is rising at a rate of 2° per hour. What will it be in 6 hr.? What was it 6 hr. ago? (In both cases, use the formula change = time $\times$ rate, the positive time direction being toward the future and a positive rate being a rate of increase, as in Examples 6, 7 of Section 4.)
25. Now 60°, the temperature is falling at a rate of 2° per hour. What will it be in 6 hr.? What was it 6 hr. ago?
26. Along an east-west road, an auto travels east (positive direction) at 40 miles per hour. The car passes milepost no. 250 at 2 P.M. Where was it at 11 A.M.? (Use directed numbers, substituting into the formula $d = vt$, as in Section 5.)

27. Along the road of Problem 26, an auto travels west at 40 miles per hour, passing milepost no. 210 at 1 P.M. Where was it at 11.30 A.M.?
28. Make a picture of a number line and show on it, by arrows, each of the following:

    (a) $2 + 3$ (b) $3 + (-1)$

    (c) $1 + (-4)$ (d) $-2 + (-3)$

29. A body thrown upward at time $t = 0$ with a speed of 80 feet per second, will have its velocity subsequently given by $v = 80 - 32t$. Find v when $t = 3$. What is the physical meaning of the answer?
30. The generator in a car charges the battery as needed ($+$), and starting, running, and the use of accessories discharge it ($-$). Discuss how this process may operate during a short trip, relating the discussion to directed numbers.

6. WHY WE NEED IRRATIONAL NUMBERS

In everyday life we can put up with many inaccuracies. The extent of the error that may be tolerated depends upon the situation. A man may cut the grass a day or two earlier or later than he planned, but if he wishes to leave a bus at a certain stop, the leeway is cut to seconds. It is a matter of small concern if the housewife prepares one tablespoon too many of mashed potatoes for dinner, but an extra teaspoon of salt in the stew may spoil the meal. The novice mechanic who grinds an extra hundredth of an inch from the cylinder wall of an automobile engine will be urged to seek another trade.

A similar situation is found in the scientific laboratory. No physicist can nor ever will be able to measure the length of a metal bar exactly. He may be able to measure it to the nearest .00000000001 in. For practical purposes such approximate measurement is fully adequate.

Are the decimals, then, adequate for such practical purposes? With them we may approximate any number as closely as we please, to the nearest .1, or the nearest .01, or the nearest .001, . . . , or the nearest .000000000000000000001, . . . ; there is no limit to the minuteness of the error-range that we may enforce.

Now possibly *absolute precision* of measurement is never entirely *necessary*, but there are many circumstances in which such exactness is highly convenient. We often wish to state the sizes of groups accurately, in terms of natural numbers. In preparing a dessert recipe, the cook could just as well apportion the ingredients on the theory that 8.003 people were to be served instead of exactly 8. But what would we think of the guest who observed that about 8.003 people were seated at the table? Monetary accounts and other inventories are supposed to be exact, to facilitate checking, and for legal and other reasons.

When we use natural numbers as precise measures, we will often find ourselves also compelled to use fractions as precise measures. If 12 rolls are to be distributed equally among 3 people, each person must get just $\frac{1}{3}$ of the dozen, not .3 (30%), nor .33, nor .333, etc. This is still a case of theoretical convenience rather than practical necessity. Who cares whether he receives 4 rolls or 4.00000000007 rolls?

Among the decimal numerals we studied so far there are no names for many fractions: $\frac{1}{3}$, $\frac{2}{7}$, etc. Hence these decimal numerals are inadequate for some purposes.

From the sixth grade on, we meet a profuse variety of applications of the simple geometry of the Euclidean plane, from shopwork and common arts and crafts to machine design and analytic dynamics. At the very least, we would wish our number system to tie in with this geometry, so that exact numerical lengths could be assigned to all line segments, circular arcs, etc. The Greeks discovered that the rational numbers did not meet this requirement, as we shall now see.

Consider this problem (Fig. 9-6): Given a right triangle with legs each of unit length, how long is the hypotenuse?

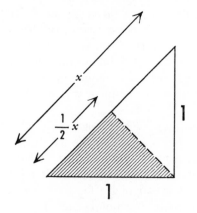

Fig. 9-6

Our first step in attacking the problem is to assume that it has an answer, i.e., that there really is a number that gives exactly the length of the hypotenuse. We denote this number by x, as marked on the figure. We mark the mid-point of the hypotenuse and inspect the shaded right triangle whose leg length is $\frac{1}{2}x$. This triangle is similar to the original, because it is also a 45°–45° right triangle. Hence the corresponding sides of the two triangles are in the proportion

$$\frac{\frac{1}{2}x}{1} = \frac{1}{x}$$

Multiplying both sides by $2x$ gives

$$x^2 = 2, \qquad \text{so that} \qquad x = \sqrt{2}.$$

We may approximate the value of $\sqrt{2}$ with a decimal numeral, say 1.41. That 1.41 is only approximately equal to $\sqrt{2}$ can be verified by squaring 1.41:

$$(1.41)^2 = 1.9881.$$

Occasionally we may wish to have a much better approximation for $\sqrt{2}$, say 1.4142135. That this is also only approximately equal to $\sqrt{2}$ can be verified by squaring:

$$(1.4142135)^2 = 1.99999982358225.$$

The point is that there is no name of the form a/b for $\sqrt{2}$ ($b \neq 0$; a, b whole numbers) and therefore no decimal numeral for $\sqrt{2}$. Thus, $\sqrt{2}$ is *not* a rational number. We shall prove in the next section that there is no rational number whose square is equal to 2.

If we should limit ourselves to rational numbers, we would have no number for the length of the hypotenuse in a right triangle with each leg 1 unit long.

7. IRRATIONALITY OF $\sqrt{2}$

There is no rational number whose square is 2.

Sometime before 430 B.C., a Greek mathematician, probably a member of the group called *Pythagoreans*, made this outstanding mathematical discovery. It was the forerunner of many famous "impossibility proofs" that have made their impact felt upon the course of Western culture. The other proofs have been given in modern times, but most of them relate to problems left unsolved by the Greeks—squaring the circle, doubling the cube, and trisecting an angle.

When the Pythagoreans learned of the proof, consternation swept their ranks. The philosophy of this famous school of Greek thinkers stemmed from the dictum that "number rules the universe." Here, *number* had reference only to the natural numbers and to their ratios, the positive rationals. That the dominion of number did not even embrace geometry, must have been as shocking to the Pythagoreans as though the sun had chosen to vanish overnight or water had ceased to be wet. Even so, they and their successors recognized the fundamental and profound importance of the new knowledge. Plato said, "He who does not know the proof of the incommensurability of the diagonal of the square with its side, is not a man but a beast." Euclid included a proof in his *Elements*.

The discovery had an unfortunate consequence. It quite likely led Greek mathematicians to take the devious detour that finally brought them to a dead end insofar as arithmetic and algebra were concerned. Since geometric objects had turned out not to be universally measurable in terms of their number scheme, they set about developing a "geometric algebra." They interpreted operations like adding and multiplying geometrically, carrying them out as constructions with line segments, surfaces, and solid objects. They could not make use of relations involving fourth and higher powers; cubing a line segment to produce a solid object was as far as they could go. Euclid's Book V dealt with proportions. To develop the subject in geometric terms he had to establish some thirty propositions. Today, with an efficient numerical algebra, we handle that theory in a few lines.

In the proof to follow we shall need this fact: *A natural number is even or odd according as its square is even or odd.* To show this, first note that, by taking $n = 1, 2, 3, \ldots$ successively, we get *all* the even naturals from the form $2n$ and *all* the odd naturals from the form $2n - 1$. Give the square of each form:

SQUARES OF EVENS

$$(2n)^2 = 4n^2$$

SQUARES OF ODDS

$$(2n - 1)^2 = 4n^2 - 4n + 1$$

Since $4n^2$ is divisible by 2, the square of an even natural is even. Since $4n^2 - 4n$ is divisible by 2, the square of an odd natural number is odd. Hence if the square of a natural number is known to be even, the number cannot be odd (since then its square will be odd) and so must be even. Likewise, a natural number whose square is odd must itself be odd.

Theorem   There is no rational number whose square is 2.

Proof. Let us suppose that there is some positive rational number whose square is 2. If we can demonstrate this supposition to be contradictory, then we shall have proved the theorem. (We need not worry about the negative case, for a negative rational whose square was 2 would have the absolute value equal to that of a positive rational with square 2.)

Let x denote such a positive rational ($x^2 = 2$). Since the positive rationals are the nonzero fractions, x is the quotient of some two natural numbers. Now we may choose a simple or fractional name for any fractional number. Therefore, we can express x in this way:

$$x = \frac{P}{Q}$$ The quotient of two natural numbers P and Q that are relatively prime, i.e., have 1 as their only common factor.

From $x^2 = 2$ we get

$$\frac{P^2}{Q^2} = 2, \qquad \text{so} \qquad P^2 = 2Q^2.$$

The equation $P^2 = 2Q^2$ states that P^2 is even. According to our earlier result, therefore, P *is even*. This means that $P/2$ is a natural number that we shall call I. Then $P = 2I$, and

$$2Q^2 = P^2 = (2I)^2 = 4I^2, \qquad \text{whence} \qquad Q^2 = 2I^2.$$

So Q^2 is even, and therefore Q *is even*.

We have shown that *both* P and Q are *even*, which directly contradicts the previous stipulation that P and Q are prime to each other. What forced us into this impossible predicament was our initial assumption that there was some positive rational with square 2. Hence that assumption is false.

Our modern **real number system** is an extension of the rational number system. A larger aggregate, it *does* include a number whose square is 2, namely $\sqrt{2}$; also one whose square is 3, namely $\sqrt{3}$; and many other *irrational* numbers.

Put yourself in the position of a mathematician who has at his disposal only the rational numbers and who is constructing from them candidates for admission to a new, "larger" real number system. From your point of view the expression $\sqrt{2}$ is thus not yet a number. But you have O.K.'d its application for membership. It is a "number-to-be."

Can $\sqrt{2} + 1$ be rational? If it is, call it R. Then $R - 1 = \sqrt{2}$, so that $R - 1$ is not rational. But $R - 1$ is a difference of rationals and so must be rational (for a difference of rationals is a rational). This contradiction shows that there is no rational number of the form $\sqrt{2} + 1$. By similar argument, no form $a + b\sqrt{2}$, with a, b rational and $b \neq 0$, can represent a rational. Yet there are as many such forms as there are rationals. So there are at least as many numbers-to-be missing from the rational system as there are numbers in the system.

Any root combination you can write (avoiding even roots of negatives) is likely to represent such a missing number-to-be:

$$\sqrt{2} + \sqrt{3}; \qquad \sqrt[3]{2}; \qquad \sqrt{4\sqrt{3} - \sqrt[3]{71}}; \qquad \sqrt{2 - \sqrt[5]{3}}.$$

There are various algebraic procedures that generate many other candidates. And there are certain special number candidates of major mathematical importance that are irrational numbers: π, for example, representing the ratio of the circumference of a circle to the length of its diameter.

As a matter of fact, yours is a hopeless task. The large portion of the numbers-to-be cannot be singled out and identified. The only way to get the all-inclusive number system that you aim toward is by a gross approach that gives the whole in one fell swoop. Such a scheme is described next.

8. THE REAL NUMBER SYSTEM

Consider the number line used as a model in Section 5 (Fig. 9-2). It is a line along which the integers are evenly marked, in both directions, from the origin. Imagine that the finite decimals are also marked at appropriate positions along it. These pepper the line evenly and "densely." Let us agree to call such decimals as 1.63, 215.6759, and .00016 **terminating decimals.** They have a finite number of digits.

The tenths separate the line into equal-length segments, any consecutive ten of them making up a unit length. The hundredths likewise give an even separation, and include the tenths. The thousandths include both tenths and hundredths. The set of all the finite decimals may thus be thought of as spaced evenly along the line. Furthermore, choose any tiny segment of the line and you will find within it a decimal marker (infinitely many, in fact). For example, any segment of length one-millionth includes nine or ten ten-millionth markers. For this reason the set of decimals is said to be a **dense set.**

The terminating decimals reveal the pattern of the entire line, even as the separate tiny dots of light on a TV picture-tube screen give a total image to the viewer. Of course these decimals miss many positions on the line, including many rational positions. Thus $\frac{1}{3}$ is missed, for this corresponds to nonterminating decimal, .333 . . . .

It turns out that each point on the line may be assigned a nonterminating decimal numeral. Conversely, every nonterminating decimal numeral may be assigned to a point on the line. This is a key to the all-inclusive number system, which we seek and which we call the **real number system.**

The set of real numbers consists of all rational numbers and all irrational numbers. Each rational number has a name of the form a/b ($b \neq 0$; a, b integers). No irrational number has a name of this form.

It is easy to see that any terminating decimal has a corresponding name of the form a/b ($b \neq 0$). For example, .1307 = 1,307/10,000. In the next section we shall show that any rational number can be given as a terminating decimal or as a *nonterminating repeating* decimal. An irrational number can only be approximated by a nonrepeating nonterminating decimal.

Having introduced the set of real numbers, we can establish a one-to-one correspondence between the set of points of the number line and the set of real numbers: To each point of the number line there is assigned exactly one real number and vice versa.

In summary, we list the properties possessed by the set of real numbers for the operations of addition and multiplication. We use R to denote the set of real numbers.

1. Closure: $\forall_x \forall_y (x + y) \in R$
   $\forall_x \forall_y (xy) \in R$
2. Commutative properties: $\forall_x \forall_y \ x + y = y + x$
   $\forall_x \forall_y \ xy = yx$
3. Associative properties: $\forall_x \forall_y \forall_z (x + y) + z = x + (y + z)$
   $\forall_x \forall_y \forall_z (xy)z = x(yz)$
4. Left-distributive property: $\forall_x \forall_y \forall_z \ x(y + z) = (xy) + (xz)$
5. Existence of additive identity: There exists an additive identity, namely 0, such that $\forall_x \ x + 0 = x$.
6. Existence of multiplicative identity: There exists a multiplicative identity, namely 1, such that $\forall_x \ x \cdot 1 = x$.
7. Property of additive inverse:
   $\forall_x \exists_{-x}$ such that $x + (-x) = 0$ (read: For every x there exists $-x$ such that . . .).
8. Property of multiplicative inverse:

   $\forall_{x \neq 0} \exists_{1/x}$ such that $x \cdot \dfrac{1}{x} = 1$.

Any set of elements and two operations having all the properties enumerated above is called a **field**. The set of real numbers is a **number field**.

Problem Set 3

1. Draw a line segment of unit length (length = 1 unit). With this as the base, erect a right triangle of altitude 1 (1 unit). As noted in Section 6, the hypotenuse of this triangle will be of length $\sqrt{2}$. Now use this hypotenuse as the base and on it erect another right triangle of altitude 1. Show its hypotenuse to be of length $\sqrt{3}$. Continue this procedure until you have constructed a segment of length $\sqrt{18}$. (If your constructions are accurate, the successive altitudes of the triangles will form a polygonal spiral turning through a total angle of 364°47'.)
2. Draw a circle of diameter 3. Draw a diameter. Draw a chord perpendicular to this diameter and dividing it in the ratio of 2 to 1. Show that the length of the chord is twice $\sqrt{2}$.
3. In the quotation of Section 7, Plato used the term "commensurable." Look up the meaning of this term, and explain Plato's reference.

4. Prove $\sqrt[3]{2}$ irrational.
5. Assuming $\sqrt{2}$ irrational, show $3\sqrt{2} - 8$ irrational. Will the same type of argument serve for $\sqrt{2} + \sqrt{3}$?
6. Give an example showing that the set of irrational numbers is not closed under

   (a) addition   (b) multiplication
   (c) subtraction   (d) division

7. Q = the set of rational numbers
   T = the set of irrational numbers
   R = the set of real numbers
   $\emptyset$ = the empty set
   True or false?

   (a) $Q \cup T = R$
   (b) $Q \cap T = \emptyset$
   (c) $T \subset R$
   (d) $R \subset Q$
   (e) $R \cup \emptyset = \emptyset$
   (f) $R \cap \emptyset = \emptyset$
   (g) $Q \cap R = Q$
   (h) $T \cap R = T$
   (i) $\bar{T} = Q$
   (j) $\bar{Q} = R$
   (k) $\bar{R} = \emptyset$
   (l) $\overline{Q \cup T} = R$

8. Show why $\sqrt{1+1} = \sqrt{1} + \sqrt{1}$ is false.
9. Give the one property which the set of integers is lacking in order to be a field.
10. Verify that the set of rational numbers is a field.
11. A given number may, when represented in numeration systems with certain bases, have a terminating numeral, but still have nonterminating numerals in other bases. In base ten, for example, $\frac{1}{3} = .333 \ldots$, whereas in base six $\frac{1}{3} = .2$. Give other instances.
12. Will every rational number have a terminating numeral in some numerical base? What is the least base with respect to which the number $\frac{7}{24}$ (base-ten representation) has a terminating numeral? $\frac{2}{13}$?
13.* Construct a line segment of length $\sqrt[4]{2}$.
14.* Let P be a point of the line segment $\overline{AB}$. Denote $AP = x$ and $AB = y$. If P is such that $\dfrac{y}{x} = \dfrac{x}{y-x}$, then P is called a "golden section" of $\overline{AB}$. Show that if $x = 1$, then $y = \frac{1}{2}(1 + \sqrt{5})$. Construct a rectangle of length y and width x. The Greeks considered such a rectangle to have an especially pleasing shape.
15.* In the base-three numeration system, squares end in 0 or 1, because $0^2 = 0$,

$1^2 = 1$, $2^2 = 11$. Hence if $2Q^2 = P^2$, Q^2 and P^2 must both end in 0. Explain these statements, then use them to prove $\sqrt{2}$ irrational.[1]

16.* Frame a proof of the irrationality of $\sqrt{2}$ according to the scheme outlined in Problem 15, but with respect to the base-ten system.

9. REPEATING DECIMAL NUMERALS

Some nonterminating decimal numerals are repeating. In such a numeral there appears a certain finite sequence or "block" of digits. The rest of the numeral is simply the unending repetition of that same block of digits.

This is a handy notation: Write the block to be repeated only once, placing a bar over the digits. *Examples:*

$$.\overline{3} = .333 \ldots$$
$$23.\overline{072} = 23.072072072 \ldots$$
$$5.0\overline{72} = 5.0727272 \ldots$$

Each repeating decimal numeral represents a rational number. To get the fractional form, multiply by the power of ten whose exponent equals the number of digits in the block. Then subtract the original number. To find a fractional form for $.\overline{3}$, for example, let $N = .\overline{3}$. Then

$$\begin{aligned} 10N &= 3.\overline{3} \qquad (= 3.333 \ldots) \\ - \quad N &= .\overline{3} \qquad (= .333 \ldots) \\ \hline 9N &= 3 \qquad \text{so that } N = \tfrac{3}{9} = \tfrac{1}{3}. \end{aligned}$$

Example 1 Find a fractional form for $.34\overline{17}$.

$$\begin{aligned} \text{Let} \qquad N &= .34\overline{17}. \\ 100N &= 34.17\overline{17} \qquad (= 34.171717 \ldots) \\ - \quad N &= .34\overline{17} \qquad (= .341717 \ldots) \\ \hline 99N &= 33.83 \qquad \text{so that } N = \frac{3383}{9900}. \end{aligned}$$

Starting with a numeral of the form a/b ($b \neq 0$; a, b whole numbers), we shall see that we can obtain a decimal numeral by division. It will either be a terminating decimal numeral or a repeating decimal numeral.

Example 2 Find the decimal numeral for $\frac{1}{125}$.

$$\begin{array}{r} 0.008 \\ 125\overline{)1.000} \\ \underline{1\,000} \\ 0 \end{array} \qquad \text{Thus } \tfrac{1}{125} = 0.008.$$

[1] *American Mathematical Monthly*, 63, **4** (April 1956), p. 247.

Example 3 Find the decimal numeral for $\frac{3}{7}$.

	LIST OF REMAINDERS	EXPLANATION

```
        .4 2 8 5 7 1
    7)3.                    3      Once a remainder is duplicated, the
      2 8                          portion of the division included be-
      ‾‾‾‾                         tween the equal remainders must
      2 0                    2     repeat thereafter. Some remainder
      1 4                          must be duplicated, for the num-
      ‾‾‾‾                         ber of possible remainders, zero
        6 0                  6     included, is only equal to the
        5 6                        divisor.
        ‾‾‾‾                       Hence 3/7 = .428571‾‾‾‾‾‾.
          4 0                4
          3 5
          ‾‾‾‾
            5 0              5
            4 9
            ‾‾‾‾
              1 0            1
                7
              ‾‾‾‾
                3            3
```

Every nonrepeating nonterminating decimal numeral names an irrational number. Two such irrationals are:

$$.101001000100001000001 \ldots$$
$$.123456789101112131415 \ldots$$

It is left to the student to detect the patterns followed in writing these, also to verify that neither decimal numeral is repeating.

One further number classification is of some interest. An *algebraic* number is a real number that is a solution of some algebraic equation, like $x^7 - 3x^4 + 8 = 0$. Other real numbers are termed *transcendental*. All rationals are algebraic, being solutions of linear equations. Thus $-\frac{5}{18}$ is the solution of $18x + 5 = 0$. Some irrationals are algebraic. Thus $\sqrt{2}$ is a solution of $x^2 - 2 = 0$. But most irrationals are transcendental. The number π was shown by Lindemann in 1882 to be a transcendental. Here is a decimal transcendental:

$$.110001000000000000000001 \ldots$$

The 1's occupy the places numbered 1!, 2!, 3!, etc., where $1! = 1$, $2! = 1 \times 2 = 2$, $3! = 1 \times 2 \times 3 = 6$, etc.

Problem Set 4

1. Derive fractional numerals in simplest terms for these repeating decimals:

(a) $.\overline{1}$ (b) $.\overline{6}$ (c) $3.\overline{27}$ (d) $.58\overline{3}$

(e) $.\overline{01}$ (f) $.1\overline{6}$ (g) $.08\overline{3}$ (h) $.\overline{076923}$

2. Verify: (a) $4 \times .\overline{3} = 1.\overline{3}$, (b) $.\overline{7} + .\overline{8} = 1.\overline{6}$.
3. Express as repeating decimal numerals:

(a) $\frac{2}{3}$ (b) $\frac{3}{11}$ (c) $\frac{8}{13}$ (d) 5

(e) $\frac{1}{11}$ (f) $\frac{5}{7}$ (g) $\frac{1}{2}$ (h) $\frac{5}{12}$

4. Find the repeating decimal numeral for $\frac{4}{13}$.
5. Present an argument that in the decimal numeral for $\frac{1}{43}$ there can be at most 42 nonzero digits in the repeating "block."
6. Show that

(a) $.\overline{9} = 1$ (b) $.\overline{1} = \frac{1}{9}$

(c) $.\overline{3} = \frac{1}{3}$ (d) $1.\overline{9} = 2$

7. Three examples of nonrepeating decimal numerals, representing irrationals, were cited in the text. Give two more examples.
8. Give arguments to show that your examples in Problem 7 are nonrepeating numerals.
9. Show the following to be algebraic numbers:

(a) $\frac{2}{3}$ (b) $1 + \sqrt{2}$

(c) $\sqrt{3}$ (d) $\sqrt{2} - \sqrt{3}$

10. Show that in the binary numeration system $\frac{1}{11} = .\overline{01}$.
11.* In the binary numeration system $1 = .\overline{1}$ (just as in base-ten system, $1 = .\overline{9}$). But $.\overline{1} = \frac{1}{10} + \frac{1}{100} + \frac{1}{1,000} + \ldots$, equivalent to $\frac{1}{2} + \frac{1}{4} + \frac{1}{8} + \ldots$ in base ten. Does this justify the assertion that $\frac{1}{2} + \frac{1}{4} + \frac{1}{8} + \ldots = 1$?

BIBLIOGRAPHY

Hacker, Sidney G., Wilfred E. Barnes, and Calvin T. Long, *Fundamental Concepts of Arithmetic*. Englewood Cliffs, N.J.: Prentice-Hall, Inc., 1963, pp. 229–245.

Kline, Morris, *Mathematics—A Cultural Approach*. Reading, Mass.: Addison-Wesley Publishing Company, Inc., 1962, pp. 54–81.

Lay, L. Clark, *Arithmetic: An Introduction to Mathematics*. New York: The Macmillan Company, 1961, pp. 257–275.

Nichols, Eugene D., *Modern Elementary Algebra*. New York: Holt, Rinehart and Winston, 1965, Chaps. 3, 4.

———, R. T. Heimer, and H. Garland, *Modern Intermediate Algebra*. New York: Holt, Rinehart and Winston, Inc., 1965, Chap. 1.

———, R. Kalin, and H. Garland, *Arithmetic of Directed Numbers*. New York: Holt, Rinehart and Winston, Inc., 1962.

Osborn, Roger, M. Vere DeVault, Claude C. Boyd, and W. Robert Houston, *Extending Mathematics Understanding*. Columbus, Ohio: Charles E. Merrill Books, Inc., 1961, pp. 87–96.

Peterson, John A., and Joseph Hashisaki, *Theory of Arithmetic*. New York: John Wiley & Sons, Inc., 1963, pp. 193–235.

Rademacher, Hans, and Otto Toeplitz, *The Enjoyment of Mathematics*. Princeton, N.J.: Princeton University Press, 1957, pp. 147–160.

Schaaf, William L., *Basic Concepts of Elementary Mathematics*. New York: John Wiley & Sons, Inc., 1960, pp. 138–154.

School Mathematics Study Group, *Studies in Mathematics, vol. VIII, Concepts of Algebra*, prelim. ed. New Haven: Yale University Press, 1961, pp. 73–218.

10

ELEMENTARY
NUMBER
THEORY

1. PRIME AND COMPOSITE NUMBERS

In this chapter we shall consider the set of natural numbers to be the universal set. We shall explore interesting aspects of some subsets of the set of natural numbers.

The number 1 is singled out, since it is the only natural number that is divisible by only one number: itself. Every other natural number is divisible by itself and by 1. Some are divisible by no other number. These are called **primes.** The rest are called **composite.** The first few primes are:

$$2, 3, 5, 7, 11, 13, 17, 19, 23, 29, 31, 37, \ldots .$$

We shall learn later that any composite number can be expressed as a product of primes, also that there is essentially only one way in which this factoring can be done. *Example:* $6 = 2 \times 3$.

Since every natural number other than 1 is either a prime or a product of primes, *the primes are the keys to the natural numbers.* That which we find out about the primes, we may apply toward learning things about all the natural numbers. By this approach, we shall be able to justify various common arithmetic processes, especially those having to do with fractions.

2. FINDING PRIMES

"How can I tell if a number is prime?" If a *formula* for telling primes is expected, the questioner will be disappointed. Such a "formula," known as *Wilson's Theorem,* does exist, but its value is theoretical rather than practical, and there is no reason to believe that a truly practical formula can be found.

Wilson's Theorem **The number N is prime if and only if the number $(N - 1)! + 1$ is divisible by N.** Examples : For $N = 7$, $(N - 1)!$ $= 6! = 1 \times 2 \times 3 \times 4 \times 5 \times 6 = 720$, and 721 is divisible by 7. For $N = 6$, $(N - 1)! + 1 = 121$, not divisible by 6. The expression $(N - 1)! + 1$ rapidly becomes too large to be dealt with conveniently. For $N = 97$, the numeral for $96! + 1$ has 150 digits.

Finding primes is essentially a matter of testing divisors in turn: 2, 3, 4, 5, 6, 7, ... Composite divisors, however, need not be tried, for they themselves have smaller divisors that will already have been eliminated in the trials. For example, a number that is not divisible by 2 cannot be divisible by 6. (A number divisible by 6 has the form $6n = (2 \times 3)n = 2 \times (3n) = 2m$, and hence is also divisible by 2.)

Is 37 prime? We try to divide it by 2, and this cannot be done. We try 3, which fails. Since 4 is a multiple of 2, we need not try it. We try 5, then 7, then 11, ... Need we keep on?

As a matter of fact, we could have ended the trials before 7. For $7 \times 7 = 49$, which exceeds 37. Hence if 7 or some higher number were a divisor of 37, the quotient would be less than 7 and would *itself* be a factor of 37. Our earlier trials, through 6, have rejected this possibility. *Conclusion:* 37 is prime.

When the considerations above are made more general, the following rule results: To find out if the number N is prime, test the primes in turn (2, 3, 5, 7, 11, . . .) for divisibility into N, but do not test beyond $\sqrt{N}$ (i.e., beyond the largest natural number whose square is less than or equal to N).

Example 1 Is 97 prime?

Yes. For 97 is not divisible by 2, 3, 5, or 7. This is far enough, since $10^2 = 100 > 97$, while 8 and 9 are composite. Note that if 11 is tried, the quotient will be 8 (and remainder 9); that the quotient turns out to be less than the divisor is an automatic *stop* signal.

Example 2 Is 1943 prime?

Mentally noting that $50^2 = 2500 > 1943$, we have the comforting knowledge that we need not test past 50. (We could actually narrow the bound to 43.) We test successively: 2, 3, 5, 7, 11, 13, 17, 19, 23, 29. Lo! 29 is a divisor. (The prime factorization is: $1943 = 29 \times 67$.)

Comment. Some of the small books of mathematical tables designed for school and ready reference use contain tables listing the prime factors of all numbers up to 1000 or more.

A practical device for listing all primes less than some given number was designed about 230 B.C. After its Greek inventor, it is called *Eratosthenes' Sieve.*

To set up the Sieve, list the natural numbers up to some last one, say 100. Cross out 1. Now go through the list striking out all the multiples of 2 (except 2 itself): 4, 6, 8, ... Next, strike out all multiples of 3 still on the list (except 3 itself): (6), 9, (12), 15, ... The next number still on the list is 5. Strike out all its multiples. Next, those of 7. This is far enough, since 8, 9, 10 are no longer on the list and $11^2 = 121 > 100$. The 25 numbers that remain are the primes under 100.

3. HOW MANY ARE THE PRIMES?

If a person did not know the answer, he might reasonably conjecture that really *big* numbers must necessarily be divisible by some smaller ones—that the primes come to an end. This possibility occurred to Euclid. He ruled it out by proving that **there is no greatest prime.**

With some care and concentration, we can follow this remarkable proof. Let us suppose that there *is* a largest prime. Call it P. Form the product of the natural numbers from 1 to P, inclusive: $1 \times 2 \times 3 \times \cdots \times P$. This product is usually denoted by $P!$, read "P factorial." Now add 1 to this product, and call the new number N:

$$N = P! + 1 = (1 \times 2 \times 3 \times \cdots \times P) + 1.$$

Since this new number N exceeds the largest prime P, it must be composite, hence divisible by some number other than 1 and itself. Let X be the smallest such number. If X were composite, some divisor of it would also divide into N, contradicting our provision that X is the smallest divisor of N (other than 1). Therefore X is prime. Since P is the largest prime, X is among the numbers 1, 2, 3, . . . , P. Consequently, X divides evenly into $P! = 1 \times 2 \times 3 \times \cdots \times P$. But then X *cannot divide into* N, a remainder of 1 being left when the division is attempted.

Our original supposition that there is a largest prime has led us to an impossible conclusion, a contradiction. We are forced to admit that the supposition is itself impossible—and we conclude that there is no largest prime. This means that the primes are scattered along the whole infinite sequence of the natural numbers and are themselves infinite in number.

The primes do indeed gradually thin out as the natural numbers mount in size. There are 25 primes under 100, a rate of 25%. There are 50,847,478 primes under 1,000,000,000, a rate of 5%.

4. SOME OBSERVATIONS ABOUT PRIMES

When listing primes, we discover that each prime greater than 3 seems to be either 1 less or 1 more than a multiple of 6:

$$5 = (6 \times 1) - 1$$
$$7 = (6 \times 1) + 1$$
$$11 = (6 \times 2) - 1$$
$$13 = (6 \times 2) + 1$$
$$17 = (6 \times 3) - 1$$
$$19 = (6 \times 3) + 1$$

and so on.

We also notice that some pairs of primes are made up of two primes differing by 2:

$$3,5; \quad 5,7; \quad 11,13; \quad 17,19; \quad \text{and so on.}$$

These are called **twin primes.** How many pairs of twin primes are there? No one knows. It is one of the unproved conjectures in mathematics that there is an infinite number of pairs of twin primes. Some of the larger primes that are twin primes are

$$209,267 \quad \text{and} \quad 209,269$$
$$1,000,000,009,649 \quad \text{and} \quad 1,000,000,009,651.$$

Another unproved conjecture is that every even number greater than 2 can be shown as a sum of two primes (not necessarily different):

$$4 = 2 + 2$$
$$6 = 3 + 3$$
$$8 = 5 + 3$$
$$10 = 5 + 5 = 7 + 3$$
$$12 = 7 + 5$$
$$14 = 7 + 7 = 11 + 3$$

and so on.

No one as yet made a proof that this is possible for every even number.

The advent of electronic computers has advanced the knowledge about primes a great deal. In 1963, Donald B. Gillies, using a computer at the University of Illinois, discovered what is the largest known prime: $2^{11213} - 1$. As of today, perhaps a larger prime has been discovered.

Problem Set 1

1. Test each number to find if it is prime or composite:

(a) 71	(g) 127	(m) 269	(s) 403	(y) 827
(b) 83	(h) 133	(n) 299	(t) 437	(z) 943
(c) 87	(i) 151	(o) 301	(u) 439	(A) 1003
(d) 91	(j) 187	(p) 307	(v) 611	(B) 1007
(e) 101	(k) 233	(q) 323	(w) 613	(C) 1009
(f) 103	(l) 253	(r) 347	(x) 817	(D) 1011

2. Construct the Sieve of Eratosthenes for the numbers from 1 to 100 as explained at the end of Section 2. List the 25 primes found.
3. The following are prime numbers:

(a) 71   (b) 107   (c) 709   (d) 719   (e) 827

Show that each of these numbers is 1 less or 1 more than some multiple of 6.
4. Give 5 pairs of twin primes using no primes under 20.
5. Check to see whether each of the following is a pair of twin primes:

(a) 821 and 823
(b) 809 and 811
(c) 431 and 433
(d) 617 and 619

6. Show each of the following even numbers as a sum of two primes or a sum of a prime and itself:

(a) 16	(c) 22	(e) 80	(g) 100
(b) 18	(d) 40	(f) 92	(h) 200

7. Prove that if a number is divisible by 8, then it is divisible by 2.
8. Apply Wilson's theorem to N equal to 4, 5, and 11.

5. TWO MOTIVATIONS FOR NUMBER STUDY

Perhaps the Greeks stood so much in respect and awe of numbers as individuals and as members of special groups that they were unable to conceive of them in a "classless society," that is, as in practical arithmetic, where particular numbers are no more important nor significant than others. The Greeks expended much energy toward the discovery and exploitation of special and novel properties of numbers. We can discern the polar motivations that spurred their studies:

I. (*Rational*). An intellectual drive of the sort that has always stimulated "pure" research in every field, a powerful and compulsive urge that is nevertheless kept under control by rigorous logical discipline.

II. (*Intuitive*). A spiritual, aesthetic, or mystical zeal, marked by impatience with and distrust of rationalism, a conviction that inner meanings and ultimate truths may be intuitively sensed, grasped by miraculous insights.

Nearly every subject of broad importance is still approached in both ways today, although seldom by the same person. In older times, a Kepler might partition his activity between astronomy and astrology. Nowadays, astronomy is a serious subject, astrology either a recreational diversion or a fraud—no one can be professionally involved in both. There are spheres of activity in which the intuitive is the serious side, the rational the frivolous. In the arts—in painting, for example—either approach may be serious and important.

Under the rational approach, the study of the structure of the natural numbers and of the special relationships found within this structure has become the field of pure mathematics called "Number Theory." Specialists in this field have claimed it to be the most abstruse and difficult of the many branches of mathematics—"the most brilliant gem in the diadem of the Queen of the Sciences."

Under the intuitive approach, the same study has degenerated in various ways. We may lump these under the heading "Numerology." In some esoteric and mystical religions we still find forms of number worship. The Rosicrucians are steeped in mystic number lore. There are also the less imaginative "numerologists" who ply their absurd trade in many urban areas.

Euclid devoted a chapter of his *Elements* to *perfect* numbers. A perfect number is defined to be one that is the sum of its own divisors, where 1 is counted as a divisor but the number itself is not. Such divisors are called **proper divisors**. The smallest perfect number is 6 ($= 1 + 2 + 3$). The first five are: 6, 28, 496, 8128, and 33,550,336.

Euclid proved that whenever the natural number n is such that $2^{n+1} - 1$ is a prime number, then multiplying this prime by 2^n produces a perfect number. Euclid conjectured that all perfect numbers could be obtained by this process. But this problem presented such difficulty that 20 centuries rolled by until Euler proved the conjecture for *even* perfects. Whether or not there is an *odd* perfect number is not known to this day.

Should the ambitious student be tempted to try to find an odd perfect number by experiment, let him take heed as follows: He should begin with numbers larger than two million and consider only those with five or more distinct prime factors . . . ! The "to be or not to be" entity, the odd perfect number, must satisfy these criteria, among others.

Euclid's contribution belongs to the great body of serious mathematics. His was surely a rational motivation. Yet the study of perfect numbers may well have been *initiated* as a result of the intuitive type of motivation. Under the latter approach, the study assumed a wholly "non-Euclidean" (and nonmathematical) aspect, as the following quotations reveal.

St. Augustine wrote: "Six is a number perfect in itself, and not because God created all things in six days; rather the inverse is true, God created all things in six days because this number is perfect, and it would remain perfect even if the work of the six days did not exist."

The Jewish philosopher Philo Judaeas wrote, " . . . such great sanctity is there in the number seven, that it has a pre-eminent rank beyond all the numbers in the first decade. . . . it displays a great and comprehensive power, contributing to the improvement of all terrestial things and affecting even the periodical changes of the moon. And in what manner it does this, we must consider. The number seven when compounded of numbers beginning with the unit, makes eight-and-twenty, a perfect number, ..."[1]

A modern mathematician, inspecting the very *definition* of the perfect numbers, would regard the definition as a wholly arbitrary construction, which has proved felicitous in that it has led to some interesting problems. No virtue resides in any definition as such, but virtue may accumulate as a definition is constantly used in a fruitful way.

The Greeks called a pair of numbers *amicable* if the proper divisors of each added up to the other. Check this for the pair 220, 284. From Greek times through the medieval period, much was written about these numbers and their divine or mystic relation to human friendship. Yet no second pair was found until the year 1636, when the famous mathematician Fermat constructed the pair 17296, 18416. Amateurs as well as professional mathematicians have since dabbled with this notion, finding some 390 pairs. But having led to no problems of special interest or importance, the notion has dwindled to the status of a mathematical "curiosity."

6. NUMBER LORE

In the Pythagorean lexicon, *even* numbers were feminine or earthly in their nature, *odd* numbers masculine or celestial. The number *One* was not included in this scheme, being regarded as the source of all numbers.

Each of the first few dozen numbers partook of special divine or mystical significance. *Five* and *six* referred to *marriage*, being the sum and product, respectively, of 2 and 3, the first female and male numbers.

[1] For a fuller quotation, see Oystein Ore, *Number Theory and Its History* (New York: McGraw-Hill, 1948), p. 27.

Four, as a product of equals (2 × 2) or as a "balance" of equals (2 + 2) connoted *justice*.

We ourselves speak of "foursquare justice." Of phrases like this in use today, some are relics of the far past, others recent acquisitions based on associations as irrational as those cited above. The difference is that we regard these phrases merely as colorful aspects of our language, whereas our predecessors took them seriously.

The Egyptian *hieratic* was an "alphabetic" type of numeral scheme, in which numbers were represented by the letters of the alphabet, in order. The Greeks also used such a scheme, augmenting their alphabet with one archaic and two Phoenician symbols:

α	β	γ	δ	ε	ϛ	ζ	η	θ
1	2	3	4	5	6	7	8	9

ι	κ	λ	μ	ν	ξ	ο	π	ϙ
10	20	30	40	50	60	70	80	90

ρ	σ	τ	υ	φ	χ	ψ	ω	ϡ
100	200	300	400	500	600	700	800	900

A Greek accustomed to using this scheme would naturally often think of the corresponding number when he used a word. The Greek word for *amen* is αμην, and from the table we find the corresponding number to be $1 + 40 + 8 + 50 = 99$. In many old editions of the Bible, the number 99 appears as a substitute for the word *amen*.

From the simple association of word and number, the Greeks and their successors proceeded further. They projected the occult personality of the number through the word onto the object named by the word. In *Number, the Language of Science* (page 39), Dantzig refers to an instance in which a poet took "revenge" upon an enemy named Thamagoras by showing this name to have the same number as the word λοιμοσ (loimos), a sort of pestilence.

The Hebrews also represented numbers alphabetically. Interpreting words according to their numbers became for them a popular occupation. The subject was known as *gematria*. Many evidences of its use are found in the Bible and in other of their writings, even unto the present day.

Gematria was a popular weapon on the theological battlegrounds of the late Middle Ages. The number of the Beast of the Revelation being 666, the sanguine scholars of the day took lusty enjoyment in affixing this symbol onto all and sundry who displeased them. Peter Bungus, Catholic theologian, succeeded in showing that a form of the name of Martin Luther gave 666 as its numerical equivalent. Not to be outdone, the Lutheran Michael Stifel retaliated as follows: The name of the Pope at that time, written in Latin capitals, was LEO DECIMVS X. The letters of this title which correspond to Roman numerals are LDCIMVX. Take away the M to remove the "mystery" (Latin: *mysterium*), and there remains the roman number D C L X V I = 666. In this medieval "logic," Pope = Antichrist.

Many a stage and screen star chooses the name that he or she will go by according to the "number" of the name (with $a = 1$, $b = 2$, . . . , $z = 26$), a number that he is told will suit his personality type and career aims. Set beside its vigorous ancestor gematria, however, modern *numerology* makes a feeble showing. The average scientist has no patience with stupidities like numerology, palmistry, phrenology, and astrology, but he usually feels that it is not worth while to take time and energy from his work to combat such relatively innocuous frauds. They gradually wither and die.

Problem Set 2

1. Show that the following numbers are perfect:

   (a) 28   (b) 496

2. For what small values of n is $2^n(2^{n+1} - 1)$ a perfect number?

3. Show that the numbers 220 and 284 form an "amicable pair."

4. In 1866, an Italian schoolboy, Nicolo Paganini, published the amicable pair 1184, 1210. Can you verify his result? (*Hint:* $1184 = 2^5 \times 37$; $1210 = 2 \times 5 \times 11^2$.)

5. Demonstrate that from 2 on there is at least one prime number between any number and its double. Do this for the numbers from 2 through 10.

6. A number is called a *deficient number* if the sum of its proper divisors is less than the number. Give examples of three deficient numbers.

7. A number is called an *abundant number* if the sum of its proper divisors is greater than the number. Give examples of three abundant numbers.

7. GREATEST COMMON DIVISOR

The *basic division relation* is a principal tool used in the investigation of the basic properties of natural numbers. We recall its form:

dividend = divisor $\times$ quotient + remainder   (remainder < divisor)

The **greatest common divisor** (GCD) of a pair of natural numbers is just what the name suggests. It is the largest natural number that divides each number of the given pair. Thus 4 is the GCD of the pair 8, 20. We express this fact by writing

$$\text{GCD } (8,20) = 4.$$

When each number of the pair is prime, the GCD will be 1. But the GCD may be 1 in other cases, as for the pair 8, 15. In such a case, the numbers of the pair are said to be *relatively prime*; 8 and 15 are relatively prime.

The *direct* way to find a GCD would be to list the set of divisors of each number (the number itself included), and to pick out the largest divisor appearing in both sets:

> Set of divisors of 8: {1,2,4,8}
> Set of divisors of 20: {1,2,4,5,10,20}
> ∴ GCD (8,20) = 4   (∴ means therefore.)

The most usual way to find a GCD is to construct it out of the common factors of both numbers. This method will be taken up later, after we have established the needed factoring principles.

Euclid developed a technique for finding the GCD that was based on the division relation. His process, called the *Euclidean Algorithm*, is applied as follows:

We are to find the GCD of 84 and 270. Divide the *smaller* (84) into the *larger* (270). The *remainder* is 18. As will soon be shown, the original GCD is equal to the GCD of the remainder 18 and the smaller given number 84:

$$\text{GCD } (84,270) = \text{GCD } (18,84).$$

remainder (270 ÷ 84)

This procedure is *repeated*. Since each remainder is less than the one before, a zero remainder must eventually be obtained. But we stop one step earlier, when it is apparent that the next division will produce the remainder 0:

GCD (84,270) = GCD (18,84) = GCD (12,18) = GCD (6,12) = 6.

When the division produces the remainder 0, as with 6 into 12, then the smaller number (6) is obviously a divisor both of itself and of the larger number (12), and so must be the GCD. Hence the final step: GCD (6,12) = 6.

To see the "why" of the process, consider the basic division relation resulting from the division of 84 into 270:

$$270 = 84 \times 3 + 18.$$

Any divisor of both 84 and 270 must also divide 18. This can be seen from the following: $270 - 84 \times 3 = 18$. Now any divisor of both 84 and 270 is a divisor of $270 - 84 \times 3$, which is equal to 18.

Therefore, the GCD of 84 and 270 is a *divisor* of 18 and 84. If it is not the *greatest* such divisor, then we shall have

$$GCD\ (84,270) < GCD\ (18,84).$$

But this is impossible. For it may be seen from the same division relation previously written that GCD (18,84), being a divisor of 18 and 84, is also a divisor of 270, so that GCD (18,84) is a *divisor* of 84 and 270, and hence cannot exceed GCD (84,270).

The conclusion is:

$$GCD\ (84,270) = GCD\ (18,84).$$

It is apparent that this numerical illustration furnishes the complete pattern for a general proof justifying the Euclidean Algorithm. (It would only be necessary to repeat the steps of the argument using letters in place of the specific numbers 84 and 270.)

Examples

1. GCD (6,15) = GCD (3,6) = 3.
2. GCD (391,544) = GCD (153,391)
   = GCD (85,153)
   = GCD (68,85)
   = GCD (17,68) = 17.
3. GCD (8,15) = GCD (7,8) = GCD (1,7) = 1.

The GCD is found most quickly by using "nearest" division, with remainder of least absolute size, instead of our usual "under" division with positive remainder. Consider GCD (18,84). In reducing this earlier, we divided 18 into 84, with quotient 4 and remainder 12. "Nearest" division produces the quotient 5 and remainder −6. Neglect the minus sign, and write

$$GCD\ (18,84) = GCD\ (6,18) = 6.$$

Similarly,

$$GCD\ (391,544) = GCD\ (153,391)$$
$$= GCD\ (68,153) = GCD\ (17,68) = 17.$$

$$GCD\ (8,15) = GCD\ (1,8) = 1.$$

The argument by which the Euclidean Algorithm was justified for ordinary division is equally valid with respect to nearest division, since the proof depends only upon the *form* of the division relation, the size of the remainder (or its sign) being irrelevant.

One obvious application of the GCD is to the simplification of fractional numerals. Because GCD (391,544) = 17, we know that

$$\frac{391}{544} = \frac{17 \times 23}{17 \times 32} = \frac{23}{32}.$$

Is this answer in lowest terms? To put the question another way: Are 23 and 32 relatively prime? Yes. For if they shared a divisor larger than 1, the product of that divisor with 17 would obviously be a common divisor of 391 and 544, contrary to our determination of 17 as the greatest such divisor. (In general, if a and b are two natural numbers with GCD $(a,b) = g$, then $a' = a/g$ and $b' = b/g$ are relatively prime.)

The GCD of three or more numbers is found by finding the GCD of the first two, next of that GCD and the third number, etc. To find GCD (48,72,108,150), for example, we have successively:

$$\text{GCD } (48,72) \ = 24$$
$$\text{GCD } (24,108) = 12$$
$$\text{GCD } (12,150) = \ 6 \qquad (Answer)$$

8. LEAST COMMON MULTIPLE

The **least common multiple** (LCM) of a pair of natural numbers is the smallest natural number that is divisible by each number of the pair. Thus the LCM of 8 and 12 is 24, written

$$\text{LCM } (8,12) = 24.$$

The LCM of a pair of natural numbers may be found by dividing the product of the numbers by their GCD. In practice, this operation is best performed by dividing the GCD into *one* of the numbers of the given pair, then multiplying this quotient by the other number.

The proof of this procedure is postponed to the next section. Note, however, the following: g denotes the GCD of the two numbers a and b; then we have $a = ga'$, $b = gb'$. Hence the product ab contains the factor g twice, whereas it is needed only once to go with either a' or b' to produce a multiple of a or b: $ga'b' = (ga')b' = ab'$ (multiple of a); $ga'b' = a'(gb') = a'b$ (multiple of b). Hence the extra factor g (= GCD of a,b) may be divided out.

Example 1 Find LCM (8,12).

$$\text{GCD } (8,12) = \text{GCD } (4,8) = 4.$$
$$\text{LCM } (8,12) = \frac{8 \times 12}{4} = 2 \times 12 = 24.$$

Example 2 Find LCM (84,270).

From Section 7, GCD (84,270) = 6.

$$\text{LCM } (84,270) = \frac{84 \times 270}{6} = 14 \times 270 = 3,780.$$

Example 3 Find LCM (36,56,60).

Outline of Solution The LCM of three or more numbers may be found by the same "successive" type of procedure as shown for the GCD at the end of Section 7:

GCD (36,56) = 4.   ∴ LCM (36,56) = 504.
GCD (60,504) = 12.   ∴ LCM (60,504) = 2520   (*Answer*).

Problem Set 3

1. Find the GCD of each pair of numbers by listing all the divisors of each number of the pair and picking out the GCD:

   (a) (4,6)   (b) (8,12)   (c) (6,18)   (d) (30,42)

2. In which cases are the numbers of the pair relatively prime?

   (a) (1,12)   (b) (4,9)   (c) (50,63)   (d) (20,35)

3. Using the relation $84 = 60 + 24$, give an argument to show that any divisor of 60 and 84 must also be a divisor of 24.
4. Continue on with the argument begun in Problem 3, as in Section 7, to show that GCD (60,84) = GCD (24,60).
5. Complete the task begun in Problems 3 and 4 above by *proving* that GCD (24,60) = GCD (12,24) = 12.
6.* Prove that, if GCD $(a,b) = g$, then $a' = a/g$ and $b' = b/g$ are relatively prime.

In Problems 7 to 18, find the GCD for each pair of numbers by the Euclidean Algorithm.

7. (9,16)   11. (42,90)   15. (806,1116)
8. (22,46)   12. (74,111)   16. (1936,3630)
9. (30,42)   13. (260,611)   17. (1728,5400)
10. (35,66)   14. (264,1512)   18. (6912,20160)

19–30. For the pairs of numbers in Problems 7 to 18, find the LCM's by the method of Section 8.
31. Find the GCD and LCM for each number triple:

   (a) (12,18,42)   (b) (36,48,60)   (c) (180,288,432)

9. PRIME-PRODUCT THEOREM

The GCD *of a pair of numbers can always be given as a difference between some two multiples of the numbers.*

This can be shown in any particular case by writing down the division relations obtained at each stage of applying the Euclidean Algorithm, then solving for the GCD in terms of the original numbers by proceeding backwards from last to first relation, in turn.

Thus in finding GCD (18,84) = 6, the steps were:

$$\text{GCD (18,84)} = \text{GCD (12,18)} = \text{GCD (6,12)}.$$

The corresponding division relations are

$$84 = \underline{18} \times 4 + \underline{12},$$
$$18 = \underline{12} \times 1 + \underline{6} \qquad (\text{GCD} = 6).$$

Solve these for the remainders 6 and 12 and write them in reverse order:

$$6 = 1 \times \underline{18} - 1 \times \underline{12},$$
$$12 = 1 \times \underline{84} - 4 \times \underline{18}.$$

The first equation expresses the GCD, 6, in terms of 12 and 18. Eliminate the smaller (12) by replacing it with the expression given for it in the second equation:

$$6 = 1 \times \underline{18} - 1 \times (1 \times \underline{84} - 4 \times \underline{18})$$
$$= 1 \times \underline{18} - 1 \times \underline{84} + 4 \times 18$$
$$= 1 \times \underline{18} + 4 \times \underline{18} - 1 \times \underline{84}$$
$$= (1 + 4) \times \underline{18} - 1 \times 84$$
$$= 5 \times \underline{18} - 1 \times 84.$$

Thus the GCD of 18 and 84 has been expressed as a multiple of 18 minus a multiple of 84.

One consequence of this result is the following:

Any common divisor of a pair of numbers is also a divisor of their GCD.

Since a common divisor of two numbers is a divisor of any multiple of either number, it is also a divisor of any difference of such multiples (by the distributive law).

Another consequence is the following theorem:

Prime-Product Theorem   If a prime divides a product of two natural numbers, then it must divide at least one of them.

This theorem is much used in simple arithmetic, generally without the computer being aware that he is using it. To find out if 242 × 331 is divisible by 3 or not, for example, we need but test 3 into 242 and 3 into 331, without multiplying out. The *prime* is very necessary to the hypothesis. Thus 4 divides the product 2 × 6. Yet 4 divides neither 2 nor 6. The proof given below is standard. An unusual proof is given on page 25 of *Biomathematics*, by Cedric Smith, Hafner, New York, 1954.

Proof. Let M and N denote any two natural numbers. Let P denote a prime number that divides the product MN. Let us suppose that P does not divide M. We propose to show that P must then divide N.

Since P is prime, its only divisors are 1 and P. But we are supposing that P is not a divisor of M. Hence GCD $(P,M) = 1$. This may be expressed as a difference between some multiples of P and M:

$$1 = aP - bM.$$

(The a and b are some unknown whole numbers. We may have the order wrong, the proper relation then being $1 = aM - bP$. But the argument is the same in either case.) Multiply each term of the equation by N:

$$N = aPN - bMN.$$

Now observe that P divides both terms on the right side of this equation, because, first, P is a factor in aPN, and second, by the theorem's hypothesis, P divides the factor MN of bMN. According to the distributive property, therefore, P is a factor of the right side of the equation. Hence P divides N.

A more general form of the prime-product theorem, proved by an argument quite like that above, is: If a number that divides a product is relatively prime to one factor of the product, then it divides the other factor. We may use this to prove the next theorem.

Theorem **Any common multiple of a pair of numbers is a multiple of their LCM.**

Proof. Suppose that M is a common multiple of the numbers a and b. Denote $g = $ GCD (a,b). Then $a = ga'$ and $b = gb'$, where a' and b' are relatively prime. Using the fact that M is a multiple of a, write

$$M = ha = hga',$$

where h is some natural number. Since M is also a multiple of b, and $b = gb'$, we know that

$$hga' \text{ is divisible by } gb',$$

hence that

$$ha' \text{ is divisible by } b'.$$

Since b' and a' are relatively prime, we find from the generalized prime-product theorem that

$$h \text{ is divisible by } b'.$$

Write $h = kb'$, where k is some natural number, and substitute into the previously written expression for M:

$$M = hga' = kb'ga' = k(ga'b') = k\left(\frac{ab}{g}\right).$$

In Section 8, we noted that $ga'b'$ *is* a common multiple of a and b, and we have just now found that *every common multiple* of a and b is a multiple of $ga'b'$. Therefore $ga'b'$ is the *least* common multiple of a and b. Not only have we proved that any common multiple of a pair of numbers is a multiple of their LCM, but we have also established the formula cited in Section 8:

$$\text{LCM} = \frac{\text{product}}{\text{GCD}}.$$

10. FUNDAMENTAL THEOREM OF ARITHMETIC

Fundamental Theorem of Arithmetic   Every composite number can be expressed uniquely as a product of primes.

This theorem assures us that there is essentially only one way of completely factoring a given number. The prime factors, to be sure, may be given in different orders: $12 = 2 \times 2 \times 3 = 2 \times 3 \times 2$, etc. However, it is not the order, but the number of times each prime appears, that is essential: two 2's and one 3 in the case of 12.

There is nothing really obvious about this theorem. The student is surely long accustomed to using it, and familiarity may have bred contempt. Let the student ask himself: "When I factor a number, how can I be sure that there are not other ways of factoring it that are entirely different from the particular one my work has produced?"

Is it *obvious*, for example, that the following equalities are impossible —just because all the factors are prime?

$$13 \times 37 = 19 \times 29,$$
$$23 \times 47 = 7 \times 11 \times 13.$$

Analyzing the first of these numerical cases will give us a clue to the method of proving the fundamental theorem. If it is true that

$$13 \times 37 = 19 \times 29,$$

then the product 19×29 must be divisible by the prime 13. According to the prime-product theorem, therefore either 19 or 29 must be divisible by 13. Yet these numbers are all primes, and we know that one prime cannot divide into a different prime. The possibility that $13 \times 37 = 19 \times 29$ is ruled out.

The above is essentially the pattern of the second part of the proof of the theorem. The first part consists of showing that every composite number can be factored in *some* way as a product of primes. The argument just involves a close look at the usual way in which we factor numbers. We try 2, and if 2 divides the number, then we try 2 again on the quotient, and again. . . . When 2 is not a factor any longer, we try 3, and keep trying so long as 3 is a factor; then 5 . . . , 7 . . . , 11 . . . ; but we need not try primes larger than the number itself (or even larger than its square root), so that the process will surely end, the final quotient being 1. The various prime divisors used are the required factors. The process is applied to the number 126 at the right, with the result

$$
\begin{array}{r}
2)\overline{126} \\
3)\overline{63} \\
3)\overline{21} \\
7)\overline{7} \\
\overline{1}
\end{array}
$$

$$126 = 2 \times 3 \times 3 \times 7.$$

The second part of the proof now consists of showing that the prime factorization obtained as above is *unique*. Suppose that some two different prime factorizations are equal. We may arrange the factors in each systematically, 2's first, if any, then 3's, then 5's, and so on. We shall have a setup like this, where the letters P, Q, P', Q', and the various blanks in the parentheses, denote primes:

$$P \times Q \times (\ \ ) \times (\ \ ) \times \cdots = P' \times Q' \times (\ \ ) \times (\ \ ) \times \cdots .$$

According to a simple extension of the prime-product theorem, since the prime P divides the number denoted on the left and thus also the same number denoted differently on the right, P must divide into some one of the factors P', Q', $(\ \ )$, $(\ \ )$, ... Hence P must equal that factor. Since these factors are arranged so that they never become smaller in left-to-right order, P cannot be smaller than P'. On the other hand, by the same argument in reverse (P' must divide one of P, Q, $(\ \ )$, $(\ \ )$, . . .), P' cannot be smaller than P. Hence

$$P = P'.$$

Upon dividing through by P, we have

$$Q \times (\ \ ) \times (\ \ ) \cdots = Q' \times (\ \ ) \times (\ \ ) \times \cdots .$$

Repeating the argument, we find

$$Q = Q'.$$

Next we may divide through by Q, and so on. Every factor on the left is shown in turn to equal the corresponding factor on the right, and vice versa. The "two" factorizations are one and the same.

11. USING FACTORS

Practical arithmetic leans heavily upon factoring procedures to effect numerical simplifications. Needed GCD's and LCM's may be found without factoring, by the Euclidean Algorithm. But where the numbers involved are small, as they usually are in practical operations with fractions, then it is easier to form GCD's and LCM's from the prime factors of the numbers.

Example 1 Find the GCD and LCM for the pair (84,270) by factoring.

Factor each number into prime factors by successive division (see right):

$$84 = 2 \times 2 \times 3 \times 7 \qquad (= 2^2 \times 3 \times 7),$$
$$270 = 2 \times 3 \times 3 \times 3 \times 5 \qquad (= 2 \times 3^3 \times 5).$$

```
2)84      2)270
2)42      3)135
3)21      3) 45
   7      3) 15
             5
```

There is one common factor 2, and one 3. Hence

$$\text{GCD } (84,270) = 2 \times 3 = 6.$$

An economical way to construct a number divisible by both 84 and 270 is to write all the factors of 270 (the one with more factors), then to supply those factors of 84 that are missing, the *second* 2 and the 7:

$$\text{LCM } (84,270) = (2 \times 3 \times 3 \times 3 \times 5) \times (2 \times 7)$$
$$= 270 \times 14 = 3,780.$$

Note. The factoring method may be justified as follows: Let the numbers be a and b, with GCD $= g$, so that $a = ga'$ and $b = gb'$. Let d be the product of the common prime factors of a and b. Then d is obviously a common divisor of a and b. Then, $g = kd$. Hence $a = kda'$ and $b = kdb'$. Hence if $d \neq g$, so that $k > 1$, there is some prime factor of k that is a common prime factor of a and b and that was not included in forming d, a contradiction. It is left to the student to justify the LCM construction.

Example 2 Find the GCD and LCM for (36,56,60) by factoring.

Factor by successive division:

```
2)36     2)56     2)60
2)18     2)28     2)30
3) 9     2)14     3)15
   3        7        5
```

$$36 = 2 \times 2 \times 3 \times 3 \qquad (= 2^2 \times 3^2),$$
$$56 = 2 \times 2 \times 2 \times 7 \qquad (= 2^3 \times 7),$$
$$60 = 2 \times 2 \times 3 \times 5 \qquad (= 2^2 \times 3 \times 5).$$

As in Example 1, construct the GCD and LCM by inspection:

$$\text{GCD } (36,56,60) = 2 \times 2 = 4,$$

$$\text{LCM } (36,56,60) = (2 \times 2 \times 3 \times 3) \times (2 \times 7) \times (5) = 2,520.$$

Problem Set 4

1. In each case, express the GCD of the pair of numbers as a difference between multiples of the numbers.

   (a) (18,30)   (b) (35,66)   (c) (63,168)   (d) (264,1512)

2. Using the relation obtained in 1(d), $24 = 23 \times 264 - 4 \times 1512$, show that every common divisor of 264 and 1512 is a divisor of 24.

3. (a) Is 142×705 divisible by 7?
   (b) Is 200×333 divisible by 6?
   (c) Is 200×301 divisible by 6?
   (*Hint:* A number is divisible by 6 only if it is divisible by both 2 and 3.)

4. To help yourself to understand the argument for the prime-product theorem, trace through it for the numerical case $M = 4$, $N = 6$, $P = 3$.

5. Taking $a = 18$, $b = 30$ (hence $g = 6$), trace through the argument in Section 9 for the theorem: "Any common multiple of a pair of numbers is a multiple of their LCM."

6. Show by the method of Section 10 (without multiplying out) that the equation $23 \times 19 = 11 \times 37$ is an impossibility.

7. What does it mean when we say that 12 and 25 are relatively prime?

In Problems 8 to 25, find GCD's and LCM's by factoring.

8. (30,42)	11. (74,111)	14. (1936,3630)
9. (35,66)	12. (264,1512)	15. (1728,5400)
10. (42,90)	13. (806,1116)	16. (6912,20160)

17. (2,4,6)	20. (36,48,60)	23. (4,6,8,10)
18. (6,10,15)	21. (180,288,432)	24. (24,54,60,72)
19. (12,18,42)	22. (1344,1536,2880)	25. (216,288,504,600)

12. DIVISIBILITY RULES

It is convenient to be able to tell whether a number is divisible by 2, 3, or certain other small numbers, without having to carry out the division.

For 2, 5, or 10, the rules are particularly simple. A number is divisible by 2, 5, or 10 if and only if the value of the units digit in its base-ten numeral is divisible by 2, 5, or 10, respectively. In other words:

1. A number is divisible by 2 if its units digit is 0, 2, 4, 6, or 8.
2. A number is divisible by 5 if its units digit is 0 or 5.
3. A number is divisible by 10 if its units digit is 0.

The rules are derived by considering the *structure* of a base-ten numeral. Inspect this numerical illustration:

$$2{,}436 = 2 \times 1000 + 4 \times 100 + 3 \times 10 + \underset{\substack{Units \\ digit}}{6}$$

Since 10 is divisible by 2, 5, and 10, so are 100 and 1,000. The long bold-type portion of the numeral above names a number that is divisible by 2, 5, and 10—and this will be true with *every* number, not just with the number 2,436 used in illustrating the structure. Hence if the units digit is divisible by 2, so is the number, and conversely. This follows in the case of 5 and 10.

A number is divisible by 4 if and only if the last two digits in its base-ten numeral (tens, units) form a number divisible by 4. The number 100, hence 1,000, etc., is divisible by 4, and any number can be split as shown in this illustration:

$$\textit{Value of the Last two digits}$$
$$2{,}436 = \mathbf{2 \times 1000} \; + \; \mathbf{4 \times 100} + 3 \times 10 \; + \; 6$$

A number is divisible by 3 (or 9) if and only if the *sum of* the digit values in its base-ten numeral is divisible by 3 (or 9).

The "why" of this rule depends upon the fact that every power of ten is one more than an "all-nines" number:

$$10 = 9 + 1; \quad 100 = 99 + 1; \quad 1{,}000 = 999 + 1; \quad \text{etc.}$$

Using 2,436 as an illustration once more, we write:

$$2{,}436 = 2 \times 1000 + 4 \times 100 + 3 \times 10 + 6$$
$$= 2 \times (999 + 1) + 4 \times (99 + 1) + 3 \times (9 + 1) + 6$$
$$\textit{Sum of digit values}$$
$$= \mathbf{2 \times 999} \; + \; \mathbf{4 \times 99} \; + \; \mathbf{3 \times 9} + 2 + 4 + 3 + 6$$

Since any all-nines number is divisible by 3 and by 9, the first bold-type portion of the numeral above names a number that is divisible by 3 and by 9—and again this will be so for every number. The remaining portion is just the sum of the digit values of the numeral.

In the case of the number 2,436, the sum of the digit values is $2 + 4 + 3 + 6 = 15$. Since 15 is divisible by 3, so is 2,436. Since 15 is not divisible by 9, neither is 2,436. Incidentally, the sum of the digit values may itself be tested for divisibility by adding *its* digit values. Thus, for 15, we have $1 + 5 = 6$, divisible by 3, but not by 9.

As a second illustration, take the number 88,769. Adding digit values: $8 + 8 + 7 + 6 + 9 = 38$. Adding again: $3 + 8 = 11$. Adding again: $1 + 1 = 2$. Since this is divisible by neither 3 nor 9, the number 88,769 is itself divisible by neither 3 nor 9.

The powers of ten differ from multiples of 11 by -1 and $+1$ alternately:

$$10 = 11 - 1 \qquad 100 = 99 + 1$$
$$1000 = 1001 - 1 \qquad 10000 = 9999 + 1 \qquad \text{etc.}$$

Hence if the digit values of a numeral are alternately added and subtracted, beginning with the units digit and proceeding from right to left, the resulting "alternating digit sum" may be tested for divisibility by 11. For 2,436, we have $6 - 3 + 4 - 2 = 5$. Hence 2,436 is not divisible by 11.

For 74,712, we have: $2 - 1 + 7 - 4 + 7 = 11$. Since 11 is divisible by 11, so is 74,712.

To explain this rule, consider the following analysis:

$$74{,}712 = 7 \times 10{,}000 + 4 \times 1{,}000 + 7 \times 100 + 1 \times 10 + 2$$
$$= 7 \times (9{,}999 + 1) + 4 \times (1{,}001 - 1) + 7 \times (99 + 1) + 1$$
$$\times (11 - 1) + 2$$
$$= 7 \times 9{,}999 + 7 + 4 \times 1{,}001 - 4 + 7 \times 99 + 7 + 1 \times 11$$
$$- 1 + 2$$
$$= \mathbf{7 \times 9999 + 4 \times 1001} + 7 \times 99 + 7 - 4 + 7 - 1 + 2$$
$$\uparrow$$

divisible by 11, since 9,999,
1,001, and 99 are each divisible by 11.

Thus for 74,712 to be divisible by 11, $7 - 4 + 7 - 1 + 2$ must be divisible by 11. This analysis can be generalized to any number.

13. CASTING OUT NINES

It was once the practice in our schools to have pupils check numerical computations by "casting out the nines." The *nines excess* of a number is the remainder obtained when the number is divided by 9. The nines excess of 5 is 5; of 9 is 0; of 12 is 3; of 43 is 7; of 100 is 1. Carrying out a division is actually unnecessary, because the nines excess of a number is equal to the nines excess of the sum of the digit values in its base-ten numeral. The number 4,873 has a digital sum of $4 + 8 + 7 + 3 = 22$; this number (22) has a digital sum of $2 + 2 = 4$. Being less than 9, this last number is equal to its own nines excess. Hence the nines excess of 4,873 is 4.

The proof follows the pattern of the proof of the rule for divisibility by 9 given in Section 12. With 4,873 as a numerical illustration, we have:

$$4{,}873 \;=\; 4 \times 1{,}000 \;+\; 8 \times 100 \;+\; 7 \times 10 \;+\; 3$$

Sum of digit values

$$=\; \mathbf{4 \times 999} \;+\; \mathbf{8 \times 99} \;+\; \mathbf{7 \times 9} \;+\; 4 + 8 + 7 + 3$$
$$=\; \text{(a multiple of 9)} + (4 + 8 + 7 + 3)$$

Hence when 9 is divided into 4,873, it divides the number named in the bold-type, so that the remainder must equal the remainder obtained from dividing 9 into the *sum of the digit values*. This argument is obviously of general type, applicable to any number.

Let a given numerical computation involve only addition, subtraction, and multiplication. **If the computation is carried out with the nines excesses in place of the original numbers, the nines excess of this result will equal the nines excess of the result of the original computation.**

Proof. Suppose two numbers a and b are added. Let their nines excesses be denoted by E_a and E_b. Then by definition of nines excess:

$$a = \text{(a multiple of 9)} + E_a,$$
$$b = \text{(a multiple of 9)} + E_b.$$

Since the sum of two multiples of 9 is again a multiple of 9, we find:

$$a + b = \text{(a multiple of 9)} + (E_a + E_b).$$

Hence $a + b$ and $E_a + E_b$ have the same nines excess. Similarly, $a - b$ and $E_a - E_b$ have the same nines excess. (In this case, $E_a - E_b$ may be negative. Thus if $a = 50$ and $b = 17$, $a - b = 33$, with excess 6, while $E_a - E_b = 5 - 8 = -3$. Add 9 to the -3 to bring it into the usual 0-to-8 nines-excess range: $-3 + 9 = 6$.)

If the numbers a and b are multiplied, we have:

$$\begin{aligned}
ab &= (9m + E_a)(9n + E_b) \\
&= (9 \times 9mn) + 9nE_a + 9mE_b + E_aE_b \\
&= 9 \times (9mn + nE_a + mE_b) + E_aE_b \\
&= \text{(a multiple of 9)} + E_aE_b.
\end{aligned}$$

(In the above, m and n denote whole numbers, the quotients obtained when 9 is divided into a and b, respectively.) Hence the nines excess of ab is equal to that of E_aE_b.

Any computation involving addition, subtraction, and multiplication may be made in steps each involving the performance of one operation on two numbers. The results shown above for two numbers can therefore be extended to apply to computation involving several numbers and operations.

Checking by "casting out the nines" consists of repeating calculations with nines excesses in place of original numbers.

CHECKING AN ADDITION		CHECKING A SUBTRACTION	
	Excesses		*Excesses*
2436	6	2407	4
218	2	− 982	1
+1602	0	~~1525~~ Wrong;	3
4256 ✓	8	1425 ✓	

In onetime school use, a special framework was used for the multiplication check:

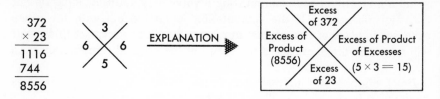

In case a multiplication does not check as a whole, the trouble can be localized by checking the computation of each partial product by excesses.

A *division* may be checked by forming the corresponding basic division relation, and checking that:

$$
\begin{array}{r}
28 \\
26\overline{)732} \\
52 \\
\hline
212 \\
208 \\
\hline
4
\end{array}
$$

Relation: $26 \times 28 + 4 = 732$
Excesses: $8 \times 1 + 4 = 12 \longrightarrow 3 \checkmark$

Casting out the nines fails to catch one very common numerical error, the transposition of two digits. If an answer ought to be 2,936 and is accidentally set down as 2,396, the false answer will pass the nines check because the sum of the digit values, hence the nines excess, is unchanged. *Casting out elevens* will catch a transposition error.

The elevens check takes the same form as the nines check. The rule for finding the elevens excess of a number (remainder upon division by eleven) is to form the "alternating sum" of the digit values: Add the value of the units digit, subtract the value of the tens digit, add the value of the hundreds digit, subtract the value of the thousands digit, etc. (See Section 12 regarding divisibility by 11.) For the number 180,739, for example, we find: $9 - 3 + 7 - 0 + 8 - 1 = 20$. For 20, we find: $0 - 2 = -2$. Adding 11 gives 9. Hence the elevens excess of 180,739 is 9. The double check, by both nines and elevens, is sometimes used in connection with large-scale machine computation.

Although these checking schemes have a limited sphere of usefulness, they cannot be trusted too far. It is not correct to suppose that the success of a check by casting out nines means that the odds are 8 to 1 in favor of the answer being right. Suppose that someone writes down a numeral for a number x between 1 and 1,000,000,000, making an entirely random choice. If a friend now guesses a number y at random in the same range, there is a true chance of about 1 in 9 that x and y will have the same nines excess. But this is by no means the chance that y is "right," that is, that $y = x$. In other words, a check by casting out nines can hardly help—and may mislead—a student who is so poor that he hardly ever gets a right answer.

Problem Set 5

1. Test for divisibility by 2, 5, and 4:

(a) 23	(f) 132	(k) 1,296	(p) 80,806
(b) 30	(g) 477	(l) 5,291	(q) 222,222
(c) 42	(h) 561	(m) 20,700	(r) 353,343
(d) 60	(i) 700	(n) 47,232	(s) 591,926
(e) 72	(j) 855	(o) 60,006	(t) 938,190

2. Test the numbers in Problem 1 for divisibility by 3.
3. Test the numbers in Problem 1 for divisibility by 9.
4. Test the numbers in Problem 1 for divisibility by 11.
5. Show that a number is divisible by 6 if and only if it is divisible by both 2 and 3. What numbers of Problem 1 are divisible by 6?
6. Show that a number is divisible by 12 if and only if it is divisible by both 3 and 4. What numbers of Problem 1 are divisible by 12?
7. Present an argument that, if x and y are each divisible by z, so is $x + y$.
8. Why is 0 divisible by any nonzero whole number?
9. Present an argument that each whole number whose numeral in base ten consists of an even number of 9's ($\underbrace{999 \cdots 9}_{\substack{\text{even number} \\ \text{of 9's}}}$) is divisible by 11.

In Problems 10 to 21, carry out the indicated computations, then check by casting out nines.

10. $\begin{array}{r} 2,307 \\ 563 \\ +4,128 \\ \hline \end{array}$　11. $\begin{array}{r} 10,786 \\ 2,341 \\ +30,064 \\ \hline \end{array}$　12. $\begin{array}{r} 9,999 \\ 999 \\ +9,090 \\ \hline \end{array}$

13. $\begin{array}{r} 232 \\ -\ 76 \\ \hline \end{array}$　14. $\begin{array}{r} 540 \\ -205 \\ \hline \end{array}$　15. $\begin{array}{r} 10,000 \\ -\ 9,999 \\ \hline \end{array}$

16. 26×37　17. 42×762　18. $397 \times 5,042$
19. $5,000 \div 27$　20. $69,321 \div 89$　21. $24 \times 34 \times 75$

22–33. Check the results in Problems 10 to 21 by casting out elevens.
34. Present an argument that every number in the sequence 11; 1,001; 100,001; 10,000,001; . . . is divisible by 11.
35.* Verify that $37 \times 27 = 999$ and $37 \times 27,027 = 999,999$. Then show that number is divisible by 37 if the sum of the numbers formed by successive triples of digits, from right to left, is divisible by 37. (Thus for 435,823 we find $823 + 435 = 1,258$, and for 1,258 we find $258 + 1 = 259 = 7 \times 37$. Hence 435,823 is divisible by 37.) Test (l), (q), (r), (s), (t) of Problem 1 for divisibility by 37.

36.* The rule for divisibility by 7 is illustrated with the number 25,554,844. Divide the numeral into groups of three digits, each starting from the right: 844; 554; 25 (the last group may have one, two, or three digits).
(i) Form the sum of the odd-place groups:

$$
\begin{array}{r}
844 \\
+\ 25 \\
\hline
869
\end{array}
$$

(ii) Form the sum of the even-place groups (there is only one such group here):

$$554$$

(iii) Subtract the number in (ii) from that in (i):

$$
\begin{array}{r}
869 \\
-554 \\
\hline
315
\end{array}
$$

(iv) If 315 is divisible by 7, so is the original number. Since $315 = 7 \times 45$, it is divisible by 7. Thus, 25,554,844 is divisible by 7.
Using this rule, test each of the following numbers for divisibility by 7:

(a) 74,572,526   (b) 1,230,659,365

37.* We may test 315 for divisibility by 7 as follows: Multiply 5 by 2 (10) and subtract the product from 31; thus $31 - 10 = 21$. Since 21 is divisible by 7, so is 315. Using this rule, test each of the following numbers for divisibility by 7:

(a) 861   (b) 903   (c) 569

38.* The rule in Problem 37 can be extended to larger numbers. This is illustrated on 84,455.

$$
\begin{array}{r}
84{,}455 \\
2 \times 5 = \quad 10 \\
\hline
8{,}435 \\
2 \times 5 = \quad 10 \\
\hline
833 \\
2 \times 3 = \quad 6 \\
\hline
77 \\
2 \times 7 = 14 \\
\hline
-7
\end{array}
$$

Therefore, 84,455 is divisible by 7. Using this rule, test each of the following numbers for divisibility by 7:

(a) 86,107   (b) 23,157   (c) 306,501

39.* Derive a rule for divisibility by 8.
40.* Derive a rule for divisibility by 99.

BIBLIOGRAPHY

Adler, Irving, *Magic House of Numbers*. New York: The John Day Company, Inc., 1957.

Dantzig, Tobias, *Number, the Language of Science*. New York: The Macmillan Company, 1954.

Gardner, Martin, *Mathematics Magic and Mystery*. New York: Dover Publications, Inc., 1956, pp. 156–174.

————, "The Remarkable Lore of the Prime Numbers," *Scientific American* (March 1964), pp. 120–128.

Jones, Burton W., *The Theory of Numbers*. New York: Holt, Rinehart and Winston, Inc., 1960, pp. 55–61.

Mazkewitsch, D., "Some Criteria for Divisibility," *School Science and Mathematics* (November 1963), pp. 678–687.

Merrill, Helen Abbot, *Mathematical Excursions*. New York: Dover Publications, Inc., 1933.

Meyer, Jerome S., *Fun With Mathematics*. New York: Fawcett World Library, 1958, pp. 57–70.

Rademacher, Hans, and Otto Toeplitz, *The Enjoyment of Mathematics*. Princeton, N.J.: Princeton University Press, 1957, pp. 9–13, 66–73, 129–139.

Stewart, B. M., *Theory of Numbers*, 2d ed. New York: The Macmillan Company, 1964, pp. 15–19, 33–61.

11

COMPUTATIONAL TOPICS

1. POWERS

Power Notation   (Base)^{Exponent}

(The exponent tells how
2^4 2 is the base   many times the base is
4 is the exponent   taken as a factor.)

As successive additions of the same natural number lead to the idea of multiplication ($3 \times 2 = 2 + 2 + 2$), so successive multiplications lead to the idea of taking **powers**. We write:

$$2^1 = \qquad\quad 2 \qquad = 2 \qquad \text{(first power of 2)},$$
$$2^2 = \qquad 2 \times 2 \qquad = 4 \qquad \text{(2 squared or second power of 2)},$$
$$2^3 = \quad 2 \times 2 \times 2 \quad = 8 \qquad \text{(2 cubed or third power of 2)},$$
$$2^4 = 2 \times 2 \times 2 \times 2 = 16 \qquad \text{(fourth power of 2), etc.}$$

Squares and cubes appear in problems about areas and volumes, as well as in other common applications. When higher powers turn up, careful attention to the meaning of the power will often save much numerical labor.

Example 1 Express $2^3 \times 2^5$ as a power of 2.
By definition:

$$2^3 \times 2^5 = (2 \times 2 \times 2) \times (2 \times 2 \times 2 \times 2 \times 2)$$
$$= 2 \times 2 \times 2 \times 2 \times 2 \times 2 \times 2 \times 2 = 2^8.$$

Example 2 Evaluate 2^8.
Instead of performing seven multiplications ($2 \times 2 = 4$; $2 \times 4 = 8$; etc.), let us take a hint from Example 1, this time breaking down instead of combining. *Three* multiplications give us $2^4 = 16$. Hence:

$$2^8 = 2^4 \times 2^4 = 16 \times 16 = 256.$$

Example 3 Evaluate: $\dfrac{5 \times 4^{10}}{4^7}$.

The seven denominator factors of 4 can be divided into seven of the ten numerator factors of 4, leaving three of them:

$$\frac{5 \times 4^{10}}{4^7} = 5 \times 4^3 = 5 \times 64 = 320.$$

Example 4 Evaluate: $2^3 \times 5^3$.

$$2^3 \times 5^3 = (2 \times 2 \times 2) \times (5 \times 5 \times 5)$$
$$= (2 \times 5) \times (2 \times 5) \times (2 \times 5) = 10^3 = 1000.$$

Example 5 Evaluate: $(\frac{2}{3})^3$.

$$\left(\frac{2}{3}\right)^3 = \frac{2}{3} \times \frac{2}{3} \times \frac{2}{3} = \frac{2 \times 2 \times 2}{3 \times 3 \times 3} = \frac{8}{27} \qquad \left(= \frac{2^3}{3^3}\right).$$

The examples above illustrate the following general patterns (we use x to refer to real numbers, m and n to refer to natural numbers, and s and t to refer to integers):

$$1. \quad \forall_x \forall_m \forall_n x^m \cdot x^n = x^{m+n}$$

$$2. \quad \forall_x \forall_s \forall_t \frac{x^s}{x^t} = x^{s-t}$$

$$3. \quad \forall_s \forall_t \forall_n \left(\frac{s}{t}\right)^n = \frac{s^n}{t^n}$$

The following is an example of pattern 2, which involves negative integers:

$$\frac{5^{-2}}{5^{-3}} = 5^{-2-(-3)} = 5^{-2+3} = 5^1 = 5.$$

2. ROOTS

Let us regard the taking of a given power as an *operation* that may be performed upon numbers. Then the *inverse operation* is that of taking the corresponding root. Figures 11-1 and 11-2 demonstrate the inverse relation. A square root is indicated by the radical symbol $\sqrt{}$. Thus: $\sqrt{25} = 5$. With higher roots, an index is placed on the radical to show the order of the root: $\sqrt[3]{8} = 2$; $\sqrt[4]{16} = 2$; etc.

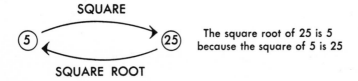

SQUARE

The square root of 25 is 5 because the square of 5 is 25

SQUARE ROOT

Fig. 11-1

CUBE

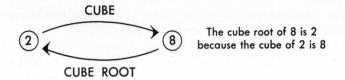

The cube root of 8 is 2
because the cube of 2 is 8

CUBE ROOT

Fig. 11-2

In elementary applications, it is almost always adequate to take account only of positive roots of positive numbers. This is the only case we shall treat. It can be proved that any positive number has one and only one positive root of each order. This theorem is too technical to establish here, and we assume it in all that follows.

Many simple problems call for finding a square root. Two sides of a right triangle, for example, may be known, with the third to be determined by using the Pythagorean relation. Since this involves the squares of the lengths of sides, the final step of the work will be the extraction of a square root. The Pythagorean relation is illustrated in Figure 11-3.

There exists an "exact" procedure, called the *Square Root Algorithm*, by which the successive digits of the root are found, one by one. This rule was at one time commonly taught in the upper elementary grades. In many school systems today, the practice is to postpone the topic to the ninth grade. This is not necessarily an instance in which standards have been "lowered." It is quite difficult to explain why the rule works, even to pupils who have had some experience in algebra. With today's emphasis on "meaning," educators generally object to presenting a rule that must be followed mechanically, without understanding. But whatever the practice in the school system, every upper grade teacher of arithmetic should be familiar with the algorithm and be ready to demonstrate it to pupils showing curiosity or aptitude.

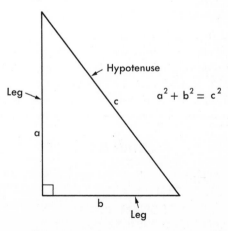

Hypotenuse

Leg

$a^2 + b^2 = c^2$

c

a

Fig. 11-3

b

Leg

When the square root rule is postponed, an approximate "division method" is often taught in its stead. And in any case, the use of *tables* is taught. In shop, field, office, and laboratory, roots are read from tables or on slide rules, or occasionally are computed by rule or by the division scheme. (The cube and higher roots are always found by approximate methods. There is an "exact" cube root rule, but it is too cumbersome to be practical.)

One useful property of the square root is illustrated by these examples:

Example 1

$$\sqrt{9 \times 16} = \sqrt{144} = 12,$$
$$\sqrt{9} \times \sqrt{16} = 3 \times 4 = 12,$$
$$\therefore \sqrt{9 \times 16} = \sqrt{9} \times \sqrt{16}.$$

Example 2

$$\sqrt{\frac{1}{4} \times \frac{25}{49}} = \sqrt{\frac{25}{196}} = \frac{5}{14},$$
$$\sqrt{\frac{1}{4}} \times \sqrt{\frac{25}{49}} = \frac{1}{2} \times \frac{5}{7} = \frac{5}{14},$$
$$\therefore \sqrt{\frac{1}{4} \times \frac{25}{49}} = \sqrt{\frac{1}{4}} \times \sqrt{\frac{25}{49}}.$$

The pattern illustrated by these examples is:

$$\forall_{x>0} \forall_{y>0} \ \sqrt{xy} = \sqrt{x} \ \sqrt{y}.$$

That a similar property does not hold for addition can be demonstrated by an example:

$$\sqrt{9 + 16} = \sqrt{25} = 5;$$
$$\sqrt{9} + \sqrt{16} = 3 + 4 = 7; \text{ and } 5 \neq 7.$$
$$\therefore \sqrt{9 + 16} \neq \sqrt{9} + \sqrt{16}$$

3. SQUARE ROOT TABLES

Multiplying a number by 100 only multiplies its square root by 10, because $\sqrt{100N} = \sqrt{100} \times \sqrt{N} = 10 \sqrt{N}$. Consequently, tables of square roots are usually arranged in the form shown at the right. The column headed $\sqrt{N}$ gives the roots of the numbers 1, 2, . . . , 10. The column headed $\sqrt{10N}$ gives the roots of the numbers 10, 20, . . . , 100.

Consider a number between 1 and 10, say 3. We read directly $\sqrt{3} \doteq 1.7$ in the $\sqrt{N}$ column. The "hundreds multiples" of 3 will have roots that are "tens multiples" of $\sqrt{3}$:

SQUARE ROOT TABLE

N	$\sqrt{N}$	$\sqrt{10N}$
1	1.0	3.2
2	1.4	4.5
3	1.7	5.5
4	2.0	6.3
5	2.2	7.1
6	2.4	7.7
7	2.6	8.4
8	2.8	8.9
9	3.0	9.5
10	3.2	10.0

$$\sqrt{300} = \sqrt{100 \times 3} = \sqrt{100} \times \sqrt{3} = 10\sqrt{3} \doteq 10(1.7)$$
$$= 17$$
$$\sqrt{30,000} = \sqrt{10,000 \times 3} = \sqrt{10,000} \times \sqrt{3} = 100\sqrt{3} \doteq 100(1.7)$$
$$= 170$$
$$\sqrt{.0003} = \sqrt{.0001 \times 3} = \sqrt{\frac{1}{10,000}} \times \sqrt{3} = \frac{1}{100}\sqrt{3} \doteq \frac{1}{100}(1.7)$$
$$= .017, \text{ etc.}$$

(Recall that "$\doteq$" means "is approximately equal to.")

The "odd-tens multiples" of 3 are "hundreds multiples" of 30, and will have roots that are "tens multiples" of $\sqrt{30}$:

$$\sqrt{30} \doteq 5.5$$
$$\sqrt{3,000} = \sqrt{100 \times 30} = \sqrt{100} \times \sqrt{30} = 10\sqrt{30} \doteq 10(5.5) = 55$$
$$\sqrt{.3} = \sqrt{\frac{1}{100} \times 30} = \sqrt{\frac{1}{100}} \times \sqrt{30} = \frac{1}{10}\sqrt{30} \doteq \frac{1}{10}(5.5) = .55,$$
$$\text{etc.}$$

All standard tables permit *interpolation*, the effect of which is to give results that could be read directly only in a table ten times as large. From our small square root table, we may determine roots to one decimal place for numbers between 1 and 10 given to tenths (1.0, 1.1, 1.2, 1.3, . . . , 9.9, 10.0) and for numbers between 10 and 100 given to units (10, 11, 12, . . . , 99, 100) In general, the table may be used to obtain square roots "accurate to two figures." (See Section 9 in this chapter for numbers given accurate to two figures.)

It is presumed that the student is familiar with the ordinary process of linear interpolation, but an example is furnished to dispel any haziness that may cloud his memory. Let us find $\sqrt{3.8}$. Locate and copy down the nearest tabular entries, those for $N = 3$ and $N = 4$, as shown below. Mentally neglect the decimal point and note that 38 is $\frac{8}{10}$ of the way from 30 to 40. Hence in the root column we wish to go $\frac{8}{10}$ of the way from 17 to 20. Since $\frac{8}{10}$ of 3 is 2 (nearest whole value), we arrive at 19. So $\sqrt{3.8} \doteq 1.9$. Set down in full, the work looks like this:

$$10 \left({}^{8} \left(\begin{matrix} N & \sqrt{N} \\ 3.0 & 1.7 \\ 3.8 & \boxed{1.9} \\ 4.0 & 2.0 \end{matrix} \right) 2 \right) 3 \qquad .8 \times 3 = 2.4$$

Problem Set 1

1. Simplify:

   (a) $3^2 \times 3^4$

   (b) $x^2 \cdot x^3$

   (c) $(\frac{2}{5}) \times (\frac{2}{5})^3$

   (d) $80^{20} \div 8^{17}$

2. Evaluate:

   (a) 2^{10} (b) $4^5 \times 5^5$

   (c) $(6 \times 3^7) \div 3^5$ (d) $(.2)^{10}$

3. Verify that the volume of air in a spherical balloon of diameter 10 in. is approximately 524 in.^{3} $(V = \frac{4}{3}\pi r^3)$.

4. The energy radiated from a hot body is proportional to the fourth power of its "absolute temperature." If the sun were half again as hot as it is, how many times more energy would it radiate?

5. Compare the energy radiated by a unit area heated to the temperature of boiling water (373° abs.) with that of a unit area heated to the temperature of the tungsten filament of an ordinary light bulb (about 3100° abs.).

6. In a half-hour an executive makes ten "yes" or "no" policy decisions. Among how many courses of action did he choose?

7. You had two parents. Each of them had two parents, and so on. How many different ancestral lines have you extending back ten generations? Is it possible that all your thirtieth generation ancestors (reached by different lines) were distinct individuals?

8. If you could triple your capital daily, beginning with one cent on the first day of the month, how much would you have on the fifteenth day?

9. If you could fold a sheet of paper 40 times, first one way and then the other alternately, the final result being a 1-in. square, how large would the sheet have been initially?

10. A germ colony doubles its number every 2 hr. 24 min. How long will it take a culture of a hundred germs to grow to a culture of a billion?

11. Draw diagrams like those in Section 2 to help explain the inverse relation between powers and roots, for each case below:

   (a) $4^2 = 16$ (c) $\sqrt{36} = 6$

   (b) $5^4 = 625$ (d) $\sqrt[3]{64} = 4$

12. A fellow student writes $\sqrt{5} = \sqrt{1+4} = \sqrt{1} + \sqrt{4} = 1 + 2 = 3$. How will you convince him of his error? Suppose he writes $\sqrt{a^2 + b^2} = a + b$. How will you straighten him out in this case?

13. Evaluate:

   (a) $\sqrt{2500}$ (b) $\sqrt{100 + 100 + 100 + 100}$

   (c) $\sqrt{2^2 \times 3^4}$ (d) $\sqrt{25 \div 4}$

14. Evaluate:

   (a) $\sqrt[3]{16} \times \sqrt[3]{4}$ (b) $\sqrt[20]{4^{30}}$

   (c) $\sqrt[4]{2500} \div \sqrt{2}$ (d) $\sqrt{10} \times \sqrt{10}$

   In Problems 15 to 17, use the small square root table in Section 3, interpolating when desirable.

15. Find the root to two figures:

   (a) $\sqrt{3.2}$ (b) $\sqrt{320}$

   (c) $\sqrt{32}$ (d) $\sqrt{.32}$

16. Find the root to two figures:

(a) $\sqrt{87}$

(b) $\sqrt{.0087}$

(c) $\sqrt{87000}$

(d) $\sqrt{8.7 \times 10^7}$

17. A 20-ft. ladder leans against a wall, with its base 10 ft. from the base of the wall. (Add further assumptions to make this a right-triangle problem.) How far up the wall does the ladder reach? Check your result by making a scale drawing.

18. What is the length of the hypotenuse in a right triangle with the following lengths of its sides:

(a) 3 and 4

(b) 5 and 12

4. THE SQUARE ROOT ALGORITHM

In Section 3 we noted that multiplying a number by 100 only multiplies its square root by 10. Writing two more digits in a numeral lengthens the numeral for the square root of the number by one digit. In finding a square root it is therefore conventional to use primes (') to **point off** the digits of the number in pairs, called *periods*. This shows how many digits the numeral for the root will have and also where they will be written (stars *) when the procedure for finding the root is carried out. *Examples:*

$$\overset{*}{\sqrt{25}}; \quad \overset{*\;\;*}{\sqrt{6'25}}; \quad \overset{*\;\;*}{\sqrt{15'42}}; \quad \overset{*\;\;*\;\;*}{\sqrt{4'27'30}}.$$

The function of the algorithm is to locate the largest whole number whose square is either equal to or less than the given number. In the *less than* case, there will be a positive remainder. Thus if the given number is 14, the root is 3, the remainder 5: $14 = 3^2 + 5$.

Let the task be to find $\sqrt{590}$. Point off: $\overset{*\;\;*}{\sqrt{5'90}}$. We find root digits in left-to-right order. To find the tens digit, we must locate the largest multiple of ten whose square is less than or equal to 590:

$$0, 10, 20, 30, 40, 50, 60, 70, 80, 90.$$

Since the squares of these numbers end in two zeros, we may neglect the 90 of the 590 and just compare them with 500. But this is equivalent to comparing the squares of the ten digit values 0, 1, 2, 3, . . . , 9 with 5. In other words, we look only at the first period (5) of the given number, and mentally run through the squares of the digits: $0^2 = 0$, $1^2 = 1$,

$2^2 = 4$, $3^2 = 9$, ... Since 2 is the largest number whose square is 5 or less, it is the root digit sought:

$$\begin{array}{c} 2 \quad * \\ \sqrt{5'90} \end{array}$$

Next we subtract 4 ($= 2^2$) from 5, then bring down the second period (90):

$$\begin{array}{c} 2 \quad * \\ \sqrt{5'90} \\ \underline{4} \\ 1\ 90 \end{array}$$

In actuality, we have subtracted $20^2 = 400$ from 590, leaving a "partial remainder" of 190. The next root digit must take care of this partial remainder, but its relationship to the remainder is not a simple one. To explore the relationship algebraically, denote that digit by x and also denote $a = 20$. Then the entire root that we are after will have the value $a + x$, and its square is to be compared with 590:

$$(a + x)^2 = a^2 + 2ax + x^2.$$

Since $a^2 = 20^2 = 400$ has already been subtracted, it is the $2ax + x^2$ portion that must take care of the remaining 190. Write this in factored form:

$$2ax + x^2 = x(2a + x).$$

Our aim is now to build up this expression, then take it away from 190 (for the various possible values of $x = 0, 1, 2, . . . , 9$).

The $2a$ is obtained by *doubling* the root digit 2 already found and writing it to the left of the 190, as shown below. This double (4) is regarded as in *tens position*, so that it is equivalent to $2a = 40$:

$$\begin{array}{cccc} & & 2 \quad * \\ & & \sqrt{5'90} \\ & & \underline{4} \\ 4 \quad * & & | 1\ 90 \end{array}$$

When any value of x ($x = 0, 1, 2, . . . , 9$) is inserted in the places indicated by the stars in the above, then the numeral now shown as 4∗ will have the value $2a + x$. When this number is multiplied by x, the desired value $x(2a + x)$ will be obtained. We wish to find the largest value of x for which $x(2a + x) \leq 190$.

The practical scheme is to estimate this x by dividing the 4 written on the left into 19 (a finger being held over the last digit of the 190). The result is $x = 4$. This is written in the starred places, the multiplication 4×44 $[= x(2a + x)$ for $a = 20$, $x = 4]$ is carried out, and the product (176) is taken from 190. [This scheme may produce too high a value for x, so that the product $x(2a + x)$ exceeds the partial remainder. When this occurs, reduce the x value by 1 and multiply again, etc.]

The above method of estimation is based upon the observation that x is usually substantially less than $2a$, so that when x is such that $x(2a) \leq$ 190, it is likely that $x(2a + x) \leq 190$. But $x(2a) \leq 190$ is equivalent to $x \leq 190/2a$, i.e. $x \leq 190/40 = 19/4$.

The completed work is shown at the right. We have determined that

$$590 = 24^2 + 14.$$

Hence $\sqrt{590} \doteq 24$. More precisely, the square root of 590 is 24, with a remainder of 14.

$$
\begin{array}{r}
2\ \ 4 \\
\sqrt{5'90} \\
4 \\
\hline
44\ \ \overline{|1\ 90} \\
|1\ 76 \\
\hline
14
\end{array}
$$

Table 11-1 shows in detail the process of taking a square root.

The work may be carried on beyond the decimal point. Suppose that we wish to find $\sqrt{598.4}$ to *four figures*. Applying the algorithm to 598 gives but two figures ($\sqrt{5'98}$). To get two more, point off two periods to the right of the decimal point, as shown in the work at the right. The work is carried out just as though the given number had been 5,984,000. The root so found is 100 times that of 598.4. It is apparent that the decimal point in the root will always be properly located if placed just above the position of the point in the given numeral.

$$
\begin{array}{r}
2\ \ 4.\ \ 4\ \ 6 \\
\sqrt{5'98.40'00} \\
4 \\
\hline
44\quad |1\ 98 \\
|1\ 76 \\
\hline
484\quad |22\ 40 \\
|19\ 36 \\
\hline
4886\quad |3\ 04\ 00 \\
|2\ 93\ 16 \\
\hline
10\ 84
\end{array}
$$

To illustrate how the occurrence of zero digits affects the work, four stages are shown in the extraction of the square root of 403 to four figures:

$$
\begin{array}{llll}
2 & 2\ \ 0. & 2\ \ 0.\ \ 0 & 2\ \ 0.\ \ 0\ \ 7 \\
\sqrt{4'03.00'00} & \sqrt{4'03.00'00} & \sqrt{4'03.00'00} & \sqrt{4'03.00'00} \\
4 & 4 & 4 & 4
\end{array}
$$

4	03		40	03 00		400	03 00 00	4007	03 00 00
									2 80 49

(4 into 0 gives 0) (40 into 30 gives 0) (400 into 3000, i.e., 4 into 30, gives 7)

Table 11-1
TAKING A SQUARE ROOT

Let us find $\sqrt{139,100}$. The first period is 13, and the largest square contained in it is 3. The first stage of the work is shown at the right, with the double of the 3 written in, in preparation for Stage 2.

Place a finger over the last digit of the 491, and divide 6 into 49, obtaining 8. This turns out to be too large. Try 7. This works. Double 37 and write it in, in preparation for Stage 3.

Place a finger over the last digit of 2200, and consider dividing 74 into 220. Estimate the result. Deleting all divisor digits after the first and dropping the same number of dividend digits, divide 7 into 22, obtaining 3. This turns out to be too large. Try 2. This works.

Hence:

$$139,100 = 372^2 + 716,$$

whence

$$\sqrt{139,100} \doteq 372.$$

Note. According to the abandoned part of the work shown in between Stage 2 and Stage 3 $139,100 = 373^2 - 29$. This negative remainder, -29, is smaller in absolute value than the positive remainder, 716. Hence we say that $\sqrt{139,100} \doteq 373$. It may be shown algebraically that the root value with least absolute remainder is always the closer to the exact root value. (To show this, begin by writing out the squares of x, $x + \frac{1}{2}$, $x + 1$.) In the present instance, therefore, we know that $372.5 < \sqrt{139,100} < 373.5$.

```
              3
        √13'91'00
              9          (Stage 1)
   6    | 4 91


              3  8
        √13'91'00
              9          No!
  68    | 4 91
        | 5 44


              3  7
        √13'91'00
              9          (Stage 2)
  67    | 4 91
        | 4 69
  74    |22 00


              3  7  3
        √13'91'00
              9          No!
  67    | 4 91          (But see
        | 4 69           the note
 743    |22 00           at left)
        |22 29
        | - 29


              3  7  2
        √13'91'00
              9          (Stage 3)
  67    | 4 91           End
        | 4 69
 742    |22 00
        |14 84
        | 7 16
```

Remarks. The algorithm is modified slightly when an abacus or electric office machine is to be used. Successive squares are built up through *cumulative addition* of the *odd* natural numbers. This is justified by the relation $(n + 1)^2 - n^2 = 2n + 1$. In the first few cases:

$$1 \qquad\quad = 1 = 1^2,$$
$$1 + 3 \qquad = 4 = 2^2,$$
$$1 + 3 + 5 = 9 = 3^2, \text{ etc.}$$

The procedure by which $\sqrt{139,100}$ may be found is shown in outline at the right. The odd numbers 1, 3, 5, . . . , 17 are cumulatively deducted from the first period (13) so long as the remainder stays positive. In this case, there are three subtractions. The number 3 is the hundreds digit of the root.

In the second stage of the work, it is not squares but expressions of form $2ax + x^2$ that must be built up by cumulative deduction. The first difference is $310^2 - 300^2 = (310 - 300) \times (310 + 300) = 6100$. The actual procedure is to deduct 1,3,5, . . . , 17 in second-period position, with each augmented by $2 \times 3 = 6$ (twice the hundreds digit) on the left.

In the third stage, the first difference is $371^2 - 370^2 = 741$. The actual procedure is to deduct 1, 3, 5, . . . in third period position, with each augmented by $2 \times 37 = 74$ on the left.

There is a routine for operating an office machine to do the above work mechanically. If there are many root digits to be found, a practical method is to determine three or four of them as above, then get twice as many by a single division operation, according to the scheme discussed next.

ABACUS WORK SCHEME

$$\sqrt{139,100}$$

Subtract	Remainder	
	13'91'00	
1'00'00	12'91'00	
3 00 00	9 91 00	3
5 00 00	4 91 00	
61 00	4 30 00	
63 00	3 67 00	
65 00	3 02 00	
67 00	2 35 00	7
69 00	1 66 00	
71 00	95 00	
73 00	22 00	
7 41	14 59	2
7 43	7 16	

Root: 372
Remainder: 716

5. APPROXIMATING ROOTS BY DIVISION

We shall describe the process of .approximating, then explain why it works. Given a number, we first divide or multiply it by one or more hundreds in order to bring it within the 1 to 100 range. The square root of this related number lies between 1 and 10, and after finding it, we may multiply it or divide it by as many tens as needed to give the root of the original number (Section 3). So we need discuss only the approximation of the square roots of numbers lying between 1 and 100.

First, we find the whole number (1, 2, 3, . . . , 10) whose square is closest to the given number. Let us illustrate the procedure by finding $\sqrt{40}$. Mentally running through the squares of the digit values, we note: $6^2 = 36 < 40 < 49 = 7^2$. The closer value is $6^2 = 36$. As the *first approximation* to the desired root, we write

$$A_1 = 6 \qquad \text{(first approximation)}.$$

In two steps, the key to the process, we get a second approximation from the first. In step 1, we divide the first approximation 6 into the number 40, and round the result to the nearest *even* number of tenths:

(1) $$40 \div 6 \doteq 6.6.$$

In step 2, we *average* the two values, the 6 and the 6.6, by adding and halving. This average is the *second approximation* to the root:

(2) $$A_2 = \frac{6 + 6.6}{2} = 6.3 \qquad \text{(second approximation)}.$$

Next we *repeat* the two steps, but with the new approximation 6.3 in place of the old. In the division of step 1, we carry out the work until we have *twice as many digits* (four) as make up the approximate value 6.3 (two), again rounding so that the last digit is *even:*

(1) $$40 \div 6.3 \doteq 6.350.$$
(2) $$A_3 = \frac{6.3 + 6.350}{2} = 6.325 \qquad \text{(third approximation)}.$$

Another repetition gives a fourth approximation:

(1) $$40 \div 6.325 \doteq 6.3241106.$$
(2) $$A_4 = \frac{6.325 + 6.3241106}{2} = 6.3245553 \qquad \text{(fourth approximation)}.$$

Still another repetition would produce a fifth approximation, expressed to 16 significant digits.

In the above example, each new approximation verifies the one before. Thus if $A_3 = 6.325$ is rounded off to two figures, $A_2 = 6.3$ is obtained (6.3|25). When such verification is obtained, the new approximation will be truly accurate (except that its last digit may be off by 1) to twice as many figures as those of the previous approximation. When the verification fails, the new approximation will be accurate to *one less* than twice as many figures. To illustrate this situation, we find a "worst" case by taking as large a number as we can that is nearer 1 than 4: take 2.4. The first approximation to $\sqrt{2.4}$ is 1. The two steps give:

(1) $$2.4 \div 1 = 2.4.$$
(2) $$A_2 = \frac{1 + 2.4}{2} = 1.7.$$

Already, A_2 does not round to A_1. Hence we round A_2 to *one less* figure, obtaining $A_2' = 2$, and continue:

(1) $$2.4 \div 2 = 1.2.$$

(2) $$A_3 = \frac{2 + 1.2}{2} = 1.6.$$

Since A_3 rounds to A_2', we may safely keep twice as many digits at the next stage:

(1) $$2.4 \div 1.6 = 1.500.$$

(2) $$A_4 = \frac{1.6 + 1.500}{2} = 1.550.$$

Since $A_4 = 1.550$ does round to $A_3 = 1.6$, even though barely, we may be sure that $\sqrt{2.4} = 1.550$ to within 1 in the last digit. (Try another repetition, obtaining $A_5' = 1.549194$.)

A handy feature about "iterative" processes is that they are generally self-correcting. Suppose that while finding $\sqrt{40}$, a student gets 6.9^+ instead of 6.7^- when he divides 6 into 40. Rounding 6.9^+ to the nearest even tenth gives 7.0. Averaging this with 6, he gets the false result $A_2 = 6.5$. Next he gets

(1) $$40 \div 6.5 \doteq 6.154.$$

(2) $$A_3 = \frac{6.5 + 6.154}{2} = 6.327.$$

Since this does not round to $A_2 = 6.5$, he replaces it with $A_3' = 6.33$ and continues:

(1) $$40 \div 6.33 \doteq 6.31912.$$

(2) $$A_4 = \frac{6.33 + 6.31912}{2} = 6.32456.$$

This nearly rounds to 6.33, hence should not be off by much more than 1 in its last digit. (Actually, it is correct in all six digits. Compare with our earlier eight-figure result.)

It is easy to see why the division method works. In the case of $\sqrt{40}$, our aim is to find the number that, when multiplied by itself, gives 40. Compare these relations:

$$\sqrt{40} \times \sqrt{40} = 40,$$
$$6 \times \quad ? \quad = 40.$$

We regarded 6 as an approximation to $\sqrt{40}$. The number symbolized by the question mark has an equal right to be regarded as an approximation to $\sqrt{40}$. We find it by dividing 40 by 6 (step 1 of the process). This gives 6.6 (to the nearest even tenth). The comparison becomes:

$$\sqrt{40} \times \sqrt{40} = 40,$$
$$6 \times 6.6 \doteq 40.$$

Of the numbers 6 and 6.6, one must be *under*, the other *over*, $\sqrt{40}$. It seems reasonable that an *average* of the two (step 2) should furnish a better approximation to $\sqrt{40}$ than does either one separately. And so it does.

6. HIGHER-ORDER ROOTS

Higher roots may be found by a similar division procedure. Setting out to find the cube root of 200, we determine the first approximation $A_1 = 6$ from the comparison

$$5^3 = 125 < 200 < 216 = 6^3.$$

Now we write:

$$\sqrt[3]{200} \times \sqrt[3]{200} \times \sqrt[3]{200} = 200,$$
$$6 \quad \times \quad 6 \quad \times \quad ? \quad = 200.$$

We find the number symbolized by the question mark by dividing 200 by $6^2 = 36$. This gives 5.6 (nearest tenth), so that

$$6 \times 6 \times 5.6 \doteq 200.$$

To get a second approximation, we average these *three* numbers:

$$A_2 = \frac{6 + 6 + 5.6}{3} \doteq 5.9.$$

The procedure is repeated:

(1) $$\frac{200}{(5.9)^2} = \frac{200}{34.81} \doteq 5.74.$$

(2) $$A_3 \doteq \frac{5.9 + 5.9 + 5.74}{3} \doteq 5.85.$$

Repeating once more:

(1) $$\frac{200}{(5.85)^2} = \frac{200}{34.2225} \doteq 5.8441.$$

(2) $$A_4 \doteq \frac{5.85 + 5.85 + 5.8441}{3} \doteq 5.8480.$$

Note that with each approximation beyond the second, we retained one less than twice the number of digits in the previous approximation. This is the rule to be followed in the case of the cube and higher roots.

Note (for advanced students only!). The following general rule may be established by algebraic analysis: Under the root-approximation process described earlier, if the relative error in a given approximation to $\sqrt[n]{N}$ is r, then the relative error in the next approximation is approximately

$$\frac{n-1}{2} r^2.$$

For a square root, $n = 2$, so that the new relative error is $r^2/2$. In the illustration concerning $\sqrt{40}$, the second approximation was $A_2 = 6.3$. A_2 being given to tenths, its absolute possible error is $\frac{1}{2}$ of .1, or .05, so that its relative possible error is $r = .05/6.3$. Computing $r^2/2$ and multiplying it by 6.3, we get the approximate absolute possible error e in the next approximation ($A_3 = 6.325$):

$$e \doteq \frac{1}{2}\left(\frac{.05}{6.3}\right)^2 (6.3) = \frac{.00125}{6.3} < \frac{.001}{2}.$$

According to this inequality, e is less than the absolute possible error to which numbers expressed in thousandths are subject. Hence it is likely that the third approximation, $A_3 = 6.325$, actually does give $\sqrt{40}$ correct to thousandths. In practice, we by-pass these technicalities and just use the "doubling the number of digits" rule, which is itself based on this technical analysis.

Problem Set 2

In Problems 1 to 6, find the integral root by the standard algorithm of Section 4. Write the result in the form: given number = (root)^2 + remainder. (Example: $45 = 6^2 + 9$, or $45 = 7^2 - 4$.) Cite the answer that corresponds to the remainder with the least absolute value. (Example: $\sqrt{45} \doteq 7$.)

1. $\sqrt{500}$ 2. $\sqrt{1000}$ 3. $\sqrt{64387}$
4. $\sqrt{676}$ 5. $\sqrt{3520}$ 6. $\sqrt{612000}$

In Problems 7 to 12, find the root to four digits. Check your answers by squaring them.

7. $\sqrt{21.08}$ 8. $\sqrt{.6300}$
9. $\sqrt{4362}$ 9. $\sqrt{.0002432}$
11. $\sqrt{883.608}$ 12. $\sqrt{2.008}$

13. Check your answers to Problems 7 to 12 as directed, by the following division process: Round each four figure value to two figures. Divide this value into the original number, obtaining a four-figure quotient. Average this quotient with the two-figure divisor. [*Examples:* $\sqrt{21.08} \doteq 4.6; 21.08 \div 4.6 = 4.583^-$; $\frac{1}{2}(4.6 + 4.583^-) = 4.591$.]

In Problems 14 to 23 find the root to the number of figures requested, using the division method of Section 5 and 6.

14. $\sqrt{20}$ (4 figs.)   19. $\sqrt{883.60800}$ (7 or 8 figs.)
15. $\sqrt{8}$ (8 figs)   20. $\sqrt[3]{10}$ (3 figs.)
16. $\sqrt{3}$ (6 figs.)   21. $\sqrt[3]{593}$ (5 figs.)
17. $\sqrt{21.08}$ (4 figs.)   22.* $\sqrt[5]{40}$ (3 figs.)
18. $\sqrt{.6300}$ (8 figs.)   23.* $\sqrt[10]{1.238}$ (5 figs.)

7. ERRORS

Physical measurement, we have pointed out, can never be absolutely precise. Even in theory, a steel rule cannot have an exact length. Under an imaginary supermicroscope, its end would show up as a disorderly molecular swarm, so that one could not tell just where the metal left off and the air began.

Man's own personal measurement errors, however, are so much larger than those inherent in our physical concepts that in ordinary discussion we may as well speak of the "true" lengths of steel rules, of the "true" speeds of moving bodies, and so on, just as though these quantities could be exactly defined.

Let a certain object have a true value T. Let M denote the value found by measuring. (M may be determined directly, or as the end result of a computation involving several direct measurements.) Then we shall regard M as an approximation to T and use it as a substitute for T in further work.

The **absolute error** (e) in using M as an approximation to T is defined as the *difference* between M and T:

$$e = M - T,$$
$$\text{absolute error} = \text{measured value} - \text{true value}.$$

Ordinarily, we simply call the absolute error the *error*.

Illustration 1

A jar contains 75 nuts. A shopper estimates by eye that the jar holds 90 nuts. Here $T = 75$, and $M = 90$. The shopper's error is $90 - 75 = 15$ (nuts). Had she estimated 70, her error would have been $70 - 75 = -5$ (nuts).

Theorem   **The error of a sum is the sum of the errors.**

In proving this theorem, we use the e, M, T notation but tag the letters with the subscripts 1 and 2, so that they will refer, respectively, to the first and second objects:

$$
\begin{aligned}
e_1 &= M_1 - T_1 \\
+\quad e_2 &= M_2 - T_2 \\
\hline
e_1 + e_2 &= (M_1 + M_2) - (T_1 + T_2) \\
&= M \text{ of sum } - T \text{ of sum } = e \text{ of sum.}
\end{aligned}
$$

Illustration 2

Let two jars contain 42 and 75 nuts, so that $T_1 = 42$ and $T_2 = 75$. Let estimates of their contents be $M_1 = 40$ and $M_2 = 80$. Then the true sum is $T = 42 + 75 = 117$, whereas the measured sum is $M = 40 + 80 = 120$. The various errors are: $e_1 = -2$, $e_2 = 5$, $e = e_1 + e_2 = 3$.

When the error is divided by the true value, the result is called the **relative error** (r) in using the measured value as an approximation to the true value:

$$\text{relative error} = \frac{\text{absolute error}}{\text{true value}},$$

$$r = \frac{e}{T} = \frac{M - T}{T}.$$

The relative error is often stated as a percent. In the nut jar illustration, with $T = 75$ and $M = 90$ so that $e = 15$, the relative error is

$$r = \frac{15}{75} = .20 = 20\%.$$

Theorem   **The relative error of a product is approximately equal to the sum of the relative errors of the factors.**

Proof.   Let T_1, T_2, T stand for the true values of the first factor, second factor, and their product $(T = T_1 T_2)$, respectively. Similarly, M_1, M_2, and $M = M_1 M_2$. Note that $e_1 = M_1 - T_1$ and $e_2 = M_2 - T_2$ may be written in the forms $M_1 = T_1 + e_1$, $M_2 = T_2 + e_2$. Then

$$M = M_1 M_2 = (T_1 + e_1)(T_2 + e_2) = T_1 T_2 + e_1 T_2 + e_2 T_1 + e_1 e_2.$$
$$e = M - T = M_1 M_2 - T_1 T_2 = e_1 T_2 + e_2 T_1 + e_1 e_2.$$

To get r, divide through by $T = T_1 T_2$;

$$r = \frac{e}{T} = \frac{e}{T_1 T_2} = \frac{e_1}{T_1} + \frac{e_2}{T_2} + \frac{e_1}{T_1} \cdot \frac{e_2}{T_2} = r_1 + r_2 + r_1 r_2.$$

If the relative errors r_1, r_2 are small, as is ordinarily the case, then their product will be much smaller. (If $r_1 = r_2 = .1$, then $r_1 r_2 = .01$; if $r_1 = r_2 = .001$, then $r_1 r_2 = .000001$.) Hence it is usually practical to neglect the product term $r_1 r_2$ and use the *approximate* relation

$$r \doteq r_1 + r_2.$$

Example 1 The true dimensions of a rectangular field are 64 ft. by 80 ft. By pacing, a boy estimates the size at 68 ft. by 86 ft., then computes the area by multiplying these values. How far off will he be?

We estimate the relative error:

$$r \doteq r_1 + r_2 = \frac{4}{64} + \frac{6}{80} = .0625 + .0750 = .1375 \doteq 14\%.$$

In actuality, $64 \times 80 = 5120$ and $68 \times 86 = 5848$, so the error is 728 sq. ft., and the relative error $725/5120 = 14\frac{7}{32}\%$.

Example 2 A balloon of radius 10 in. is inflated by further blowing to reach a radius of 11 in. What is the relative increase in its volume? The volume of a sphere is given by the formula $V = (\frac{4}{3})\pi R^3$, where R is the radius. Regard the 1-in. increase in radius as an "error." Then the relative error in the radus is $\frac{1}{10} = 10\%$. The volume is the product of five factors, $V = (\frac{4}{3}) \times \pi \times R \times R \times R$, whose relative errors are 0, 0, 10%, 10%, 10%. Adding these gives 30% as an approximation to the relative increase in the volume. (The closer value is about 33.1%.)

For a *difference* of estimated values: $e = e_1 - e_2$.
For a *quotient* of estimated values: $r \doteq r_1 - r_2$.

The proof of the difference rule is like that for a sum. With regard to the quotient we note that

$$T = \frac{T_1}{T_2} \quad \text{is equivalent to} \quad T_1 = T_2 \times T.$$

Applying the product rule to the latter relation gives

$$r_1 \doteq r_2 + r,$$

from which we get

$$r \doteq r_1 - r_2.$$

Theorems for powers and roots may also be derived from the product theorem. For example, if $T = \sqrt[3]{T_1}$, then $T_1 = T^3 = T \times T \times T$, and the product theorem gives $r_1 \doteq 3r$, so that $r \doteq \frac{1}{3}r_1$. A 6% relative error in measuring the capacity of a cubic box will therefore lead to about a 2% relative error in the estimate of its edge.

8. POSSIBLE ERRORS

In practical application, "true" values are seldom known. Hence we are unable to compute exact errors. We deal instead with **possible errors**: positive numbers that numerically exceed the unknown true errors. Relative possible errors are estimated by dividing possible errors by measured or estimated values.

Suppose that a person measures the length of a rod and gives his answer as 8.7 in. The presumption is that he measured to the *nearest tenth* of an inch. The true length may then be any number of inches between 8.65 and 8.75 (Fig. 11-4). The true error may have any value between $-.05$ and $+.05$, as readily seen in the figure. The *possible error* is taken to be .05, for this is the smallest positive number that is sure to exceed (or equal) the true error in absolute value.

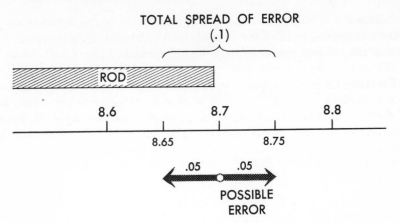

Fig. 11-4   The Possible Error in a Measurement Made to the Nearest Tenth

In computing with decimals, we must ordinarily assume that the values are correctly given, with the last digit representing a "nearest" choice. *The possible error is equal to one-half the place value of that last digit.*

Illustrations

For 2., 2.6, 5.72, .034, .0340, the possible errors are .5, .05, .005, .0005, .00005, respectively. If the value of a piece of property is quoted as $20,300 and if we assume that the fact of the figure's being given as an even hundred means that it is correct to the nearest hundred dollars, then the possible error is $50.

With the direction of the error unknown, the rule for a difference merges with that for a sum, and the rule for a quotient with that for a product.

To see why this happens, consider a quotient, $T = T_1/T_2$. Let the relative possible error be 10% for each T_1 and T_2. Then the true relative errors r_1, r_2 can fall anywhere within the range from -10% to $+10\%$. Hence their difference, $r_1 - r_2$, can fall anywhere between -20% and $+20\%$. For example, the measurer may *overestimate* T_1 by nearly 10%, so that $r_1 \doteq 10\%$, while *underestimating* T_2 by nearly 10%, so that $r_2 \doteq -10\%$. Then $r_1 \doteq r_1 - r_2 \doteq 10\% - (-10)\% = 20\%$. The relative possible error in the quotient thus turns out to be the *sum* of the relative possible errors in the numerator and denominator, just as with the product.

Computational Errors

Rule 1   With a sum or difference combination of two or more estimated values, the possible error is the sum of the possible errors of the values.

Rule 2 **With a product or quotient combination of two or more estimated values, the relative possible error is approximately equal to the sum of the relative possible errors of the values.**

Example By pacing, a man estimates the dimensions of a rectangular field to be 60 ft. by 85 ft. He knows by past experiment that his estimates of distance by pacing are usually correct within about 8%. He figures that he can cut the grass on the field at the rate of 100 ft.² per minute, but recognizes that this estimate may be off as much as 10%. At worst, how long will the mowing job take?

His time estimate is given by

$$t = \frac{60 \text{ ft.} \times 85 \text{ ft.}}{100 \text{ ft.}^2/\text{min.}} = \frac{5100}{100} \text{ min.} = 51 \text{ min.}$$

The terms 60, 85, 100 of the above product-quotient combination are subject to relative possible errors of 8%, 8%, 10%, respectively. According to Rule 2, the relative possible error r of t is approximately given by

$$r \doteq 8\% + 8\% + 10\% = 26\%.$$

From this we estimate the (absolute) possible error e of t:

$$e \doteq 51 \times 26\% = 51 \times (.26) \doteq 13 \text{ (min.)}.$$

So to be on the safe side, the man may allow 64 min. for the task. (*Note.* An "exact" computation, with 60, 85, 100 replaced by 64.8, 91.8, 90, gives about 66 min.)

9. ROUNDING DECIMAL NUMERALS

Bookkeepers and merchants are the only people who deal with decimals in full digital array. The rest of us fill our scratch pads and stud our conversation with "rounded" values: "She must be over fifty." "He makes ten thousand a year." "Eight million live in New York City." "I bought a 4½-lb. roast." "I weigh 170."

To round a numeral, mentally place a vertical bar at the position where you wish to cut it off. The digits to the right of the bar are dropped, but it may be necessary to replace some or all of them by zeros so as to maintain the place values of the other digits. The part of the numeral to the left of the bar is retained as is, or is increased by 1, according as the lopped-off portion is under or over the halfway value (|500000 . . .). The 1950 population of the continental United States was 150,697,361. In millions, this becomes:

$$150|697\ 361 \xrightarrow{\text{rounds to}} 151\ 000\ 000.$$

There is no universal agreement upon handling the halfway cases. Should 2.25 when rounded to tenths become 2.2 or 2.3? Perhaps the *even* rule is best: *Of the two choices, select the one for which the digit just left of the imaginary bar is even.* (*Examples;* 2.2|5 rounds to 2.2; 45.75|55 to 45.76; 6|50 to 600; 77|500 to 78000; etc.)

One popular rule is to increase the digit in every halfway case. This has the disadvantage of introducing an accumulative error into sums. Also, when a rounded value is divided by 2, which frequently occurs, the final value may be thrown off. Under the increase rule, 2.25 rounds to 2.3. Dividing by 2 gives 1.15, which then rounds to 1.2. The even rule, on the other hand, leads to 1.1, which is closer to the "true" value, 2.25/2 = 1.125.

Business firms usually drop a half-cent when paying a dividend or wage, but charge the full cent when billing.

Suppose that a numeral has been rounded, but that the imaginary vertical bar is still in position. Locate the first (leftmost) nonzero digit. The digits from there to the bar are called the **significant digits** of the rounded numeral. (Any zeros that precede or follow this group of digits serve only to locate the decimal point.) *Examples:*

3.142	significant digits: 3,1,4,2	number of them: 4
151|000000	significant digits: 1,5,1	number of them: 3
.0000602	significant digits: 6,0,2	number of them: 3
27.20	significant digits: 2,7,2,0	number of them: 4

When a rounded numeral names a *whole number*, there is one chance in ten that it is "ambiguous." Thus if 23,962 is rounded to *hundreds*, the result is 24,000, which appears accurate only to *thousands*. Various notational devices for showing which digits are significant, and which are not, have been suggested. Inherently awkward, none has been commonly adopted. Scientists overcome the difficulty by expressing numbers in scientific form. In the case above, in which 23,692 was rounded to hundreds, the result would be written 2.40×10^4. The presence of the otherwise superfluous zero digit reveals it to be a third significant digit.

Problem Set 3

1. According to the definition, which leads to a positive absolute error—an overestimate or an underestimate?
2. If it turns out that you have overestimated your income for the month by $40 and have underestimated your expenditures by $20, what is your net budget error?
3. Before setting out on a vacation jaunt with his family, Angus Snood made the cost estimates shown below. List each "error," estimated cost less actual cost, and verify that they add to the total error.

	ESTIMATED COST	ACTUAL COST	ERROR
Car costs	$120	$134.25	
Accommodations	90	98.00	
Food	75	68.20	
Other	50	82.15	

4. A candidate received 56,432 votes. He had expected 62,500 votes. What was the relative error in his prediction?

5. The actual dimensions of a lot are 150 ft. by 270 ft. By pacing, a boy estimates the size at 160 ft. by 290 ft. Compute the relative error in each dimension. From the actual and the estimated area values, find the relative error in the area. Verify that the results satisfy the exact formula $r = r_1 + r_2 + r_1 r_2$. How closely do they satisfy the approximate formula $r \doteq r_1 + r_2$?

6. Same as Problem 5, except that the actual and estimated dimensions are 150 ft. by 270 ft. and 140 ft. by 290 ft., respectively.

7. A carpenter measures the radius R of a circular disk, then computes the diameter and circumference from the formulas $d = 2R$, $c = 2\pi R$. If he was off by 2% in his measurement of the radius, by what per cents will his values of the diameter and circumference be off? (From now on, use the approximation $r \doteq r_1 + r_2$.)

8.* The frequency of oscillation of a simple pendulum is inversely proportional to the square root of its length. To increase the frequency 2%, how should the length be altered?

9.* A ball-bearing, although still spherical, has been worn down from its initial diameter of .750 in. to .728 in. Originally it weighed 1.02 oz. About how much does it weigh now?

10. For each value listed, give the possible error and the relative possible error (stated as decimals):

(a) 23 (b) 20 lb.
(a) $67 (d) 2.3 oz.

11. Proceed as in Problem 10:

(a) .004 (b) 21.63 cm.
(c) 3800 ft. (d) 4 ft. 2 in.

12. To the nearest ten feet, the length and width of a field are 200 ft. and 80 ft., respectively. The computed perimeter and area values are thus 560 ft. and 16,000 ft.², respectively. Replacing 200 by 195 and 80 by 75, compute the least values that the perimeter and area may have. Replacing 200 by 205 and 80 by 85, compute the greatest values that the perimeter and area may have. Estimate these same extremes by combining possible and relative possible errors in length and width. Compare results. (Thus the estimated relative possible error in the area is given by 5/200 + 5/80 = 8.75%, and 8.75% × 16,000 = 1400, so that the estimated greatest possible area value is 17,400 ft.², which compares closely with 205 ft. × 85 ft. = 17,425 ft.².)

13. To the nearest foot, the length and width of a room are 20 ft. and 12 ft. Discuss the possible errors in perimeter and area values in the same way as directed in Problem 12.

14. The base diameter and the height of a cylindrical barrel are measured as 22 in. and 28 in., respectively, each to the nearest inch. Discuss the possible error in the volume, according to the directions of Problem 12 ($V = \pi R^2 H$.)

15. A boy is clocked at $11\frac{1}{2}$ sec. in a hundred-yard dash. The time is thought to be correct to the nearest $\frac{1}{2}$ sec., whereas the 100-yd. measurement may be as much as 6 ft. off. Discuss the possible error in the speed, in feet per second, according to the directions of Problem 12.

16. How many significant figures does each decimal have?

   (a) 2.13   (b) 504.3   (c) 30.10

   (d) 762   (e) 2.008   (f) .0068

17. Proceed as in Problem 16:

   (a) 2.00   (b) 2.60×10^7

   (c) 2700   (d) 36 million

18. Round each decimal to the nearest tenth:

   (a) 20.72   (b) 6.25   (c) .063

   (d) 1.008   (e) 283.4739   (f) .05

   (g) 6.15   (h) 49.98   (i) 3.60

19. Round each numeral to three significant figures:

   (a) 29,374   (b) 6.065   (c) 2.937×10^{12}

   (d) 6,045   (e) 6,095   (f) .02937

   (g) 6.055   (h) 29.37   (i) .0083548

20.* Collect a number of adding-machine-tape receipts from a grocery store, each with at least ten entries. (Discard tapes with items under 6¢, which may represent bottle deposits, corrections, etc. Eliminate any sales-tax items.) On each tape, round each entry to the nearest 10¢, add and compare with the machine total, computing the absolute error, rounded total less machine total.

10. ADDING AND SUBTRACTING

Two numerals rounded to the same decimal place are said to be equally *precise*. Since the possible error is one-half the place value of the last significant digit, two equally precise numerals will have equal possible errors. Thus 2.62 and 780.29 each have the possible error .005, and 23,700 and 9,200 presumably each have the possible error 50. Of two numerals the one with the smaller possible error is said to be the more precise, that is, .07 is more precise than 3.6.

In adding or subtracting several numbers, it is pointless to attempt to gain more precision than is displayed by the least precise numeral, for the possible error of the sum is the sum of those of the numbers, and the error of the least precise numeral will dwarf the others (being at least ten times as big). Hence before adding or subtracting measurements, we ordinarily round all numerals to have the same degree of precision as the initially least precise numeral.

Standard Rule

Before adding or subtracting, round all numerals to the same decimal place. (The answer will then be automatically rounded to that place.)

Even in adding a number of values, there is little chance that rounding errors will accumulate sufficiently to throw the answer off substantially. Occurring both positively and negatively, the true errors will tend to cancelling out one another. Suppose, for example, that ten dollar-and-cent entries, chosen at random (like $2.43, $26.17, etc.), are rounded to the nearest dollar and added. The result will be more than a dollar away from the true sum in only about one-third of the cases, and will be more than four dollars off in less than one case out of ten thousand.

Example 1 In a news story, a man reads that the 1950 population of the "South" (16 states and the District of Columbia) was 47,197,088. He remembers that the 1950 population of the United States was about 151,000,000. What should be his estimate for the population outside the South?

The U.S. population figure is precise only to millions. Round the other value to millions, and subtract:

$$
\begin{array}{r}
151,000,000 \\
- \quad 47,000,000 \\
\hline
104,000,000
\end{array}
\quad (Answer)
$$

Example 2 A team of three men measures the road distance between two intersections. Smith drives to a certain crossroad, reading 5.4 miles on his odometer. Jones goes from there to another crossroad, measuring 7.76 miles on a fifth-wheel device attached to his car. Barry lays a surveyor's tape along the final portion, finding it to be 3.478 miles. Estimate the total distance.

Jones' and Barry's careful work is wasted. Round the numbers to *tenths*, and add. The estimate is 16.7 miles. (If the figures are added without rounding, the result is 16.638, which rounds to 16.6). It is instructive to ask, "How short might the true distance be?" Smith's figure being 5.4, it may be presumed that the true length of his portion is at least 5.35 miles. Jones' portion must be at least 7.755 miles, Barry's 3.4775 miles. The true distance is at least their sum, 16.5825 miles. Similarly, the true distance must be less than 16.6935 miles. In view of these extreme possibilities, the "best" single answer is clearly either 16.6 or 16.7, with 16.6 just a shade the more preferable.

5.4
7.8
3.5
16.7

11. MULTIPLYING AND DIVIDING

Of two numbers, the one with the smaller relative possible error is called the more *accurate*. In multiplying or dividing several numbers, it is pointless to maintain a substantially higher order of accuracy in one or more numerals than in the others.

Given a number, consider the related whole-number numeral that is composed of its significant digits in sequence. We shall call this whole-number numeral the **accuracy** of the original number. *Examples:*

23.072	has the accuracy	23072
.00730	has the accuracy	730
2900	presumably has the accuracy	29 (possibly 290 or 2900)

The relative possible error (r) of a number is half the reciprocal of its accuracy (α), in symbols:

$$r = \frac{1}{2} \cdot \frac{1}{\alpha}.$$

Thus for 23.072, the absolute possible error is $(\frac{1}{2})(.001)$ and the relative possible error is $(\frac{1}{2})(.001/23.072) = (\frac{1}{2})(1/23072)$. Halving the relative possible error doubles the accuracy, etc.

Example 1 Compare the accuracies of 26.3 and 5.41.

The accuracies are 263 and 541. Since 541 is a little more than twice 263, 5.41 is a little more than twice as accurate as 26.3.

Suppose two numbers are multiplied or divided. We know that the relative possible error of the resulting product or quotient numeral is approximately given by $r \doteq r_1 + r_2$. Denoting the accuracies of the two by α_1 and α_2 and substituting $r_1 = 1/2\alpha_1$, etc., we obtain

$$\frac{1}{\alpha} \doteq \frac{1}{\alpha_1} + \frac{1}{\alpha_2}.$$

Here, α denotes the *theoretical accuracy* of the result. (We shall wish to round the result so that its accuracy will agree with the theoretical accuracy, as nearly as possible.)

The relationship generalizes, in the obvious way, to apply to more than two numbers. Hence in any sequence of multiplications and/or divisions, **the reciprocal of the theoretical accuracy of the result is approximately equal to the sum of the reciprocals of the accuracies of the numbers.**

For illustration, take the product

$$.426 \times 158.3.$$

The accuracies of the given numbers are 426 and 1,583. Form the reciprocals and add:

$$\frac{1}{426} + \frac{1}{1,583} \doteq .002347 + .000632 = .002979 \doteq \frac{1}{336}.$$

Hence the theoretical accuracy of the product is about 336.

Multiplying 158.3 by .426 in full gives 67.4358. How shall we round this result so that its accuracy will be close to 336? Here are the two possibilities:

(1)   67.4|358   ⟶   67.4   (accuracy: 674).

(2)   67.|4358   ⟶   67   (accuracy: 67).

The test of closeness is one of ratio: 674 is only just over twice as accurate as 336, whereas 336 is nearly five times as accurate as 67. So the proper choice is 67.4. We give this as the answer to the multiplication problem:

$$.426 \times 158.3 \doteq 67.4.$$

Another way of analyzing is to compute the *extreme bounds* on the result (see the note to Example 2 below). The least and greatest values that the product could have are:

LOWER BOUND	UPPER BOUND
$.4255 \times 158.25 = 67.33 \ldots$	$.4265 \times 158.35 = 67.53 \ldots$

Clearly, 67.4 represents an appropriate choice for the answer. To retain a fourth figure, for example, citing the answer as 67.44 (67.43|58), would give a misleading impression with regard to the accuracy of the answer.

In casual computation, we would not wish to carry out exact analyses as just discussed. We usually depend upon "rough and ready" rules based on counting significant digits.

The number of significant digits provides a crude measure of accuracy. Thus a number with two significant digits has an accuracy between 10 and 99; a number with three significant digits has an accuracy between 100 and 999; etc. Cutting one significant digit away drops its accuracy by a factor of 10. But multiplying a number by itself, say, drops the accuracy only by a factor of 2, because

$$\frac{1}{\alpha_1} + \frac{1}{\alpha_1} = \frac{2}{\alpha_1} = \frac{1}{\frac{1}{2}\alpha_1}.$$

So when several numbers are multiplied or divided, the theoretical accuracy of the result is less than the accuracy of any one of the given numbers, but usually not so much less as to cause the "loss" of a significant digit, and hardly ever so much less as to cause the loss of two such digits.

This reasoning leads to the following standard computational rules. In both cases, it is assumed that the computation is one that involves only multiplications and divisions or the taking of powers and roots.

Safe Rule

In the given numbers, and throughout the computation, retain one more significant digit than is to be kept in the final answer.

Common Rule

First locate the numeral of least accuracy. Round each other numeral as far as possible without diminishing its accuracy below that of the least accurate number. As the computation proceeds, continue to round in this same way. Round the final answer to have just as many significant digits as the least accurate numeral.

The common rule is the more efficient and is fairly satisfactory for ordinary computation. Where from two to six numbers are involved, the rule gives a "wrong" result about 30% of the time (one too few or one too many significant digits). The safe rule calls for lengthier computations, and the loss of accuracy caused by it (usually unnecessarily) cannot always be tolerated.

Example 2 The length and width of a long rectangular tape are measured. To the nearest tenth of an inch, the width is 3.2 in. and the length is 912.4 in. What is the area?

We use the common rule. The area A is given by

$$A = (3.2) \times (912.4) \text{ in.}^2.$$

The accuracies of the given numerals are 32 and 9124. The least accurate numeral is 3.2. We round 912.4 to 910, so that its accuracy is 91, still larger than 32. We round the result to two "figures" (significant digits):

$$A = 3.2 \times 910 = 2912 \doteq 2900 \text{ (in.}^2) \qquad (Answer).$$

Note. Let us, for the practice, also compute the extreme bounds for the answer. Since 3.2 and 912.4 are accurate only to tenths, the *true* width and length may fall anywhere between these bounds:

$$3.15 < \text{true width (in.)} < 3.25,$$
$$912.35 < \text{true length (in.)} < 912.45.$$

The true area must therefore lie between these bounds:

$$3.15 \times 912.35 = 2873.9025 < \text{true area (in.}^2) < 2965.4625$$
$$= 3.25 \times 912.45.$$

Apparently from the given information about the length and width, we can say of the area only that it falls somewhere between 2,874 and 2,965 in.². If we must cite one number for the area, 2,900 represents a sound choice. (The apparent absolute possible error in 2,900 is 50, whereas half the spread of error from 2,874 to 2,965 is 46, an unusually good agreement.)

Example 3 Divide 12,630 by 138. (Assume these to be rounded.)

Proceeding according to the common rule, we round 12,630 no further, since rounding one more place would reduce its accuracy to 126, less than 138. We carry out the division to get three figures, as are in 138:

$$\frac{12630}{138} = 91.5|2 \ldots \doteq 91.5 \qquad (Answer).$$

Note. In computing extreme bounds for a quotient, take care. The upper bound is found by selecting the largest possible numerator and the smallest possible denominator:

$$\frac{12625}{138.5} \doteq 91.2 < \frac{\text{true}}{\text{quotient}} < 91.9 \doteq \frac{12635}{137.5}.$$

Since the apparent absolute possible error in 91.5 is only .05, whereas half the error spread from 91.2 to 91.9 is .35, it would seem that this is a case in which the common rule is "wrong." A two-figure answer (92) would be more appropriate.

Example 4 Find the value of 319.346 × 8.3029 correct to three significant digits.

Safe rule: 319.3 × 8.303 = 265|1.1479 ≐ 2650.
Common rule: 319   × 8.30 = 264|7.1   ≐ 2650.

Example 5 Evaluate $\dfrac{563 \times 607}{1234}$

With 563, the least accurate numeral, no initial rounding is needed:

$$\frac{563 \times 607}{1234} = \frac{341741}{1234} \doteq \frac{341700}{1234} \doteq 277 \qquad (Answer).$$

Note that four digits were retained in 341,700, because rounding another place would have reduced its accuracy to 342 < 563.

12. THE ACCURACY RULE

The number of significant digits provides only a crude measure of accuracy. It would therefore seem desirable to develop a simple computational rule that is based wholly upon the conception of accuracy. Such a rule is given below. Note that it differs from the common rule of section 11 only in the criterion used for rounding the final answer.

Accuracy Rule

In multiplying or dividing several numbers, first locate the numeral of least accuracy. Round each of the other numerals as far as possible without diminishing its accuracy below that of the least accurate numeral. As the computation proceeds, continue to round in the same way. Round the final answer to have no more than twice the accuracy of the least accurate numeral.

Over the range for which the common rule is wrong about 30% of the time, the accuracy rule is wrong about 10% of the time.

The rule is based upon an evaluation of what happens "on the average," when several numbers are multiplied or divided. Consider the illustration of Section 11 in which the multiplication .426 × 158.3 was analyzed. Carried out in full, the multiplication process gave the result 67.4358, though the theoretical accuracy of the answer was only 336. In lieu of testing ratios, we may determine a "ten range" centered on 336 by dividing and multiplying it by $\sqrt{10}$, which is approximately equal to 3.16. Thus:

$$\frac{336}{3.16} \doteq 106 \qquad \text{and} \qquad 336 \times 3.16 \doteq 1,060.$$

Then 67.4358 should be rounded so that its accuracy lies between those bounds: $106 < 674 < 1060$. In fact, only the upper bound, 1060, need be computed; then 67.4358 should be rounded to obtain as large an accuracy as possible which does not exceed this upper bound. In general, with a sequence of multiplications and/or divisions, we should round the final answer so that its accuracy is as large as possible, but not exceeding 3.16 times its theoretical accuracy.

To get a simple rule, we substitute the accuracy of the least accurate numeral for the theoretical accuracy of the answer. But the latter is a larger value, so that the size of the 3.16 factor needs to be reduced in compensation. Consideration of the situation in the average shows 2 to be a good choice for the factor.

Illustrations

(1) $\dfrac{98}{73} \doteq 1.34$ (accuracy: $134 < 2 \times 73 = 146$).

(2) $\dfrac{152}{206} \doteq .74$ (accuracy: $74 < 2 \times 152 = 304$).

(3) $\dfrac{(.238)(8.0371)(15.763)}{.9624} \doteq \dfrac{(.238)(8.04)(15.76)}{.962}$

$\doteq \dfrac{(.238)(126.7)}{.962}$ $(1267 > 238)$

$\doteq \dfrac{30.2}{.962}$ $(302 > 238)$

$\doteq 31.4$ $(314 < 2 \times 238 = 476)$

Note. A power is a "worst case" of a multiplication, each factor being equally inaccurate. Squaring halves the accuracy, cubing divides it by three, etc. On the other hand, accuracy is gained when a root is taken. Here is a special rule for powers and roots (the factor of 3, which appears in it being rounded from $\sqrt{10} \doteq 3.16$).

Supplementary Rule for Powers and Roots

When taking the nth power of a base, round the answer so that its accuracy does not exceed $3/n$ times the accuracy of the base. When taking the nth root of a base, round the answer so that its accuracy does not exceed $3/n$ times the accuracy of the base.

Problem Set 4

In these problems, all numerals should be taken as "rounded"—correct just to their last significant place value. Thus 2.73 is correct to the nearest hundredth, 3,760 to the nearest ten, etc.

In Problems 1 to 5, add or subtract as directed, after initial roundings:

1. 24.372
    6.29
     .8840
    +162.096

2. 2,700
     392
      57.6
    + 940

3. .0064
    .0105
    .0002
    +.073

4. 36,000
    − 8,827

5. 27.063
    − 8.4

6. Give the accuracies of the following:

(a) 237 (b) 5.70 (c) 10,000
(d) 23,700 (e) .057 (f) 6.2×10^8
(g) 2.37 (h) 5.07 (i) 1.002

7. How accurate is 2.72 in comparison with 68?

8. Any four-digit numeral is bound to be at least how much more accurate than any two-digit numeral?

9. In the most extreme case, how much more accurate can a four-digit numeral be than a three-digit numeral?

10. On the average, how much more accurate is a four-digit numeral than a three-digit numeral?

In Problems 11 to 20, compute the theoretical accuracy of the result, then round your calculated result so that its accuracy is as close as possible to the theoretical accuracy. (Use a table of reciprocals if you have one.)

11. 2.4×8.7
12. $1.02 \div 1.04$
13. 2.2×3.6
14. $3.6 \div 2.2$
15. $2.2 \div 3.6$
16. 72.3×908
17. $908 \div 72.3$
18. $\dfrac{27 \times 52}{63}$
19. $\dfrac{271 \times 52}{63}$
20. $\dfrac{86.0 \times (73.2)^2}{2,466}$

In Problems 21 to 30, compute the result (a) by the common rule (Section 11), (b) by the accuracy rule (Section 12). Then compute the extreme bounds for the answer.

21. 2.4×8.7
22. $2.2 \div 3.6$
23. $98 \div 92$
24. 6.4×8.235
25. 6.4×3.164
26. $372 \div 8.234$
27. $36.0 \times 28.2 \times 61.44$
28. $(36.0 \times 28.2) \div 61.44$
29. $61.44 \div (36.0 \times 28.2)$
30. $(234.73 \times 804.632) \div 4205$
31.* Verify that the given answers satisfy the "supplementary rule for powers and roots," cited in the note at the end of Section 12.

    (a) $(7.4)^3 \doteq 410$ (b) $\sqrt{20.4} \doteq 4.52$

    (c) $(2.0)^5 \doteq 30$ (d) $\sqrt[3]{1.500} \doteq 1.1447$

    (e) $(2.0)^{12} \doteq 4000$ (f) $\sqrt[100]{2 \times 10^{103}} \doteq 10.8$

*13. ABRIDGED MULTIPLICATION AND DIVISION

After two numbers have been multiplied out in full, several digits usually must be lopped off the result to round it to have appropriate accuracy. The aim of *abridged multiplication* schemes is to avoid doing the part of the work that produces the unwanted digits.

Consider the product 174 × 238. We usually arrange the work in the form shown on the left below. The form on the right is an alternative arrangement in which the multiplier digits are used in left-to-right order, 1, 7, 4, to get the partial products 238, 1666, and 952. Depending on the computational rule used, the result should be rounded to 41,400 or to 41,000.

$$
\begin{array}{rr}
238 & 238| \\
\times \quad 174 & \times \quad 1|74 \\
\hline
952 & 238| \\
1666 & 166|6 \\
238 & 9|52 \\
\hline
41{,}412 & 41{,}4|12
\end{array}
$$

result rounds to
41,400 or to 41,000.

We focus our attention upon the form on the right. The part of the work lying on the right of the vertical bar represents wasted effort. To abridge the process, we may just neglect the digit products 7 × 8, 4 × 8, and 4 × 3, the ones contributing to the portion of the work that is to be discarded.

One way to do this is as follows. Multiply 238 by 1, then place a dot over the units digit (8) of 238 to indicate that this digit is now "used up." The 23 that remains is multiplied by 7, giving the partial product 161, written next to the bar, as shown at the right. Then the tens digit (3) of 238 is dotted. Multiplying 2 by 4 gives the last partial product, 8. The partial products are summed, and zeros are filled into the missing places of the result (under each multiplier digit).

$$
\begin{array}{r}
23\dot{8}| \\
1|74 \\
\hline
238|
\end{array}
$$

$$
\begin{array}{r}
2\dot{3}\dot{8}| \\
1|74 \\
\hline
238| \\
161|
\end{array}
$$

Of course the result is too small. The neglected products make a contribution on the left of the bar that is just a little too large to be wholly over-looked. The lost contribution, from 7 × 8, 4 × 8, and 4 × 3, is shown on the right. It amounts to about 7 units in the place just left of the bar.

$$
\begin{array}{r}
2\dot{3}\dot{8}| \\
1|74 \\
\hline
238| \\
161| \\
8| \\
\hline
407|00
\end{array}
$$

To correct for the loss, we modify this procedure by adding 2 (in the place just left of the bar) to each partial product as it is written down. We call this process *automatic abridged multiplication*.

The rule is based upon the observation that the uncorrected scheme will, on the average, give second and later partial products that are about $2\frac{1}{2}$ units

$$
\begin{array}{rr}
7 \times 8 = & 5|6 \\
4 \times 38 = & 1|52 \\
\hline
Lost \longrightarrow & \textcircled{7}|12
\end{array}
$$

too small in the place just left of the bar. The rule is amply accurate for ordinary multiplying. A discrepancy in the final answer of 3 or more units in the place just left of the bar will occur infrequently. (Correct rounding will usually eliminate even these discrepancies.)

When one factor has fewer significant digits than the other, use it as the multiplier. (Alternative: Set the bar farther to the right and delay the dotting.) In the next illustrations, correctly rounded answers are shown in bold type; the numerals in parentheses under them give the results of multiplying out in full.

AUTOMATIC ABRIDGED
MULTIPLICATION

$$
\begin{array}{r}
2\dot3\dot8| \\
1|74 \\
\hline
240 \\
163 \\
10 \\
\hline
413|00
\end{array}
$$

$$
\begin{array}{r}
6\dot2\dot8\dot5| \\
2|408 \\
\hline
12572 \\
2514 \\
50 \\
\hline
15136|000 \\
\textbf{15140000} \\
(15134280)
\end{array}
\qquad
\begin{array}{r}
17\dot8\dot5| \\
4|67 \\
\hline
7142 \\
1070 \\
121 \\
\hline
8333|00 \\
\textbf{833000} \\
(833595)
\end{array}
\qquad
\begin{array}{r}
4.0\dot7\dot6\dot3| \\
8|9.036 \\
\hline
326106 \\
36686 \\
122 \\
26 \\
\hline
362.940 \\
\textbf{362.94} \\
(362.9374468)
\end{array}
$$

To abridge a division, set it up according to the usual arrangement, then draw a vertical bar *after the first quotient* digit (unless this digit is 1, in which case set the bar one place farther to the right and delay dotting one step). Curtail work at the bar, increase each partial product by 2 before subtracting it, and place dots over "used up" digits of the divisor numeral after each step of the work.

At the right are shown the successive steps in the division of 41,300 by 174. After the first step, we test 17 into 63, obtaining 3 for the second quotient digit. We increase the partial product $3 \times 17 = 51$ by 2 before putting it down, etc.

Note. Some textbooks on arithmetic describe abridged procedures arranged like those shown here, but require the computer to estimate mentally the corrections needed to compensate for the discarded products.

$$
\begin{array}{r}
2| \quad . \\
17\dot4)\overline{413|00.} \\
350 \\
\hline
63|
\end{array}
$$

$$
\begin{array}{r}
2|3 \quad . \\
1\dot7\dot4)\overline{413|00.} \\
350 \\
\hline
63| \\
53 \\
\hline
10|
\end{array}
$$

$$
\begin{array}{r}
2|38. \\
1\dot7\dot4)\overline{413|00.} \\
350 \\
\hline
63| \\
53 \\
\hline
10| \\
10
\end{array}
$$

Further examples:

```
        3.08              .02 408            1.1 35
267)822.        6285)151.36 00        843)957.0
    803              125 72                843
    ───              ─────               ─────
     19               25 64              114 0
     18               25 14               84 5
    ───              ─────               ─────
                         50               29 5
                         50               25 4
                      ─────              ─────
                                           4 1
                                           4 2
                                         ─────
```

*Problem Set 5

Use the automatic abridged methods to perform the indicated multiplications and divisions. Round each result according to the common rule (Section 11) or the accuracy rule (Section 12), as directed.

1. 148×462
2. $30.6 \times .618$
3. 4.23×10.76
4. 6.812×80.57
5. 2.358×3.762
6. $18.94 \div 30.6$
7. $18.94 \div .618$
8. $8.869 \div 3.762$
9. $708 \div 45.2$
10. $98 \div 96$
11. Observe that the partial products occurring in the division of Problem 7 are the same as those appearing in the multiplication of Problem 2, likewise for Problems 8 and 5. Hence the two abridged processes are inverse of each other. Why do the partial products differ in Problems 6 and 2?
12. In Problems 1 to 10, carry out the work for each without abridgment, but round according to either rule. In any case does the answer differ from the one obtained before?

*14. THE SLIDE RULE

A pair of yardsticks furnishes a crude *slide rule* for adding and subtracting numbers. The method of operation is to slide one stick along the top edge of the other. Figure 11-5 shows the addition of 5 and 8. The upper stick is slid to the right until its left (zero) end is above the 8-in. mark on the lower stick. Then below the 5-in. mark on the upper stick is read

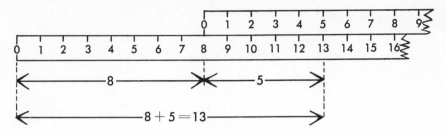

Fig. 11-5 An "Adding" Slide Rule

the answer **13** (13-in. mark on the lower stick). In this way, the abstract numerical operation 8 + 5 = 13 has been replaced by a physical operation of adding lengths: 8 in. + 5 in. = 13 in.

In subtraction, the procedure is reversed. To subtract 5 from 13, set 5 on the upper stick over 13 on the lower, then read **8** below the left end of the upper stick (Fig. 11-5 applies here too). The addition and subtraction of directed numbers may be demonstrated by replacing the yardsticks with strips of cardboard graduated with scales running from −10 to +10.

It is possible to graduate two strips with special scales so that the "adding" operation described above actually accomplishes the *multiplication* of the scale numbers, and the reverse "subtracting" operation accomplishes their *division*. The special scale is called a *logarithmic scale*, or *log* scale for short. Slide rules incorporating logarithmic, trigonometric, and other scales are extensively used by engineers, scientists, technicians, and industrial workers to expedite the many rough computations they must perform.

Children are often fascinated by the "magical" way in which the slide rule produces products, quotients, and roots. Many educators recommend the demonstration of the instrument in the middle or upper grades. Where time permits, it may be desirable that a child should make his own crude slide rule, as a mathematical experiment. The needed logarithmic scale can be constructed without technical knowledge. We will call it a *multiplying scale*. To construct it, we will apply and reapply the principle that the length-adding operation earlier described must accomplish the multiplication of the scale values.

Take two strips of cardboard, about 11 in. long and 1 to 1½ in. wide. Place two marks 10 in. apart along the edge of each strip (Fig. 11-6).

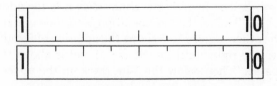

Fig. 11-6 Constructing a Slide Rule: First Stage

Mark the 10-in. length so that it is divided into eight equal portions. In speaking of these marks, we refer to their fractional positions: 0, $\frac{1}{8}$, $\frac{1}{4}$, $\frac{3}{8}$, $\frac{1}{2}$, $\frac{5}{8}$, $\frac{3}{4}$, $\frac{7}{8}$, 1. Label the zero mark with the scale value 1 and the 1 mark with the scale value 10.

Henceforth we shall refer to the 10-in. portions of the strips (scaled from 1 to 10) as upper and lower scales, the left end of each scale (0 mark) being labeled 1 and the right end (1 mark) being labeled 10.

Now slide the upper scale to the position shown in Figure 11-7, so that its left end lies above the $\frac{1}{2}$ mark on the lower scale. The $\frac{1}{2}$ mark on the upper scale will then lie above the right end of the lower strip. With

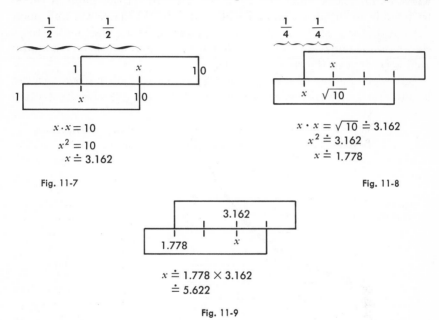

Fig. 11-7

Fig. 11-8

Fig. 11-9

this "setting" of the rule we are adding two equal lengths: 5 in. + 5 in. = 10 in. By the principle of construction, this must accomplish the multiplication of the scale value that is to be placed at the $\frac{1}{2}$ mark on the lower scale by the *same* scale value, to be placed at the $\frac{1}{2}$ mark on the upper scale. Further, the product of these equals is read as 10 (right end of lower scale). Hence the square of the scale value in question is 10, and the value itself is $\sqrt{10}$. Extract the root finding the approximate value $\sqrt{10} \doteq 3.162$. Label each $\frac{1}{2}$ mark with this scale value.

The quarter-marks are labeled by sliding the upper rule to the position shown in Figures 11-8 and 11-9. In Figure 11-8, it is seen that the value at the $\frac{1}{4}$ mark is the square root of $\sqrt{10}$, or $\sqrt[4]{10} \doteq \sqrt{3.162} \doteq$ 1.778. Likewise, the value at the $\frac{3}{4}$ mark is $\sqrt[4]{10^3} = \sqrt[4]{10} \times \sqrt{10} \doteq$ 1.778 × 3.162 $\doteq$ 5.622. The eighth-marks may be labeled by a similar procedure; we could continue to sixteenths, etc., were this desired.

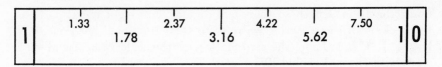

Fig. 11-10 Constructing a Slide Rule: Second Stage

Figure 11-10 shows the labeled lower scale at the present stage of construction. This is the multiplying scale that we want. But it is inconveniently labeled. We would like to have it marked to show where the whole-number scale values fall: 1, 2, 3, . . . , 10. At this point, it would be feasible to bring a standard slide rule into the classroom and point out how the 1, 1.33, 1.78, 2.37, etc. positions on its log scale match those shown on the homemade rule. The homemade rule could then be regraduated according to the slide-rule scale.

But with the aid of a graph, we can finish the job on our own. In Figure 11-11, the scale values already found (1, 1.33, 1.78, etc.) are plotted

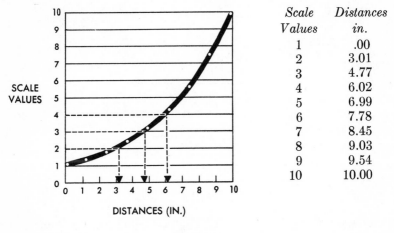

Scale Values	Distances in.
1	.00
2	3.01
3	4.77
4	6.02
5	6.99
6	7.78
7	8.45
8	9.03
9	9.54
10	10.00

Fig. 11-11

against inch distances measured from the left end of the scale (0, 1.25, 2.50, etc.). A smooth curve is drawn through the nine plotted points. The distances corresponding to whole-number scale values are now estimated by drawing horizontal lines through these values to meet the curve, then vertical lines to the distance scale. Thus the dotted lines drawn in Figure 11-11 show that the scale values, 2, 3, 4 are to be placed at distances of 3.0, 4.8, 6.0 in. The work may be checked against the figures in the table at the right (distance = 10 × log of scale value).

Now the strips may be turned over and regraduated according to the distance readings. Figure 11-12 shows the result. (The 1.5, 2.5, etc.,

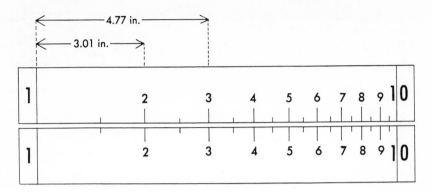

Fig. 11-12   The Slide Rule

values are also marked in. To find the first four of these, set the scales for the divisions of 3 by 2, 5 by 2, etc.)

When we give our new slide rule a tryout, we shall soon face a troublesome situation. Trying 4 × 5, we find that the answer is "off the rule." One way of handling this situation is to join two lower scales end to end to make one twice as long, as shown in Figure 11-13. The values on the second scale are ten times those on the first, the two together forming a single scale graduated from 1 to 100. A second way is much simpler. After discovering that 4 × 5 lies off the rule, set the *right* instead of the left end of the upper scale above 5 on the lower. Below the 4 on the upper scale, read **2** on the lower. Multiply this by ten to get the answer: 10 × 2 = 20. To learn why this method works, study the relationship of the shaded scale in Figure 11-13 to the rest of the figure.

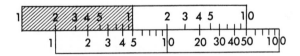

Fig. 11-13

BIBLIOGRAPHY

Bakst, A., "Approximate Computation," *Twelfth Yearbook of the National Council of Teachers of Mathematics.* New York: Bureau of Publications, Teachers College, Columbia University, 1937.

Bond, E. A., "Significant Digits in Computation with Approximate Numbers," *The Mathematics Teacher* (April 1931), pp. 208–212.

Boyer, Lee Emerson, "Elementary Approximate Computation," *The Mathematics Teacher* (October 1938), pp. 249–258.

Cullimore, A. R., *The Use of the Slide Rule.* Hoboken, N.J.: Keuffel and Esser Company, 1925.

Nichols, Eugene D., *Modern Elementary Algebra*. New York: Holt, Rinehart and Winston, Inc., 1965, Chap. 3.

Odom, M. M., and E. D. Nichols (consulting ed.), *Introduction to Exponents* (A Programed Unit). New York: Holt, Rinehart and Winston, Inc., 1964.

Scarborough, J. B., *Numerical Mathematical Analysis*. Baltimore: Johns Hopkins Press, 1930.

School Mathematics Study Group, *Intuitive Geometry*. Stanford, Calif.: Leland Stanford Junior University, 1961, chap. 9.

———, "Mathematical Methods in Science," *Studies in Mathematics, Vol. XI*. Stanford, Calif.: Leland Stanford Junior University, 1963, pp. 42–52.

———, *Mathematics Through Science, Part I: Measurement and Graphing*. Stanford, Calif.: Leland Stanford Junior University, 1963, pp. 7–11.

Shuster, Carl N., "Computation with Approximate Data," *Twentieth Yearbook of the National Council of Teachers of Mathematics*. Washington, D.C., 1948.

12

NONMETRIC
GEOMETRY

1. SPACE, POINTS, AND SEGMENTS

As the title of this chapter suggests, we shall be concerned primarily with the nonmeasurement aspects of geometric objects. That is, we shall focus our attention on the properties of geometric objects, apart from their size.

We shall consider **space** to be our universal set and shall study some of its significant subsets.

The simplest geometric object is a **point.** To suggest points, we make dots on paper and use capital letters as names for points.

$$\overset{A}{\cdot} \qquad \text{This dot represents } point \ A.$$

A point is also the smallest geometric object. To be the smallest object, it must have no size, since if it did have size, we could consider an object with one-half that size. Thus the point would not be the smallest possible object.

The next object, still quite simple but somewhat more complicated than a point, is a **segment.** Figure 12-1 shows a segment $\overline{AB}$, which is the same as $\overline{BA}$. It consists of points A and B, called **endpoints,** and all points between A and B. Note that we use the names of the endpoints with a bar over them to denote a segment $(\overline{AB})$.

In Figure 12-2, point D lies between points A and B; therefore $D \in \overline{AB}$

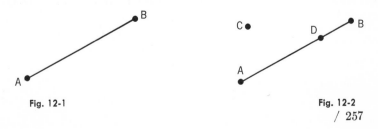

Fig. 12-1   Fig. 12-2

(read: D belongs to segment $\overline{AB}$). Point C, however, is not between A and B; therefore $C \not\subseteq \overline{AB}$ (read: C does not belong to segment $\overline{AB}$).

Two segments may have no common points: $\overline{AB} \cap \overline{CD} = \emptyset$ (read: the intersection of segments $\overline{AB}$ and $\overline{CD}$ is the empty set). See Figure 12-3. Two segments may partially overlap. In this case, the intersection

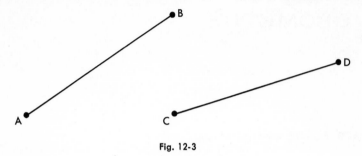

Fig. 12-3

of two segments is a segment: $\overline{AB} \cap \overline{CD} = \overline{BC}$. See Figure 12-4. Two

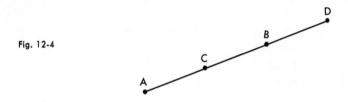

Fig. 12-4

segments may intersect in one point: $\overline{AB} \cap \overline{CD} = \{E\}$. See Figure 12-5.

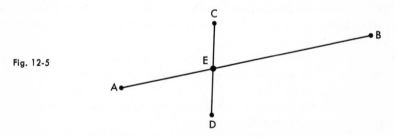

Fig. 12-5

Or two segments may have a common endpoint: $\overline{AB} \cap \overline{BC} = \{B\}$. See Figure 12-6.

Fig. 12-6

2. POLYGONS

In Figure 12-7 are pictures of several polygons. Do you observe that each polygon is a union of segments? But not every union of segments is a polygon. Explain.

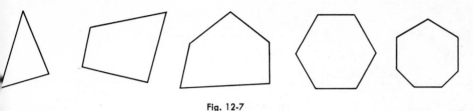

Fig. 12-7

A polygon that has the smallest possible number of sides is a **triangle.**

Definition   A triangle is a union of three segments, in which each pair of segments has one common endpoint.

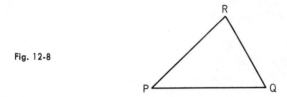

Fig. 12-8

Figure 12-8 shows triangle PQR. We abbreviate triangle PQR as $\triangle PQR$. Look at this figure and verify that each of the following statements is true:

$$\overline{PQ} \cap \overline{QR} = \{Q\}.$$
$$\overline{QR} \cap \overline{RP} = \{R\}.$$
$$\overline{RP} \cap \overline{PQ} = \{P\}.$$

According to the definition of a triangle, $\triangle PQR = \overline{PQ} \cup \overline{QR} \cup \overline{RP}$. Points P, Q, and R are called **vertices** of $\triangle PQR$.

A polygon having four sides is called a **quadrilateral.** Figure 12-9 gives a picture of a quadrilateral $NPQR$. In $NPQR$, $\overline{NP}$ and $\overline{PQ}$ are one pair of *adjacent sides*, since they have a common point. $\overline{NP}$ and $\overline{QR}$ are a pair of *opposite sides*. The vertices P and Q are *adjacent vertices* and P and R

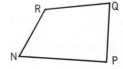

Fig. 12-9

are *opposite vertices*. Segment $\overline{PR}$, which connects the opposite vertices, is called a *diagonal*. See Figure 12-10.

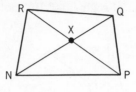

Fig. 12-10

Problem Set 1

1. Using Figure 12-11, tell whether each of the following statements is true or false:

(a) $\overline{PR} \cup \overline{RS} = \{R\}$
(b) $\overline{RM} \cap \overline{MP} = M$
(c) $\overline{RS} \cup \overline{ST} \cup \overline{TR} = \triangle RST$
(d) $MRST$ is a quadrilateral
(e) Point S lies between R and T
(f) $\overline{MP} \cup \overline{PR} \cup \overline{RT} = \triangle MPT$
(g) $\overline{MR}$ is a diagonal of quadrilateral $MPRT$
(h) $\triangle MRT \cap \triangle RST = \overline{RT}$
(i) $\triangle MPR \cap \triangle RST = \{R\}$
(j) $\triangle MPR \cup \triangle MRT =$ quadrilateral $MPRT$

Fig. 12-11

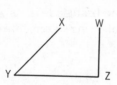

Fig. 12-12

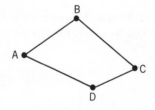

Fig. 12-13

2. Tell which part of the definition of a triangle is not satisfied in order that Figure 12-12 represent a triangle.
3. (a) Copy Figure 12-13 on your paper.
   (b) Draw pictures of the two diagonals in quadrilateral $ABCD$. Call the point of intersection of the two diagonals E.
   (c) Name the eight triangles in your picture.
   (d) Name two pairs of triangles such that the intersection of each pair is a point.
   (e) Name two pairs of triangles such that the intersection of each pair is a segment.

(f) Name two pairs of opposite sides in quadrilateral *ABCD*.

(g) Name four pairs of adjacent sides in quadrilateral *ABCD*.

(h) Using your copy of Figure 12-13, complete each of the following statements:

    (i) $\overline{AE} \cap \overline{CE} =$ ___?___

    (ii) $\overline{BC} \cap \overline{AD} =$ ___?___

    (iii) $\overline{BC} \cap \overline{DC} =$ ___?___

    (iv) $\overline{BC} \cup \overline{CD} \cup \overline{DB} =$ ___?___

    (v) $\triangle ABC \cap \triangle ACD =$ ___?___

4. Draw a picture of a triangle and a segment so that the intersection of the two consists of two points.

5. Draw a picture of a triangle and a segment so that the intersection of the two consists of one point.

6. Draw a picture of a triangle and a quadrilateral so that the intersection of the two consists of two points.

7. Draw a picture of a triangle and a quadrilateral so that the intersection of the two consists of an infinite set of points.

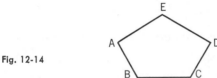

Fig. 12-14

8. The polygon of Figure 12-14 is called a **pentagon** because it has five sides.

(a) Copy it on your paper.

(b) Draw all possible diagonals in it. How many diagonals are there?

(c) If $\overline{AD} \cap \overline{BE} = \{P\}$, $\overline{AD} \cap \overline{CE} = \{Q\}$, $\overline{CE} \cap \overline{BD} = \{R\}$, $\overline{BD} \cap \overline{AC} = \{S\}$, and $\overline{AC} \cap \overline{BE} = \{T\}$, then what figure is $PQRST$?

(d) What is $\triangle BDE \cap \triangle CDE$ equal to?

9. A polygon with seven sides is called a **heptagon.** Draw a heptagon with all possible diagonals in it. How many diagonals are there?

10. (a) A polygon having eight sides is called an **octagon.** How many diagonals does it have?

(b) Tabulate the number of sides and next to it the number of diagonals for all polygons starting with a triangle and ending with an octagon. Try to discover a pattern and use this pattern to tell how many diagonals there are in a nonagon (9-sided polygon) and decagon (10-sided polygon).

3. SEPARATION

We agreed to consider space to be the set of all points. Now imagine a set of points, which resembles a flat surface, extending indefinitely in all directions. We call such a set of points a **plane.**

A plane separates all points of space that are not on the plane (for simplicity we say: a plane separates space) into two subsets, called **half-spaces**. The points of the plane that do the separating do not belong to either of the two half-spaces. If we denote space by S, the plane by p, and the two half-spaces by s_1 and s_2, then the following statements are true. Explain the meaning of each statement.

$$s_1 \cup s_2 \cup p = S.$$
$$s_1 \cap s_2 = \emptyset.$$
$$s_1 \cap p = \emptyset.$$
$$s_2 \cap p = \emptyset.$$

Explain why each of the pairs s_1 and s_2, s_1 and p, and s_2 and p is a pair of disjoint sets.

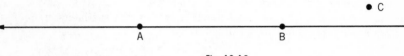

Fig. 12-15

Figure 12-15 shows a line. Points A and B are marked on the line. We use these points to name the line. We can name it $\overleftrightarrow{AB}$ or $\overleftrightarrow{BA}$. The double-headed arrow suggests a line that, unlike a segment, does not end, that is, it extends without end in both directions.

For Figure 12-15, the following statements are true:

$$A \in \overleftrightarrow{AB}; \qquad B \in \overleftrightarrow{AB}; \qquad C \notin \overleftrightarrow{AB}.$$

A line separates the points of the plane not on the line (for simplicity we say: a line separates the plane) into two subsets called **half-planes**. In Figure 12-16, $\overleftrightarrow{AB}$ separates plane p into two half-planes, a half-plane that

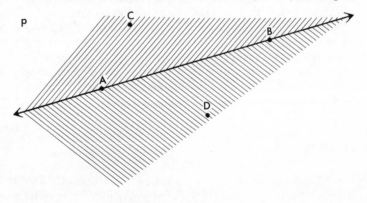

Fig. 12-16

contains point $C(p_C)$ and a half-plane that contains point $D(p_D)$. Explain why each of the following statements is true:

(1) $\overleftrightarrow{AB} \cup p_C \cup p_D = p$

(2) $\overleftrightarrow{AB} \cap p_C = \emptyset$

(3) $\overleftrightarrow{AB} \cap p_D = \emptyset$

(4) $p_C \cap p_D = \emptyset$

A point on a line separates all the remaining points on the line (for simplicity we say: a point separates the line) into two subsets called **half-**

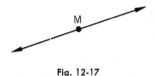

Fig. 12-17

lines. For example, point M in Figure 12-17 separates the line into a set of points to the right of M and a set of points to the left of M.

Fig. 12-18

In the statements that follow, referring to Figure 12-18, notation for a half-line is suggested. Explain why each statement is true.

(1) Q separates $\overleftrightarrow{RT}$ into two half-lines, $\overset{\circ}{\overrightarrow{QR}}$ and $\overset{\circ}{\overrightarrow{QT}}$ (the hollow dot suggests that point Q does not belong to the half-line)

(2) $\overset{\circ}{\overrightarrow{QR}} \cup \{Q\} \cup \overset{\circ}{\overrightarrow{QT}} = \overleftrightarrow{RT}$

(3) $\overset{\circ}{\overrightarrow{QR}} \cap \{Q\} = \emptyset$

(4) $\overset{\circ}{\overrightarrow{QT}} \cap \{Q\} = \emptyset$

(5) $\overset{\circ}{\overrightarrow{QR}} \cap \overset{\circ}{\overrightarrow{QT}} = \emptyset$

We frequently wish to refer to a set of points consisting of a half-line and a point. In Figure 12-18,

$$\overset{\circ}{\overrightarrow{QR}} \cup \{Q\} = \overrightarrow{QR},$$

and $\overrightarrow{QR}$ is called a **ray**.

Why is $\overrightarrow{QR} \cap \overrightarrow{QT} = \{Q\}$ true? The point Q is called the *endpoint* of $\overrightarrow{QR}$. It is also the endpoint of $\overrightarrow{QT}$.

Problem Set 2

1. Tell whether each statement is true or false. Each statement is based on Figure 12-19.

 Fig. 12-19

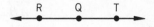

(a) $\overrightarrow{QR} \cup \overrightarrow{QT} = \overleftrightarrow{QR}$

(b) $\overset{\circ}{\overrightarrow{QR}} \cup \overset{\circ}{\overrightarrow{QT}} = \overleftrightarrow{QR}$

(c) $\overrightarrow{QR} \cap \overrightarrow{QT} = \{Q\}$

(d) $\overset{\circ}{\overrightarrow{QR}} \cap \overset{\circ}{\overrightarrow{QT}} = \{Q\}$

(e) $\overrightarrow{RT} = \overrightarrow{TR}$

(f) $\overrightarrow{RQ} \cup \overrightarrow{QT} = \overrightarrow{RT}$

(g) $\overrightarrow{TR} \cap \overrightarrow{RT} = \overline{RT}$

(h) $\overrightarrow{QT} \cup \overrightarrow{QR} = \overrightarrow{TR}$

(i) $\overset{\circ}{\overrightarrow{TR}} \cup \overset{\circ}{\overrightarrow{RT}} = \overleftrightarrow{QT}$

(j) $\{T\} \cup \overset{\circ}{\overrightarrow{TR}} = \overrightarrow{TR}$

(k) $\{Q\} \cup \overrightarrow{QT} = \overrightarrow{QT}$

(l) $\overrightarrow{QR} \subseteq \overrightarrow{TR}$

(m) $\overset{\circ}{\overrightarrow{QR}} \subseteq \overrightarrow{RT}$

(n) $\overrightarrow{QR} \subseteq \overset{\circ}{\overrightarrow{QR}}$

(o) $\overrightarrow{QT} \subseteq \overrightarrow{QT}$

2. Explain the meaning of separation of (a) space by a plane, (b) plane by a line, and (c) line by a point.

3. (a) Let $\overleftrightarrow{AB}$ separate plane k into two half-planes, k_1 and k_2. Let $\overleftrightarrow{AB} \cup k_1$ be called the *closed* half-plane k_1. Define the closed half-plane k_2.

   (b) Let k_{1C} denote the closed half-plane k_1 and k_{2C} the closed half-plane k_2. To what is $k_{1C} \cap k_{2C}$ equal?

   (c) To what is $k_{1C} \cup k_{2C}$ equal?

   (d) To what is $\overline{k_{1C}}$ equal? (*Hint:* $\overline{k_{1C}}$ is the complement of k_{1C}, which is the set of all points of k not in k_{1C}.)

   (e) To what is $\overline{k_{2C}}$ equal?

4. Using the concept of a complement of a set, describe the separation of (a) line by a point, (b) plane by a line, and (c) space by a plane.

4. ANGLES

Recall that each ray has one endpoint. For example, $\overrightarrow{AB}$ (see Figure 12-20) has endpoint A. A number of rays can be identified in Figure 12-21. Two of these rays are $\overrightarrow{YZ}$ and $\overrightarrow{WC}$. Identify four more rays in this figure.

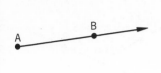

Fig. 12-20

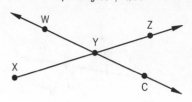

Fig. 12-21

We are now interested in those *pairs of rays* that have a common endpoint. One such pair in Figure 12-21 is $\overrightarrow{YW}$ and $\overrightarrow{YZ}$. Name one more pair of rays having a common endpoint found in Figure 12-21. These observations lead to the definition of an **angle.**

Definition   An angle is a union of two noncollinear rays having a common endpoint. The rays are called the sides of the angle. The common endpoint is called the vertex of the angle.

Notice that the rays, in order to form an angle, must be noncollinear. That is, both rays cannot be subsets of the same line.

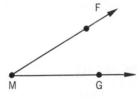

Fig. 12-22

In Figure 12-22 we have two rays with a common endpoint. Thus, it is a picture of an angle, and there are three different ways in which we can name the angle:

$\angle M$ (angle M); $\angle FMG$ (angle FMG); $\angle GMF$ (angle GMF).

In the case of the angle in Figure 12-22, we may use only one letter (the name of the vertex) when naming the angle. Often however, it is necessary to use three letters in order to tell which angle we have in mind. For example, writing $\angle A$ in reference to Figure 12-23 is not sufficient, because we would not know which of the four different angles would be intended. We must write $\angle CAB$, or $\angle BAC$, if we wish to refer to the angle in the right portion of the picture.

Fig. 12-23

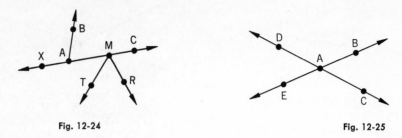

Fig. 12-24   Fig. 12-25

For Figure 12-24, we can write the true statement:

$$\angle BAM = \angle BAC.$$

We are thus stating that "$\angle BAM$" and "$\angle BAC$" are two names for the same set of points. $\angle BAM$ and $\angle BAC$ are the same angle, since $A = A$, $\overrightarrow{AB} = \overrightarrow{AB}$, and $\overrightarrow{AM} = \overrightarrow{AC}$. Do you see that "$\overrightarrow{AM}$" and "$\overrightarrow{AC}$" are two names for the same ray?

If two angles are located with respect to each other, as $\angle DAE$ and $\angle BAC$ are in Figure 12-25, then they are called a pair of **vertical angles**. They are vertical angles because they have a common vertex and because $\overrightarrow{AB}$ and $\overrightarrow{AE}$ form a line and $\overrightarrow{AD}$ and $\overrightarrow{AC}$ form a line.

5. INTERIORS OF ANGLES

Recall that a line separates those points of a plane that are not on the line into two half-planes. For example, $\overleftrightarrow{AB}$ in Figure 12-26 separates the points of the plane not on $\overleftrightarrow{AB}$ into two half-planes, one half-plane containing point C and the other half-plane containing point D.

For the purposes of this discussion, let us assign the half-plane containing C the symbol h_C, and that containing D, the symbol h_D. The line $\overleftrightarrow{AB}$

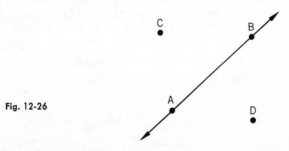

Fig. 12-26

does not belong to either half-plane. If we use p to denote the entire plane, then the following statement is true:

$$h_C \cup h_D \cup \overleftrightarrow{AB} = p.$$

An angle also separates the points of the plane, which are not on the angle, into two subsets. Refer to Figure 12-27 and decide for yourself (on the basis of the statements below) into which two subsets the plane is separated by $\angle YXZ$.

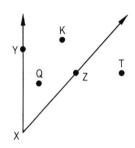

Fig. 12-27

1. K is in the **interior** of $\angle YXZ$.
2. T is in the **exterior** of $\angle YXZ$.
3. Y is on $\angle YXZ$.

From these three statements you probably understood that an angle separates the points of the plane that are not on the angle into an *interior* of the angle and the *exterior* of the angle.

To obtain a more precise idea of the interior of an angle, consider Figure 12-28, in which $\overleftrightarrow{AC}$ separates the plane into two half-planes. We denote by h_B that half-plane containing points M, D, B, and F. Line $\overleftrightarrow{AB}$ also separates the plane into two half-planes. We denote by h_C that

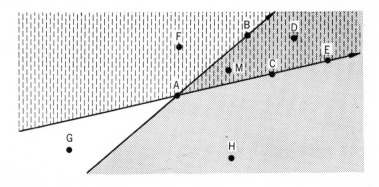

Fig. 12-28

half-plane containing points M, D, C, E, and H. That part of the plane which is doubly shaded is the intersection of h_B and h_C. We are now ready to state the definition of the interior of an angle. (See Figure 12-28.)

Definition   **The set of points $h_B \cap h_C$ is the interior of $\angle BAC$.**

It is logical to decide now that the **exterior** of $\angle BAC$ is the set of all points that are in the plane but are not in the interior of $\angle BAC$ and not on $\angle BAC$.

6. INTERIORS OF TRIANGLES

From the definition of a triangle in Section 2, it follows that $\triangle XYZ = \overline{XY} \cup \overline{YZ} \cup \overline{ZX}$ (see Figure 12-29). Copy this picture on your paper.

Fig. 12-29

Now shade h_Z (that half-plane determined by $\overleftrightarrow{XY}$, which contains point Z), h_Y, and h_X. Identify on your picture the set

$$h_X \cap h_Y \cap h_Z.$$

This set is called the *interior* of $\triangle XYZ$. Figure 12-30 shows the interior of $\triangle ABC$ (shaded portion). Those points that are not in the interior

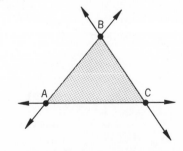

Fig. 12-30

of $\triangle ABC$ and not on $\triangle ABC$ constitute a set called the *exterior* of $\triangle ABC$. It follows then that (I = interior of $\triangle ABC$, E = exterior of $\triangle ABC$, and p = the entire plane)

$$I \cup E \cup \triangle ABC = p.$$

Problem Set 3

1. Name two rays shown in Figure 12-31.

Fig. 12-31

2. Name four angles shown in Figure 12-32. For each angle, name its vertex and its two sides.

Fig. 12-32

3. Using three letters in each case, name seven different angles shown in Figure 12-33.

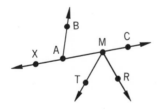

Fig. 12-33

4. Name two pairs of vertical angles in Figure 12-34.

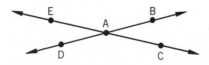

Fig. 12-34

5. Tell whether each statement that follows is true or false. Refer to Figure 12-35. Notation of Section 5 is used.

(a) $h_C \cap h_D = \emptyset$

(b) $(h_C \cup \overleftrightarrow{AB}) \cap \overleftrightarrow{AB} = \overrightarrow{AB}$

(c) $D \in h_C$

(d) $A \in (h_C \cup h_D)$

(e) $A \in \overleftrightarrow{AB}$

(f) $\{B\} \cap \overleftrightarrow{AB} = \{B\}$

(g) $h_C \cup h_D = p$

(h) $\overleftrightarrow{AB} \subseteq p$

(i) $(h_D \cap \overleftrightarrow{AB}) \cap h_C = \emptyset$

(j) $\overleftrightarrow{AB} \subseteq h_C$

(k) $C \in h_C$

(l) $h_D \cup \overleftrightarrow{AB} = h_C$

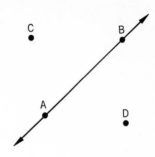

Fig. 12-35

6. The statements that follow refer to Figure 12-36. The following abbreviations are used:

$$I = \text{interior of } \angle BAC$$
$$E = \text{exterior of } \angle BAC$$
$$p = \text{the entire plane}$$

Tell whether each statement is true or false.

(a) $M \in I$

(b) $A \not\subseteq E$

(c) $A \in \angle BAC$

(d) $H \in E$

(e) $\angle BAC \cap I = \emptyset$

(f) $\angle BAC \cap E = \emptyset$

(g) $I \cup \angle BAC \cup E = p$

(h) $I \subseteq p$

(i) $E \not\subseteq p$

(j) $I \cap E = \angle BAC$

(k) $G \in E$

(l) $\angle BAC \subseteq p$

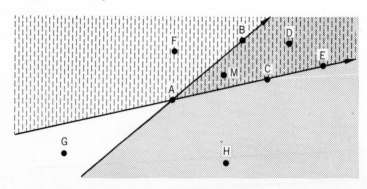

Fig. 12-36

7. (a) Prepare an illustration like Figure 12-37.

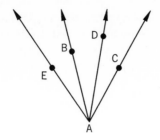

Fig. 12-37

(b) Shade that portion which is the intersection of the interiors of angles BAC and EAD.

(c) Connect E and B with a segment. Describe the points of $\overline{EB}$ that belong to the interior of $\angle EAB$.

(d) Which points of $\overline{EB}$ do not belong to the interior of $\angle EAB$?

8. Statements (a) through (s) refer to Figure 12-38. The following abbreviations are used:

$$h_A = \text{half-plane determined by } \overleftrightarrow{BC} \text{ containing point } A$$
$$h_B = \text{half-plane determined by } \overleftrightarrow{AC} \text{ containing point } B$$
$$h_C = \text{half-plane determined by } \overleftrightarrow{AB} \text{ containing point } C$$
$$I_{\triangle ABC} = \text{interior of triangle } ABC$$
$$E_{\triangle ABC} = \text{exterior of triangle } ABC$$

Tell whether each statement is true or false.

(a) $H \in (h_B \cap h_C)$

(b) $G \in (h_B \cap h_C)$

(c) $D \in (h_B \cap h_C)$

(d) $F \in (h_B \cap h_C)$

(e) $E \in (h_B \cap h_C)$

(f) $K \in (h_B \cap h_C)$

(g) $J \in (h_B \cap h_C)$

(h) $I \in (h_B \cap h_C)$

(i) $M \in (h_B \cap h_C)$

(j) $E \in I_{\triangle ABC}$

(k) $D \in I_{\triangle ABC}$

(l) $A \in E_{\triangle ABC}$

(m) $H \in E_{\triangle ABC}$

(n) $B \in \triangle ABC$

(o) $\triangle ABC \cap I_{\triangle ABC} = \emptyset$

(p) $I_{\triangle ABC} \cup E_{\triangle ABC} = p$

(q) $\overline{\triangle ABC \cup I_{\triangle ABC}} = E_{\triangle ABC}$

(r) $\overline{I_{\triangle ABC} \cup E_{\triangle ABC}} = \triangle ABC$

(s) $I_{\triangle ABC} \cap E_{\triangle ABC} = p$

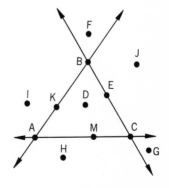

Fig. 12-38

7. SIMPLE CLOSED CURVES

You are familiar with many geometric shapes that find applications in our everyday activities. Some of these are triangles, squares, rectangles, parallelograms, and circles. All belong to the set of **simple closed curves.** Figure 12-39 shows some simple closed curves.

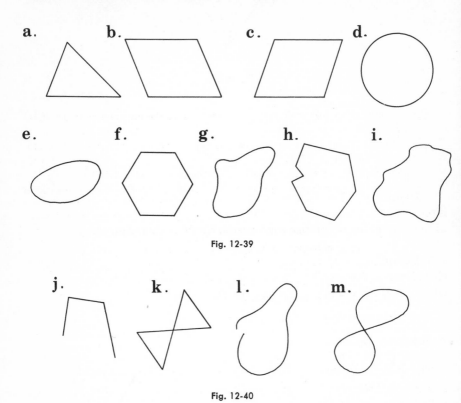

Fig. 12-39

Fig. 12-40

Each part of Figure 12-40 portrays a set of points that is not a simple closed curve. How do we tell whether a picture portrays a simple closed curve or not? We apply the following test:

To trace a picture of a simple closed curve, you must be able to start at a certain point and return to the same point without lifting the pencil from the paper and without crossing your trace at any point.

Is the conclusion that the curves in Figure 12-39*a* through *i* are simple closed curves and none of the curves in Figure 12-40*j* through *m* is such a curve consistent with the test above? Carry out the test for each curve before answering the question.

We can further classify simple closed curves into two kinds. To effect this classification, consider the simple closed curve portrayed in Figure 12-39*h*. We choose points A and B in the interior of this curve and draw a picture of $\overline{AB}$ as in Figure 12-41. Notice that not all of $\overline{AB}$ is in the interior of the curve.

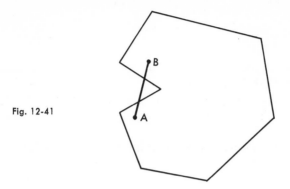

Fig. 12-41

Definition If there exists at least one pair of points A and B in the interior of a simple closed curve so that $\overline{AB}$ is not a subset of the interior of this curve, then this curve is a *concave* simple closed curve.

Definition If for every pair of points in the interior of a simple closed curve, the segment connecting these points is in the interior of the curve, then the curve is a *convex* simple closed curve.

8. BUILDING GEOMETRIC OBJECTS FROM POINTS

The simplest geometric object is a point. The next simplest object is a segment. Segment $\overline{AB}$ (Figure 12-42) consists of points A and B, called endpoints of the segment, and all points between A and B.

Fig. 12-42

It is easy to observe that, for any two points, there is one segment that contains these two points. Given three points, however, it is not always possible to have one segment that contains all three points. In Figure

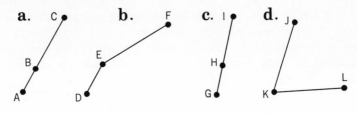

Fig. 12-43

12-43 each picture has three points. In two of these pictures there is one segment containing the three points. In each of two remaining pictures there is no one segment that contains the three points.

We are led to the definition of collinear points.

Definition   **Three points that lie on the same line are called** *collinear* **points.**

If there is no line that contains three given points, then these points are called **noncollinear points.** Do you see that any set of three non-collinear points can determine a triangle?

In building successively more and more complicated geometric objects, we can consider a point, a segment, and a triangle to be the first three steps in order of complexity. We start with one point, move to two points (two points determine a segment), then to three noncollinear points (three points determine a triangle). See Figure 12-44.

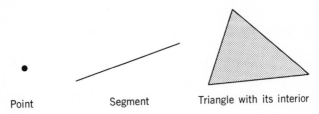

Point   Segment   Triangle with its interior

Fig. 12-44

What about four points? First, we must exercise some care. Four points can be chosen so that they determine one plane. Such points are called **coplanar points.** Suppose, however, that we choose four points in space so that they do not lie on the same plane; that is, we choose a set of four **noncoplanar points.** These points determine an object called a *tetrahedron*, shown in Figure 12-45. Thus, following this pattern, the fourth simplest object (determined by four noncoplanar points) is a tetrahedron.

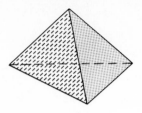

Fig. 12-45

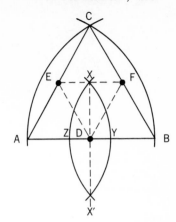

Fig. 12-46

9. TETRAHEDRON

When studying polygons, we classified them into regular polygons and all other polygons. We may also classify tetrahedra into regular tetrahedra and all others.

We now engage in a bit of a practical activity and build a model of a regular tetrahedron. For this you need a piece of paper, some Scotch tape, a pair of scissors, a ruler, a compass, and a pencil. Once equipped with these materials, follow the steps below in the order they are listed.

1. On a piece of paper, construct a picture of an equilateral triangle. To do this, start with $\overline{AB}$. Then with a compass mark arcs AC and BC as in Figure 12-46. Draw pictures of $\overline{AC}$ and $\overline{BC}$.

2. Bisect (divide into two parts of the same length) each side of $\triangle ABC$. Proceed as follows for bisecting $\overline{AB}$:

(a) Put the foot of a compass at point A and open the compass to more than half the distance from A to B.

(b) Make an arc $X'YX$ as in Figure 12-46.

(c) With the same opening of the compass and with the foot at point B, make another arc $X'ZX$. The two arcs intersect in X and X'.

(d) Connect X and X'.

(e) Point D is the midpoint of $\overline{AB}$, so $\overline{AD}$ and $\overline{DB}$ are of the same length.

3. Using a compass, mark off $\overline{AE}$ equal in length to $\overline{AD}$ and $\overline{BF}$ equal in length to $\overline{AD}$. (Why are E and F the midpoints of $\overline{AC}$ and $\overline{BC}$, respectively?)

4. Draw $\overline{ED}$, $\overline{DF}$, and $\overline{FE}$.

5. Cut out $\triangle ABC$, and fold along $\overline{ED}$, $\overline{DF}$, and $\overline{FE}$. Fasten edges with Scotch tape. You now have a model of a regular tetrahedron.

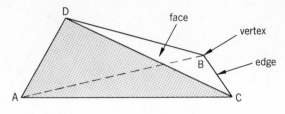

Fig. 12-47

It was fairly simple to make a model of a *regular* tetrahedron. Making a model of an irregular tetrahedron is somewhat more complicated; to do so, proceed as follows:

1. On a piece of cardboard draw a scalene triangle ABC (a triangle in which no two sides are of the same length). Label the vertices inside the triangle (see Figure 12-47).
2. Cut out the triangle.
3. On the cardboard, draw another scalene triangle with one side the same length as that of $\overline{AB}$.
4. Cut out the triangle.
5. With Scotch tape, fasten $\overline{AB}$ and the side of the second triangle of the same length.
6. Label the vertex at the top D.
7. Draw a triangle with one side the same length as $\overline{AD}$ and another side the same length as $\overline{AC}$.
8. Cut out the triangle and fasten it to your model to match the lengths of $\overline{AD}$ and $\overline{AC}$.
9. Now cut out the triangle to fit the open side; you have a tetrahedron that is not regular.

Figure 12-47 might approximate your model.

Problem Set 4

1. Tell why each curve pictured in Figure 12-40 is not a simple closed curve (see the test in Section 7).
2. Classify each curve shown in Figure 12-39 as a convex or concave simple closed curve (see definition in Section 7).
3. Explain why every circle is a convex simple closed curve.
4. Explain why every triangle is a convex simple closed curve.
5. Explain why every square is a simple closed curve.
6. Explain why every pair of points is a set of collinear points.
7. Explain why every triple of points is a set of coplanar points.
8. How many points are needed to determine a tetrahedron? What must be the condition on these points?

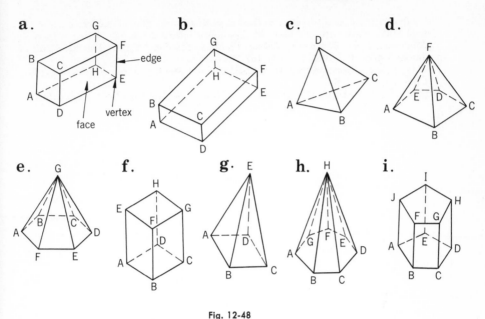

Fig. 12-48

9. In Figure 12-48 are pictures of various polyhedra (manyfaced solids). For each polyhedron count the number of vertices (V), the number of faces (F), and the number of edges (E). Make a table like the one shown below and record your results. The last column gives the number obtained by subtracting the number of edges from the sum of the number of vertices and faces. [The problem is worked for you for polyhedron 1.]

Polyhedron	Number of vertices, V	Number of faces, F	Number of edges, E	$(V + F) - E$
1	8	6	12	$(8 + 6) - 12 = 2$

BIBLIOGRAPHY

Abbott, Edwin A., *Flatland*. New York: Dover Publications, Inc., 1952.
Brumfiel, Charles F., Robert E. Eicholz, Merrill E. Shanks, and P. G. O'Daffer, *Principles of Arithmetic*. Reading, Mass.: Addison-Wesley Publishing Company, Inc., 1963, pp. 273–296.
Court, Nathan A., *Mathematics in Fun and Earnest*. New York: New American Library, 1961, pp. 28–35, 47–62, 91–98, 140–146.
Johnson, Donovan A., *Curves in Space*. St. Louis: Webster Publishing Company, 1963.
Nichols, Eugene D., *Pre-Algebra Mathematics*. New York: Holt, Rinehart and Winston, Inc., 1965, Chap. 10.
Norton, M. Scott, *Geometric Constructions*. St. Louis: Webster Publishing Company, 1963.

Ravielli, Anthony, *An Adventure in Geometry*. New York: The Viking Press, 1961.

School Mathematics Study Group, *Studies in Mathematics, Vol. IX, A Brief Course in Mathematics for Elementary School Teachers*. Stanford, Calif.: Leland Stanford Junior University, 1963, pp. 139–167, 327–353.

————, *Intuitive Geometry*. Stanford, Calif.: Leland Stanford Junior University, 1961, Chaps. 1, 3, 4, 6, 8.

Yaglom, I. M., *Geometric Transformations*. New York: Random House, Inc., 1962.

13

MEASUREMENT IN GEOMETRY

1. MEASURING

In the preceding chapter we considered geometric objects as sets of points without any reference to the size of the object. In this chapter we shall be concerned with such concepts as length, area, and volume. Although we shall not engage in the physical activity of measuring objects, we shall make computations assuming that we know certain measures of these objects.

When reporting results of measuring, we employ various units. To report the length of an object, we may use the inch, centimeter, foot, mile, kilometer, or other unit of length. The process of measuring is in the realm of physical activities. Computations involving results of measuring are activities of a mathematical nature. We must exercise some caution when performing operations in which results of measuring are involved. We must first ascertain that each measure is given in terms of the same unit.

To compute the perimeter of a triangle whose sides are 4 ft., 6 ft., and 7 ft. long, we are first satisfied that the length of each side is given in terms of the same unit (feet in this case). Next we use the mathematical model:

$$4 + 6 + 7 = 17$$

and conclude that the perimeter of our triangle is equal to 17 ft. The same mathematical model can serve when computing the perimeter of a triangle whose sides are 4 in., 6 in., and 7 in. long. In this case, however, we interpret the result of

$$4 + 6 + 7 = 17$$

as meaning 17 in., rather than 17 ft.

Should two measures be given in terms of different units, then, before using a mathematical model, we need to express each measure in terms of the same unit. We shall use the symbol $\overset{m}{=}$ to mean "is the same measure as." For example, each of the following is true:

$$1 \text{ ft. } \overset{m}{=} 12 \text{ in. (read: 1 ft. is the same measure as 12 in.)}$$
$$1 \text{ yd } \overset{m}{=} 3 \text{ ft.}$$
$$1 \text{ mile } \overset{m}{=} 5280 \text{ ft.}$$
$$1 \text{ square foot (ft.}^2) \overset{m}{=} 144 \text{ square inches (in.}^2)$$
$$1 \text{ square yard (yd.}^2) \overset{m}{=} 9 \text{ square feet (ft.}^2)$$

Frequently measures of the same object are stated in terms of different units, and one or more operations are needed before arriving at the desired result.

Example 1 Express 2 ft. 6 in. in terms of inches.
Since 1 ft. $\overset{m}{=}$ 12 in., 5 ft. $\overset{m}{=}$ 60 in. Therefore, 5 ft. 6 in. $\overset{m}{=}$ 66 in.

Example 2 Find the perimeter of a triangle in which the lengths of sides are: 14 in., 1 ft., and $1\frac{1}{2}$ ft.
We first express each measure in terms of inches. 1 ft. $\overset{m}{=}$ 12 in.; $1\frac{1}{2}$ ft. $\overset{m}{=}$ 18 in. The mathematical statement relative to the perimeter can now be written:

$$14 + 12 + 18 = 44.$$

Thus, the perimeter is equal to 44 in.

Example 3 Find the perimeter of a square in which each side is 7 in. long. The mathematical statement that is a model for this problem is:

$$4 \times 7 = 28.$$

Thus, the perimeter of the square is equal to 28 in.
In this chapter we shall be concerned with the ways of computing areas and volumes of geometric objects.

Problem Set 1

1. Give each of the following measures in inches.

   (a) 3 ft. 7 in.   (b) 3 yd. 2 ft. 11 in.
   (c) 1 yd. 2 ft. 3 in.   (d) 9 yd. 1 ft. 8 in.

2. Compute the perimeters of triangles with the following measures of sides.

   (a) 2 ft., 17 in., 9 in.
   (b) 1 yd., 2 ft., $1\frac{1}{2}$ ft.

3. Compute the perimeter of a square in which each side has the length of 7 yd.

4. True or false?

    (a) 1 yd.^{2} $\overset{m}{=}$ 1,296 in.^{2}
    (b) 1 in.^{2} $\overset{m}{=}$ $\frac{1}{144}$ ft.^{2}
    (c) 1 mile $\overset{m}{=}$ 15,840 yd.
    (d) 1 ft. $\overset{m}{=}$ $\frac{1}{3}$ yd.
    (e) 1 in. $\overset{m}{=}$ $\frac{1}{12}$ yd.

2. AREAS OF INTERIORS OF RECTANGLES AND TRIANGLES

A rectangle is a four-sided polygon, called a quadrilateral, in which opposite sides are parallel and all angles are right angles.

Fig. 13-1

The shaded region in Figure 13-1 is the interior of rectangle $ABCD$. Strictly speaking, the area of rectangle $ABCD$ is 0, because rectangle $ABCD$ is the union of four segments: $\overline{AB} \cup \overline{BC} \cup \overline{CD} \cup \overline{AD}$. That is, the boundary itself has an area of 0 in.^{2}. However, the area this boundary encloses is not 0.

    Definition   **To simplify matters, we shall agree that, whenever we say "area of a rectangle," we shall mean "area of the interior of the rectangle."**

If a rectangle has its length equal to 7 in. and width equal to 3 in., then the mathematical model for computing its area is

$$7 \times 3.$$

Thus, the area of this rectangle is 21 in.^{2}.

More generally, if the length of a rectangle is a units and the width is b units, then the area of this rectangle is ab square units.

We shall take the above as our basic assumption and *derive* from it theorems concerning areas of other geometric objects. We make one further assumption, namely, that a diagonal of a rectangle divides it into two triangles having the same area. For example, in Figure 13-2, $\triangle ABC$ and $\triangle ADC$ have the same area.

The following derivation refers to Figure 13-2. "Area$_{\triangle ABC}$" means "area of triangle ABC," and "$\square ABCD$" means "rectangle $ABCD$."

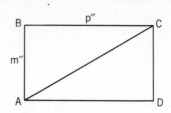

Fig. 13-2

First step. Area of the rectangle $ABCD = mp$ in.²

Second step. Area$_{\triangle ABC}$ = area$_{\triangle ACD}$.

Therefore, area$_{\square ABCD} = 2 \times$ area$_{\triangle ABC}$.

Therefore, $mp = 2 \times$ area$_{\triangle ABC}$.

Therefore, area$_{\triangle ABC} = \frac{1}{2}mp$.

The conclusion is that the area of triangle ABC is one-half of the area of rectangle $ABCD$. Of course, this would be true in *any* rectangle, since we did not choose any special rectangle.

In triangle ABC in Figure 13-2, we can consider $\overline{BC}$ the base and $\overline{AB}$ the altitude upon this base. Thus, we proved above that the *area* of a right triangle is equal to one-half of the product of the measures of its base and the altitude upon this base. Study the following generalization of this formula to any triangle (Figure 13-3).

$$A_{\triangle PQD} = \frac{1}{2}mh$$
$$A_{\triangle RQD} = \frac{1}{2}nh$$
$$A_{\triangle PQR} = A_{\triangle PQD} + A_{\triangle RQD} = \frac{1}{2}mh + \frac{1}{2}nh$$
$$= \frac{1}{2}h(m+n)$$
$$= \frac{1}{2}hb.$$

Thus, the area of any triangle is equal to one-half of the product of the measures of one of its sides and the altitude upon this side.

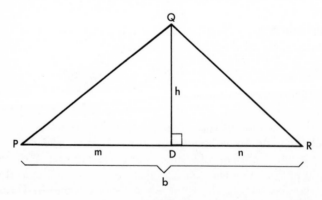

Fig. 13-3

As another example of a derivation or proof, let us assume that the sum of the measures of the three angles in any triangle is 180° and prove that the sum of four angles in any quadrilateral is 360°. Refer to Figure 13-4 when studying this proof. We use "$m(\angle A)$" to mean "measure of angle A."

Fig. 13-4

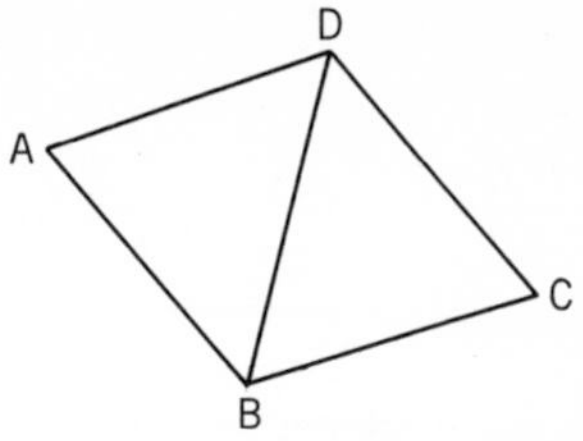

$$m(\angle A) + m(\angle ADB) + m(\angle ABD) = 180°$$
$$m(\angle C) + m(\angle CDB) + m(\angle CBD) = 180°$$
$$m(\angle A) + m(\angle ADC) + m(\angle C) + m(\angle CBA) = 360°$$

And we have thus proved the theorem we set out to prove.

Problem Set 2

1. Is every quadrilateral a rectangle?
2. Is every rectangle a quadrilateral?
3. Compute the area of each rectangle with the given length and width.

   (a) 4 in., 2 in.
   (b) 1.5 in., 0.6 in.
   (c) 2 in., 1 in.

   (d) 12 in., $\frac{3}{4}$ ft.
   (e) 2 ft., 7 in.
   (f) 3 yd., 2 ft.

4. Find the following areas (Figure 13-5):

   (a) Area$_{\square ABCD}$
   (b) Area$_{\triangle ABC}$
   (c) Area$_{\triangle ACD}$

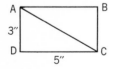

Fig. 13-5

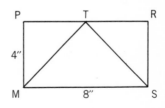

Fig. 13-6

5. Find the following areas (Figure 13-6):

   (a) Area$_{\square MPRS}$
   (b) Area$_{\triangle MPT}$ (T divides $\overline{PR}$ into two segments of equal length.)
   (c) Area$_{\triangle TRS}$
   (d) Area$_{\triangle MTS}$

6. Find the following areas, if $\overline{YV}$, $\overline{VW}$, and $\overline{WU}$ are of the same length, and $\overline{XT}$ and $\overline{TZ}$ are of the same length (Figure 13-7).

(a) Area$_{\square XYUZ}$
(b) Area$_{\triangle XYV}$
(c) Area$_{\triangle WUZ}$
(d) Area$_{\triangle XVT}$
(e) Area$_{\triangle XWZ}$
(f) Area$_{\triangle XYW}$
(g) Area$_{\triangle XUZ}$

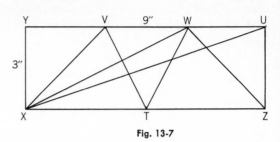

Fig. 13-7

7. Find the areas of triangles when given the measure of one side (first number) and the measure of the altitude upon this side (second number).

(a) 5 in., 15 in.   (d) $\frac{1}{2}$ ft., $\frac{1}{3}$ ft.
(b) 1 ft., $5\frac{1}{2}$ in.   (e) $\frac{3}{4}$ ft., 8 in.
(c) 3.6 in., 2.8 in.   (f) 1 yd., 2 ft.

8. Use Figure 13-8 to prove that the sum of the measures of the four angles in a quadrilateral is equal to 360°.

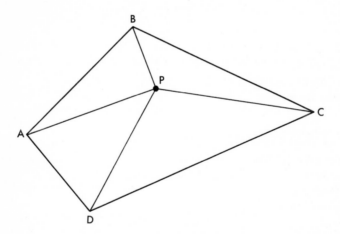

Fig. 13-8

3. AREA OF A PARALLELOGRAM

A parallelogram is a special kind of a quadrilateral (four-sided polygon). It has all the following properties:

1. Its opposite sides are parallel (name two pairs of parallel sides in Figure 13-9).

2. Its opposite sides have the same length.

3. Its opposite angles have the same measure (name two pairs of opposite angles having the same measure in Figure 13-9).

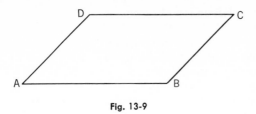

Fig. 13-9

4. Its adjacent angles are supplementary angles; that is, the sum of their measures is equal to 180°. (Name four pairs of adjacent angles in Figure 13-9.)

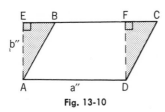

Fig. 13-10

Now let us consider $\square ABCD$ in Figure 13-10. In this picture $\overline{EA} \perp \overline{AD}$ (read: $\overline{EA}$ is perpendicular to $\overline{AD}$) and $\overline{FD} \perp \overline{AD}$. Knowing that $\overline{AD}$ and $\overline{BC}$ have the same length (why?) and that $\overline{EA}$ and $\overline{FD}$ have the same length (why?), we could easily prove that $\triangle AEB$ and $\triangle DFC$ have the same area. If this is so, then we can reason out the conclusion concerning the area of a parallelogram.

We know that $AEFD$ is a rectangle. Its area is ab square inches. Since triangles AEB and DFC have the same area, the area of parallelogram $ABCD$ is the same as the area of the rectangle $AEFD$. Explain why this is true. The area of the parallelogram, therefore, is also ab square inches.

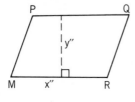

Fig. 13-11

Definition   The area of a parallelogram is equal to the product of the measures of the base and the altitude (see Figure 13-11).

$$\text{Area}_{\square MPQR} = xy \text{ in.}^2$$

Problem Set 3

1. Tell which of the following statements are true and which are false.

   (a) Every parallelogram is a rectangle.
   (b) Every rectangle is a parallelogram.
   (c) Every parallelogram is a quadrilateral.
   (d) Every quadrilateral is a parallelogram.
   (e) Every square is a quadrilateral.
   (f) No triangle is a quadrilateral.
   (g) No quadrilateral has a larger area than any triangle.
   (h) Some rectangles have no right angles.
   (i) Every parallelogram has two diagonals.
   (j) Diagonals of a parallelogram have exactly one point in common.
   (k) Every square is a parallelogram.
   (l) A diagonal of a parallelogram divides the parallelogram into two triangles with the same area.

2. Compute the area of the parallelogram *EFGH*. The measures of the base and altitude are as shown in Figure 13-12.

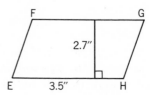

Fig. 13-12

3. The area of the parallelogram *IJKL* is 24 in.² (Figure 13-13). Compute the length of its altitude $\overline{JM}$, if the length of $\overline{IL}$ is equal to 8 in.

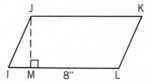

Fig. 13-13

4. The area of the parallelogram *NOPR* is 48 in.² (Figure 13-14). Compute the length of $\overline{NR}$.

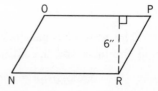

Fig. 13-14

5. Compute the area of the parallelogram pictured in Figure 13-15.

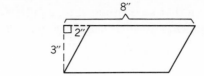

Fig. 13-15

6. If the area of $\triangle VUW$ is equal to 1.5 in.² and the lengths of $\overline{SV}$ and $\overline{VW}$ are 5 in. and 1 in., respectively, compute the area of $\square STUV$ (Figure 13-16).

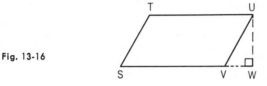

Fig. 13-16

4. AREAS OF REGULAR POLYGONS AND EQUILATERAL TRIANGLES

Definition   A regular polygon is a polygon in which all sides have the same length and all angles have the same measure.

A triangle that meets the conditions of this definition is called an **equilateral triangle.** Since the sum of the measures of the three angles in any triangle is 180°, it follows that each angle of an equilateral triangle has the measure equal to 60°.

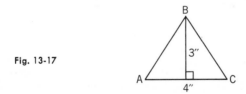

Fig. 13-17

We already know that, to compute the area of a triangle, we need to know the measure of one side and the measure of the altitude upon that side. For example, to compute the area of the triangle pictured in Figure 13-17, we multiply

$$\tfrac{1}{2} \times 4 \times 3 = 6.$$

Since the lengths are given in inches, the area of this triangle is equal to 6 in.².

We would like to explore whether it is possible to know the area of an equilateral triangle once we know the measure of one of its sides. Of course, this amounts to knowing the measure of each side of the equilateral triangle (why?).

First we observe that an altitude in an equilateral triangle divides the base into two segments of equal length (Figure 13-18).

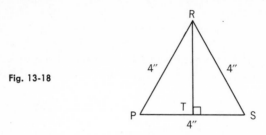

Fig. 13-18

We need to recall that in every right triangle the square of the measure of the hypotenuse is equal to the sum of the squares of the measures of the two legs (legs are sides making the right angle). For Figure 13-19, the following is true:

$$a^2 + b^2 = c^2.$$

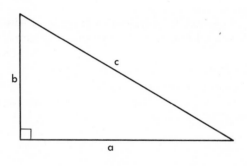

Fig. 13-19

Returning to a part of Figure 13-18 that is shown in Figure 13-20, we can make the following computations, which give us the length of the altitude $\overline{RT}$.

$$4^2 = 2^2 + h^2$$
$$16 = 4 + h^2$$
$$h^2 + 4 = 16$$
$$h^2 = 16 - 4$$
$$h^2 = 12$$
$$h = \sqrt{12} \doteq 3.4$$

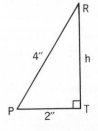

Fig. 13-20

Knowing the measure of a side in an equilateral triangle, we can compute the measure of an altitude. In the triangle with sides 4 in. long, the

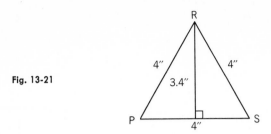

Fig. 13-21

altitude is about 3.4 in. long (Figure 13-21). Now we can compute the area of the triangle: $\text{Area}_{\triangle PRS} \doteq \frac{1}{2} \times 4 \times 3.4 = 6.8$ in.^{2}. If we wanted to know the exact area, we would use $\sqrt{12}$ for the measure of the altitude:

$$\text{Area}_{\triangle PRS} = \tfrac{1}{2} \times 4 \times \sqrt{12} = 2\sqrt{12} \text{ in.}^2.$$

We are now ready to generalize the above development to arrive at a formula that can be used to compute the area of any equilateral triangle (Figure 13-22).

$$(BD)^2 + \left(\frac{s}{2}\right)^2 = s^2$$

$$(BD)^2 = s^2 - \left(\frac{s}{2}\right)^2 = s^2 - \frac{s^2}{4} = \frac{4s^2 - s^2}{4} = \frac{3s^2}{4}$$

$$BD = \sqrt{\frac{3s^2}{4}} = \frac{\sqrt{3}\sqrt{s^2}}{\sqrt{4}} = \frac{s\sqrt{3}}{2}$$

$$\text{Area of } \triangle ABC = \frac{1}{2} \cdot s \cdot \frac{s\sqrt{3}}{2} = \frac{s \cdot s\sqrt{3}}{2 \cdot 2} = \frac{s^2\sqrt{3}}{4}.$$

Thus, to compute the area of an equilateral triangle, replace s in $s^2\sqrt{3}/4$ by a numeral giving the measure of the side of the triangle.

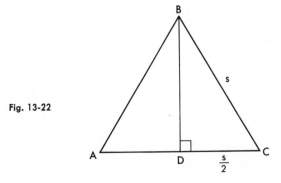

Fig. 13-22

Problem Set 4

1. Without measuring, tell which polygons in Figure 13-23 appear to be regular polygons.

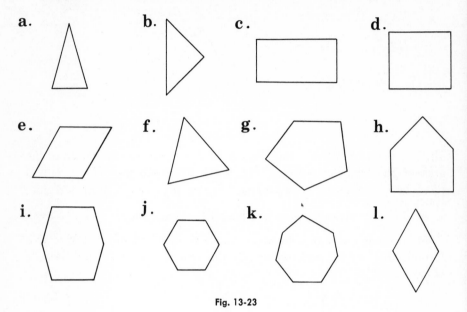

a.   **b.**   **c.**   **d.**

e.   **f.**   **g.**   **h.**

i.   **j.**   **k.**   **l.**

Fig. 13-23

2. Compute the area of each of the equilateral triangles in Figure 13-24. (Compute the measure of an altitude first.)

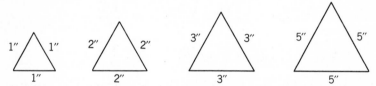

Fig. 13-24

3. Knowing that an altitude upon the base of an isosceles triangle bisects the base, compute the area of each of the isosceles triangles in Figure 13-25. ("Bisects" means "divides into two segments of the same length"; an isosceles triangle has two sides of the same length.)

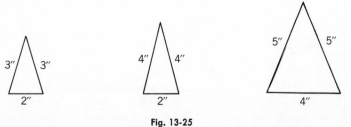

Fig. 13-25

4. Using the formula, compute the areas of equilateral triangles whose sides have the following measures:

   (a) 6 in.
   (b) $\sqrt{3}$ in.
   (c) $\frac{1}{2}$ in.
   (d) $\sqrt{12}$ in.
   (e) 27 in.

5. If the area of an equilateral triangle is $7^2 \sqrt{3}/4$ in.², how long is its side?
6. If the area of an equilateral triangle is $3 \sqrt{3}/2$ in.², how long is its side?

5. CIRCLES AND INSCRIBED REGULAR POLYGONS

In the picture of the circle (see Figure 13-26) with center P, every point on the circle is the same distance from point P. This distance is 2 in. $\overline{PA}$ is one of many radii (singular: radius) of this circle. Two inches is the measure of each radius of this circle. The segment $\overline{AB}$ is one of many diameters of this circle.

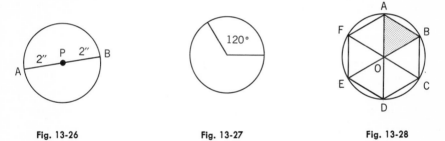

Fig. 13-26   Fig. 13-27   Fig. 13-28

We can use the center of a circle for a vertex of an angle whose sides are two radii of the circle. Such an angle is called a **central angle.** For example, in Figure 13-27 we show a central angle whose measure is 120°.

We now turn our attention to regular polygons that are inscribed in circles. For a polygon to be inscribed in a circle, all its vertices must be on the circle. In Figure 13-28 we have hexagon $ABCDEF$ inscribed in a circle.

Let us take a closer look at one of the triangles, say, $\triangle OAB$. We can immediately observe that it is an isosceles triangle, because $\overline{AO}$ and $\overline{BO}$ have the same length (why?). Also angles OBA and OAB have the same measure (why?). It follows then that each angle of $\triangle OAB$ has the measure 60°, since the measure of $\angle AOB$ is equal to 60°. Thus, $\triangle OAB$ is an *equiangular* and, therefore, an **equilateral** triangle.

It is not difficult to observe that the area of the hexagon in Figure 13-28 is smaller than the area of the circle in which the hexagon is inscribed. We shall now make certain observations that will eventually lead us to the formula for the area of a circle. In order to understand this development fully, follow the steps below and answer each question.

1. (a) Draw a picture of a circle having a radius of any length you choose. Inscribe a regular hexagon in it by measuring off six angles of 60° each from the center of the circle.

(b) Divide each angle into two 30° angles, obtaining 12 angles, each having a measure of 30°. Connect the points on the circle to form a dodeca-gon (12-sided polygon).

(c) Is the area of the dodecagon less than or greater than the area of the circle?

(d) Is the area of the dodecagon less than or greater than the area of the hexagon?

(e) Is the perimeter of the dodecagon shorter than or longer than the perimeter of the hexagon?

2. (a) If you were to divide each 30° angle in your picture into two angles of the same size, how many angles would you obtain?

(b) What would be the size of each angle?

(c) How many sides would there be in the polygon obtained by connecting the new points on the circle?

Now answer the questions below, which refer to Figure 13-29.

1. What kind of a polygon is $A'B'C'D'E'F'$?

2. What kind of a polygon is $AA'BB'CC'DD'EE'FF'$ (read: A' as A prime)?

Let us call the polygon in Question 1 polygon X and the polygon in Question 2 polygon Y.

3. Which polygon has a larger area, X or Y?

4. Which polygon has a longer perimeter, X or Y?

5. How many sides does the polygon $AA''A'B''BC''B'D''CE''C'F''$ $DG''D'H''EI''E'J''FK''F'L''$ have? (Read: A'' as A double prime.)

Let us call the polygon in Question 5 polygon Z.

6. (a) Of the three polygons, X, Y, and Z, which has the greatest area?

(b) Which has the longest perimeter?

7. (a) How do the areas of the polygons compare with the area of the circle as the number of sides increases?

(b) How do the perimeters compare with the circumference of the circle?

Definition   We say that the limit of the area of the polygon, as the number of sides increases indefinitely, is the area of the circle.

8. Make a statement similar to this definition about the circumference of the circle in relation to the perimeter of polygons.

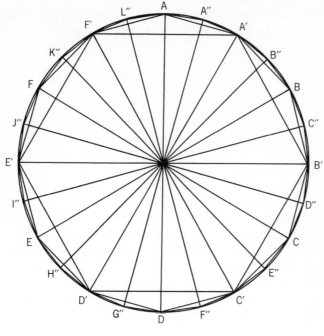

Fig. 13-29

6. AREA OF A CIRCLE

We know that the ratio of the circumference of any circle to the length of a diameter is the same number for every circle. This number is π (read: pi), which is approximately equal to 3.14. Thus, the circumference of any circle is a little more than three times as long as any diameter of that circle. If the measure of a diameter is d, then the circumference is πd or $\pi \cdot 2r$, where r is the measure of a radius. This is illustrated in Figure 13-30.

$$2\pi r \doteq 2 \times 3.14 \times 1 = 6.28.$$

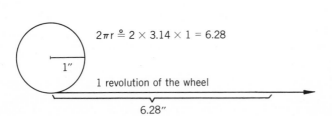

Fig. 13-30

Now look at Figure 13-31. It shows a regular polygon inscribed in a circle. We make the following observations in reference to Figure 13-31.

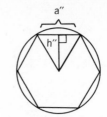

Fig. 13-31

1. If the altitude of the triangle shown in Figure 13-31 is h inches long and the base is a inches long, then the area of the triangle is equal to $\frac{1}{2}ah$ square inches.

2. If the number of sides in the regular polygon inscribed in the circle is n, then there are n triangles like the one shown, each having the area equal to $\frac{1}{2}ah$ square inches.

3. The area of the inscribed regular polygon is then equal to $\frac{1}{2}(ah)n$ or $\frac{1}{2}n \cdot ah$.

4. Should we inscribe, in the circle shown, regular polygons with more and more sides, then (a) the limit of the perimeters of the polygons would be the circumference of the circle, and (b) the limit of the lengths of the altitudes of triangles would be the length of a radius of the circle.

We show the last two observations in an abbreviated form:

$$\text{perimeter of polygon} \to \text{circumference of circle}$$
$$p \to c$$

(read: perimeter of polygon *tends to* or *approaches* circumference of circle).

$$\text{altitude of triangle} \to \text{radius of circle.}$$
$$h \to r.$$

Now let us recall the formula for the area of the inscribed polygon we obtained in item 3:

$$\text{area of polygon} = \frac{1}{2}(ah)n \qquad \text{or} \qquad \frac{1}{2}n \cdot ah.$$

Since $a \cdot n$ is equal to the perimeter p of the polygon, we can write

$$\text{area of polygon} = \frac{1}{2}ph.$$

But, as the number of sides in the polygons increases indefinitely, p approaches c and h approaches r. Thus,

$$\frac{1}{2}ph \xrightarrow{\text{approaches}} \frac{1}{2}cr.$$

We know, however, that the circumference of the circle c is equal to $2\pi r$. Therefore,

$$\text{area of circle} = \frac{1}{2}\, cr = \frac{1}{2}\,(2\pi r)r = \pi r^2.$$

This formula enables us to compute areas of circles. The only thing we need to know is the measure of a radius of the circle.

Problem Set 5

1. Draw a picture showing a central angle.

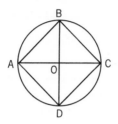

Fig. 13-32

2. (a) Inscribe a square in a circle, like the square $ABCD$ in Figure 13-32. Using a compass, bisect each of the angles AOB, COB, DOC, and AOD. Draw a regular, inscribed, octagon (eight sides).

   (b) How does the area of the octagon compare with the area of the square?

   (c) How does the perimeter of the octagon compare with the perimeter of the square?

   (d) How does the area of the octagon compare with the area of the circle?

   (e) How does the perimeter of the octagon compare with the circumference of the circle?

   (f) Now, using a compass, bisect appropriate angles to obtain a regular, inscribed, 16-sided polygon.

   (g) Is the area of the 16-sided polygon greater or less than the area of the octagon?

   (h) Is the area of the 16-sided polygon greater or less than the area of the circle?

   (i) Is the perimeter of the 16-sided polygon longer or shorter than the perimeter of the octagon?

   (j) Is the perimeter of the 16-sided polygon longer or shorter than the circumference of the circle?

3. What is the circumference of a circle with a radius of 2 in.? Give an answer in terms of π, then compute the approximate answer using $\pi \doteq 3.14$.

4. What is the area of a circle with a radius of 5 in.? Give two answers, as in Problem 3.

5. Find the circumferences and the areas of circles having the following measures

of radii. Give two answers, one in terms of π and the other computed (approximately) using $\pi \doteq 3.14$.

(a) $\frac{1}{2}$ in.
(b) 3 in.
(c) 10 in.
(d) 1 ft.
(e) 6 ft.

6. A diameter of a circle measures 20 in.

(a) What is the area of the circle? (Give the answer in terms of π.)
(b) What is the area of a square inscribed in this circle?
(c) Find the difference between the area of the circle and the area of the inscribed square. (Give the answer in terms of π, then compute an approximate answer using $\pi \doteq 3.14$.)

7. (a) Compute the area of a regular hexagon inscribed in the circle of Problem 6.
(b) Find the difference between the areas of the circle and the inscribed hexagon. Compute two answers as in Problem 6(c).
(c) Which difference is larger: that in 6(c) or that in 7(b)?
(d) Is your answer in (c) consistent with what you have learned?

8. Compute to two decimal places the circumferences and areas of the circles with the following measures of radii (use $\pi \doteq 3.14$):

(a) 1 in.
(b) 3 ft.
(c) 2.5 in.
(d) $5\frac{1}{2}$ ft.
(e) 10 miles

9. What distance does a wheel with a diameter of 2 in. cover when making 100 revolutions?
10. To the nearest whole number, how many revolutions does a wheel with a radius of 10 in. measure make when traveling 1 mile?
11. A diameter of a wheel measures 32 in. If the wheel moves along the road with a speed of 65 mph, how many revolutions, to the nearest whole number, does it make in 1 hour?
12. Approximately how many revolutions does the wheel in Problem 11 make in 1 hour when traveling at 130 mph?

7. VOLUMES OF PRISMS

Solids whose faces are parallelograms are called **prisms.** If both the bases and the faces happen to be rectangles, then the solid is called a **rectangular prism.**

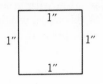

Fig. 13-33

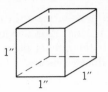

Fig. 13-34

In measuring areas of plane geometric objects, we used a square unit of measure. A square with a side of length 1 in. may serve as such a unit (Figure 13-33).

In measuring volumes of solid objects, we use a cubic unit of measure. For example, a cube with an edge of length 1 in. may serve as such a unit (Figure 13-34).

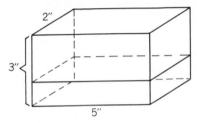

Fig. 13-35

Consider a rectangular solid like the one shown in Figure 13-35. The dimensions of this rectangular prism are: length, 5 in.; width, 2 in.; and height, 3 in. One layer of cubes, shown in the picture, has the volume equal to 5×2 or 10 cubic inches (in.^{3}). Since the height is 3 in., there are three such layers, or the volume of the prism is $5 \times 2 \times 3$ or 30 in.^{3}.

Definition   **A rectangular prism with the dimensions l in., w in., and h in. has the volume $V = lwh$ in.^{3}.**

Problem Set 6

1. Compute the volume of rectangular prisms with the following dimensions:

   (a) 1 in., 2 in., 3 in.
   (b) 3.2 in., 2.5 in., 6.0 in.
   (c) $\frac{1}{2}$ ft., $\frac{1}{3}$ ft., 2 ft.
   (d) 12 centimeters (cm.), 20 cm., 30 cm.
   (e) 25 meters, 2 meters, 4 meters
   (f) $2\frac{1}{2}$ in., $4\frac{1}{2}$ in., $6\frac{1}{2}$ in.

2. Given a piece of metal in the shape of a rectangular prism with dimensions 4 in., 7 in., and 12 in., compute its weight, if 1 in.³ of this metal weighs $\frac{1}{4}$ lb.

3. Compute the ratio of the volumes of the first rectangular prism to the second if their dimensions are as follows:

    (a) 2 in., 3 in., 5 in. (first prism); 4 in., 3 in., 5 in. (second prism)
    (b) 2 in., 3 in., 5 in.; 4 in., 6 in., 5 in.
    (c) 2 in., 3 in., 5 in.; 4 in., 6 in., 10 in.
    (d) 2 in., 3 in., 5 in.; 6 in., 9 in., 15 in.

4. Look at your answers from Problem 3 and answer the following questions:

    (a) If one of the three dimensions of a rectangular prism is doubled while the other two are unchanged, how is the volume changed?
    (b) If each of two dimensions of a rectangular prism is doubled while the third is unchanged, how is the volume changed?
    (c) If each of the three dimensions of a rectangular prism is doubled, how is the volume changed?

5. In 7 hours a laborer dug out a hole in a form of a rectangular solid 4 ft. by 4 ft. by 6 ft. How many cubic yards of dirt did he remove per hour? Give your answer to the nearest tenth.

6. A cube with an edge of 2 ft. is filled with water. What does the water weigh? (*Hint:* one cubic foot of water weighs 62.5 lb.)

7. One cubic yard of black soil is called "one load." A truck has the dimensions 6 ft. by 4 ft. by 2 ft. How many loads does it carry when it is filled? Give your answer to the nearest tenth of the load.

8. SURFACE AREAS AND VOLUMES OF CYLINDERS

Given two parallel lines, k and l, as shown in Figure 13-36. Imagine that line l "moves" at a constant distance d from line k. The resulting object is a cylindrical surface. The *surface* is called a **cylinder.** The set of points "enclosed" by the cylinder is the interior of the cylinder; its measure is called the volume.

Since we shall be mainly concerned with the study of parts of cylinders included between two parallel planes, we shall use the word *cylinder* to refer to this kind of an object.

Fig. 13-36

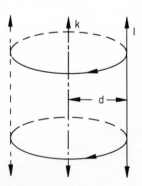

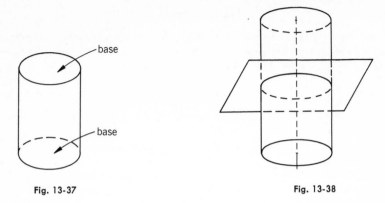

base

base

Fig. 13-37   **Fig. 13-38**

A right cylinder is a geometric solid like the one shown in Figure 13-37. Observe that a base of a cylinder is a circular region.

Figure 13-38 shows a cylinder with a line passing through the centers of the two bases. Such a line is called the **axis** of the cylinder. From the picture it is evident that, if a cylinder is cut by a plane perpendicular to the axis, then the intersection of this plane and the cylinder is a circle.

The entire surface of the cylinder consists of two bases (circles) and the lateral surface, as shown in Figure 13-39. If you should unfold the lateral surface of the cylinder, you would obtain a rectangular region. The length of one of its sides would be equal to the circumference of the base of the cylinder and of the other to the height of the cylinder. This is shown in Figure 13-40.

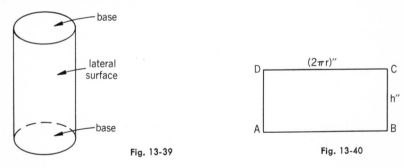

base

lateral
surface

base

Fig. 13-39   **Fig. 13-40**

It is easy to see from this picture that the area of the lateral surface is equal to $2\pi rh$ (why?). Since the area of the two bases is equal to $2\pi r^2$ (why?), the total surface area of a cylinder is given by the formula

$$2\pi rh + 2\pi r^2 \qquad \text{or} \qquad 2\pi r(h + r).$$

What are r and h in this formula?

To find the volume of a cylinder, we multiply the area of the base by the height:

$$V = \pi r^2 h.$$

Problem Set 7

1. In each pair, the first number gives the length of a radius of a base of a cylinder and the second number gives the height of the cylinder. Compute the lateral area for each cylinder. Leave the answers in terms of π.

   (a) 3 in., 7 in.   (b) 5 in., 1 ft.   (c) 2 ft., 8 in.

2. Compute the entire area for each cylinder in Problem 1. Leave the answers in terms of π.
3. Find the volumes of cylinders in Problem 2. Leave the answers in terms of π.
4. A cylindrical water tank has the following dimensions: radius of a base, 2 ft.; height, 8 ft. Compute the approximate weight of the water if the tank is half filled. Use $\pi \doteq 3.14$. (*Hint:* one cubic foot of water weighs 62.5 lb.)

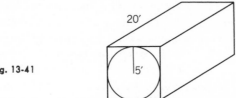

Fig. 13-41

5. In Figure 13-41, a cylinder fits exactly into the rectangular solid. The length of a radius of a base of the cylinder is 5 ft.; the height of the cylinder measures 20 ft. Compute the volumes of the cylinder and rectangular solid. By how many cubic feet does the volume of the rectangular solid exceed the volume of the cylinder? (Give the answer to one decimal place.)
6. A radius of the base of a cylindrical tank measures 12 ft. Its height is 25 ft. What is the weight of gasoline filling the tank, if a cubic foot of gasoline weighs 44.2 lb.?

9. SURFACE AREAS AND VOLUMES OF PYRAMIDS

Figure 13-42 shows a pyramid. The base of this pyramid is a square and the four triangular faces are congruent triangles. It is, therefore, a **regular pyramid.**

Fig. 13-42

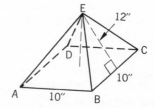

It is easy to find the total surface area of this pyramid. We need to compute the area of the base and add it to four times the area of one of the triangles.

Here are the computations for the area of the pyramid shown in Figure 13-42.

$$10^2 + 4 \times (\tfrac{1}{2} \times 10 \times 12) = 100 + 4 \times 60 = 100 + 240 = 340 \text{ in.}^2.$$

Did you follow these computations? What is the meaning of 10^2? Of $\tfrac{1}{2} \times 10 \times 12$? Of $4 \times (\tfrac{1}{2} \times 10 \times 12)$?

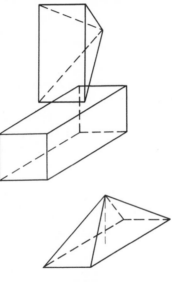

Fig. 13-43

In order to understand the volume of a pyramid, perform the following experiment. Out of cardboard make a rectangular solid like the one shown in Figure 13-43. Choose your own dimensions. Leave an opening at the top. Then make a model of a pyramid having a base of the same size as that of the rectangular solid and an altitude of the same measure. Remove the base of the pyramid in order to be able to fill it up with sand. Now fill the model of the pyramid with sand and empty it into the rectangular solid. Repeat the process. How many pyramids full of sand does the rectangular solid contain? Did you find it to be 3?

Since the volume of a rectangular solid is given by bh (b = area of base; h = measure of altitude), the experiment leads us to the conclusion that the volume of a pyramid is given by

$$\tfrac{1}{3}bh.$$

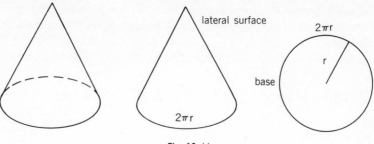

Fig. 13-44

10. VOLUMES OF CONES

Figure 13-44 shows a cone. Its lateral surface is part of a circle together with its interior, and the base is a circle with its interior.

As in the case of a cylinder, the cone is a part of a more general object generated by a line. To imagine this object, consider the line l rotating as shown in Figure 13-45. The resulting set of points is a surface; this *surface* is a more "general" **cone.**

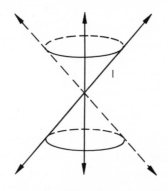

Fig. 13-45

Recall our agreement that, whenever we said "area of a rectangle," we meant "area of the interior of the rectangle." We shall make the same agreement about volume here. Whenever we say "volume of a cone," we shall mean "volume of the interior enclosed by the cone."

To find out how the volumes of a cylinder and a cone with bases and altitudes of the same length compare, we need models. If your instructor has such models, you may want to experiment to see how many times the contents of the cone will fit into the cylinder.

Volume of cylinder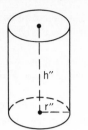

3 X (volume of cone)

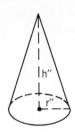 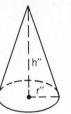 

Fig. 13-46

You will find the volume of a cylinder is three times that of a cone having the same size base and altitude, as is apparent from Figure 13-46.

Volume of cylinder   3 × (Volume of cone)

$$\text{Volume of cylinder} = \pi r^2 h$$
$$\text{Volume of cone} = \tfrac{1}{3}\pi r^2 h$$

Problem Set 8

1. Compute the total area and volume of a pyramid whose base is a square with a side 7 in. long and whose altitude is 34 in. (*Hint:* To find the length of the altitude of a triangular face, observe that $\triangle ABC$ is a right triangle.)

2. A pyramid has for its base a square with a side of 15 in. The altitude of the pyramid is 12 in. long. What is the volume of the pyramid? (See Figure 13-47.)

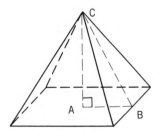

Fig. 13-47

3. Compute the volumes of cones with given length of a radius of the base (first number) and the altitude (second number). Leave answers in terms of π.

(a) 2 in., 5 in.   (d) 2 in., 10 in.   (g) 6 in., 10 in.
(b) 4 in., 5 in.   (e) 2 in., 15 in.   (h) 6 in., 15 in.
(c) 6 in., 5 in.   (f) 4 in., 10 in.   (i) 4 in., 15 in.

4. On the basis of your answers to Problem 3, answer the following questions:

(a) Two cones have bases with radii of the same length. The height of cone A is twice the height of cone B. How do the volumes of cones A and B compare?

(b) Two cones have bases with radii of the same length. The height of cone A is three times the height of cone B. How do the volumes of cones A and B compare?

(c) Two cones have bases with radii of the same length. The height of cone A is n times the height of cone B. How do the volumes of cones A and B compare?

(d) Two cones have the same height. The radius of the base of cone A is twice as long as the radius of the base of cone B. How do the volumes of cones A and B compare?

(e) Two cones have the same height. The radius of the base of cone A is three times as long as a radius of the base of cone B. How do the volumes of cones A and B compare?

(f) Two cones have the same height. The radius of the base of cone A is n times as long as a radius of the base of cone B. How do the volumes of cones A and B compare?

(g) The height and radius of cone A are each twice the height and radius of cone B. How do the volumes of cones A and B compare?

(h) The height and radius of cone A are each three times the height and radius of cone B. How do the volumes of cones A and B compare?

(i) The height and radius of cone A are each n times the height and radius of cone B. How do the volumes of cones A and B compare?

(j) The height of cone A is n times the height of cone B. The radius of cone A is n times the radius of cone B. How do the volumes of cones A and B compare?

Bibliography

Botts, Truman, "Linear Measurement and Imagination," *The Arithmetic Teacher* (November 1962), pp. 376–382.

Brumfiel, Charles F., Robert E. Eicholz, Merrill E. Shanks, and P. G. O'Daffer, *Principles of Arithmetic*. Reading, Mass.: Addison-Wesley Publishing Company, Inc., 1963, pp. 297–329.

Coxford, Arthur F., Jr., "Piaget: Number and Measurement," *The Arithmetic Teacher*, (November 1963), pp. 419–427.

Crouch, Ralph, and George Baldwin, *Mathematics for Elementary Teachers*. New York: John Wiley & Sons, Inc., 1964, pp. 243–314.

Dutton, Wilbur H., *Evaluating Pupils' Understanding of Arithmetic*. Englewood Cliffs, N.J.: Prentice-Hall, Inc., 1964, pp. 150–176, 334–353.

Goldmark, Bernice, "Geometry in the Primary Grades," *The Arithmetic Teacher* (April 1963), pp. 191–192.

Lamb, Pose M., "Geometry for Third and Fourth Graders," *The Arithmetic Teacher* (April 1963), pp. 163–194.

Lopshits, A. M., *Computation of Areas of Oriented Figures*. Boston: D. C. Heath and Company, 1963.

Nichols, Eugene D., *Pre-Algebra Mathematics*. New York: Holt, Rinehart and Winston, Inc., 1965, Chap. 11.

Piaget, Jean, Barbel Inhelder, and Alina Szeminska, *The Child's Conception of Geometry*. London: Routledge and K. Paul, 1960.

Ransom, William R., *Geometry Growing*. Washington, D.C.: National Council of Teachers of Mathematics, 1961.

School Mathematics Study Group, *A Brief Course in Mathematics for Elementary School Teachers, Studies in Mathematics, Vol. IX*. Stanford, Calif.: Leland Stanford Junior University, 1963, pp. 169–201, 355–388.

———, *Intuitive Geometry*. Stanford, Calif.: Leland Stanford Junior University, 1961, Chaps. 2, 5, 7.

———, *Mathematical Methods in Science, Studies in Mathematics, Vol. XI*. Stanford, Calif.: Leland Stanford Junior University, 1963, pp. 1–42, 210–242.

———, *Mathematics Through Science, Part I: Measurement and Graphing*. Stanford, Calif.: Leland Stanford Junior University, 1963, pp. 1–71.

Titchmarsh, E. C., *Mathematics for the General Reader*. New York: Doubleday & Co., Inc., 1959, pp. 59–74.

Youden, W. J., *Experimentation and Measurement*. New York: Scholastic Book Services, 1962.

14

COORDINATE
GEOMETRY

1. FIVE-BY-FIVE ARRAY OF POINTS

In Chapter 12 we considered geometric objects as sets of points and studied various properties of some of the more significant geometric objects. In Chapter 13 we considered sizes of geometric objects and learned to compute lengths, areas, and volumes of various objects. Now we shall see how arithmetic and elementary algebra can be used to study some types of geometric objects.

We begin by considering an array of 25 points arranged in 5 rows and 5 columns, as shown in Figure 14-1. The point marked △ is in the fourth column and in the second row. To describe it briefly we shall use the pair of numbers (4,2). The point marked ⊙ is in the third column and in the fourth row, and is described by the pair (3,4).

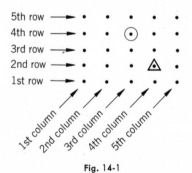

Fig. 14-1

In Figure 14-2 the point corresponding to (4,2) is marked △ and the point corresponding to (2,4) is marked ⊙. Notice that, although (4,2) and (2,4) contain the same numbers, they refer to *two different points*. What makes the difference is the order of listing the numbers in each pair: (2,4)

306 /

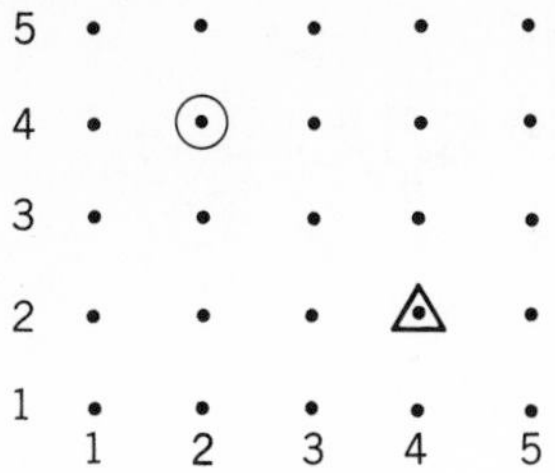

Fig. 14-2

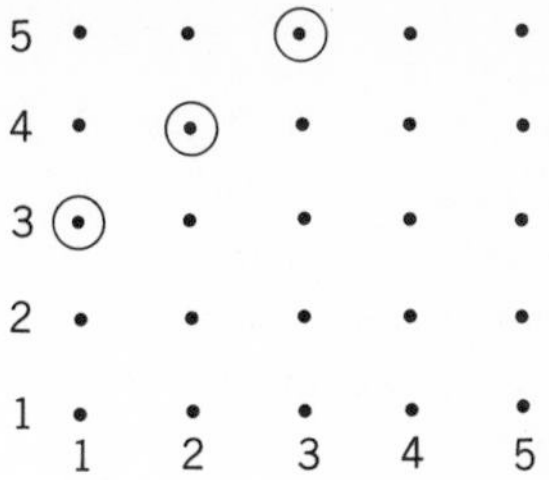

Fig. 14-3

is not the same as (4,2). We call such pairs of numbers **ordered pairs of numbers.** Each ordered pair has a **first member** and a **second member.** In the ordered number pair (2,4), for example, 2 is the first member and 4 is the second member.

We shall illustrate how to locate points, on a 5-by-5 array of points, that meet certain specified conditions. In each example the conditions are specified for that particular set of points. The points belonging to the specified set of points are marked ⊙ in each case.

Example 1 The second member is 2 more than the first member (Figure 14-3). All such ordered pairs are (1,3), (2,4), and (3,5).

Example 2 The first member is 4. We shall agree that, if the *second* member is not mentioned, then it can be each of the numbers 1 through 5. (If the *first* member were not mentioned, then it could be each of the numbers.) All such ordered pairs in which the first member is 4 are (4,1), (4,2), (4,3), (4,4), and (4,5) (Figure 14-4).

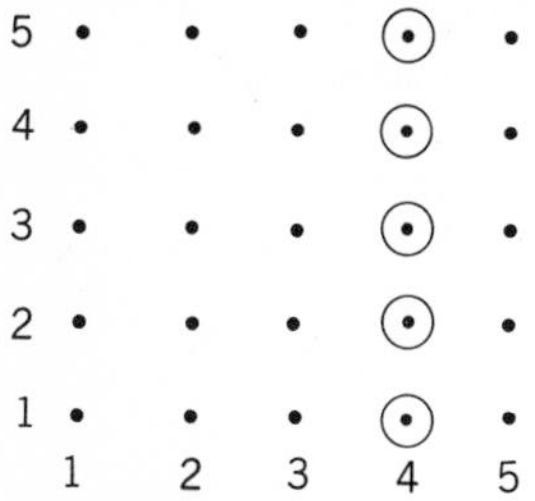

Fig. 14-4

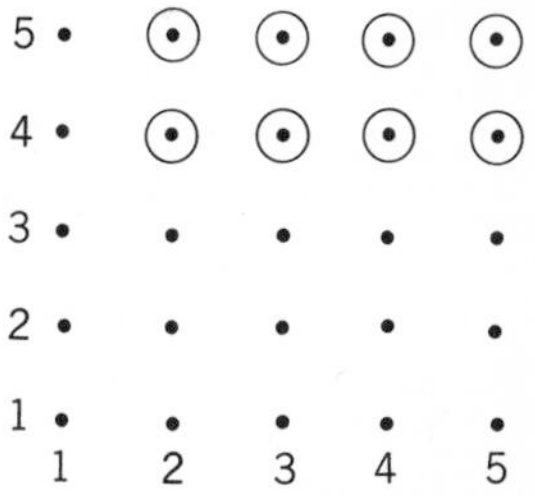

Fig. 14-5

Example 3 The first member is greater than or equal to 2 and the second member is greater than or equal to 4 (Figure 14-5). All such ordered pairs are (2,4), (2,5), (3,4), (3,5), (4,4), (4,5) (5,4), and (5,5).

Example 4 The first member is less than 3. (Since the second member is not mentioned, it can be each of the numbers 1 through 5.) All such ordered

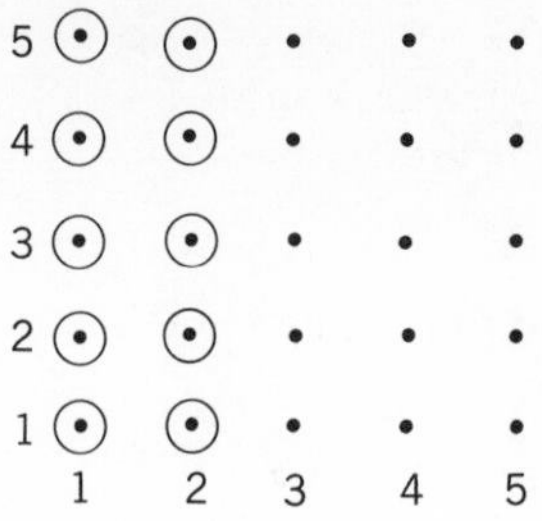

Fig. 14-6

pairs are (2,1), (2,2), (2,3), (2,4), (2,5), (1,1), (1,2), (1,3), (1,4), and (1,5) (Figure 14-6).

Problem Set 1

1. Explain why (1,5) and (5,1) are two different ordered number pairs.
2. Explain why (1 + 2,4) and (3,3 + 1) are the same ordered number pair.
3. On 5-by-5 arrays mark, like this ⊙, all points corresponding to the ordered number pairs meeting the given conditions. First list all ordered pairs meeting these conditions. In cases where there are no such points, state that it is the empty set.

 (a) The first member is the same as the second member.
 (b) The first member is twice the second member.
 (c) The second member is twice the first member.
 (d) The first member is three times the second member.
 (e) The second member is three times the first member.
 (f) The first member is one less than the second member.
 (g) The first member is one more than the second member.
 (h) The second member is three more than the first member.
 (i) The second member is four less than the first member.
 (j) The first member is five less than the second member.
 (k) The first member is 2. (Recall that, if one of the two members is not mentioned, it can be each of the numbers 1 through 5.)
 (l) The second member is 2.
 (m) The first member is 5.
 (n) The first member is 6.
 (o) The second member is 5.
 (p) The first member is greater than or equal to 3, and the second member is greater than or equal to 3.
 (q) The first member is less than 6, and the second member is less than 6.
 (r) The first member is less than 2; the second member is less than 2.
 (s) The first member is greater than or equal to 5, and the second member is greater than or equal to 5.
 (t) The first member is greater than 5.
 (u) The second member is greater than 5.
 (v) The first member is less than or equal to 1.

(w) The second member is less than or equal to 1.

(x) The first member is greater than 4.

(y) The second member is greater than 4.

2. SQUARE AND RECTANGULAR ARRAYS

An array of points like the 5-by-5 array is called a **finite lattice of points.** A finite lattice can have any finite number of rows and any finite number of columns.

If the number of columns and rows is the same, the lattice is a **square lattice.** If the number of rows is different from the number of columns, the lattice is a **rectangular lattice.** For example, a 5-by-5 lattice has the same number of rows as it does columns; therefore it is a square lattice. A 3-by-7 lattice has 3 rows and 7 columns and is a rectangular lattice. In general, an x-by-y lattice has x rows and y columns. If $x = y$, then an x-by-y lattice is a square lattice. If $x \neq y$, then an x-by-y lattice is a rectangular lattice.

Instead of writing "x-by-y lattice," we shall write "x x y lattice." Thus, "10 x 10 lattice" means "10 by 10 lattice."

We shall illustrate how to locate points on a 10 x 10 lattice. To facilitate the descriptions of conditions upon the first and second members of the ordered number pairs, we shall use (x,y) to mean an ordered pair in which the first member is x and the second member is y. The points belonging to the desired sets are marked $\odot$.

Example 1 $x < 3$ and $y > 8$; all ordered pairs that meet these conditions are (1,9), (1,10), (2,9), (2,10). Do you see that, for each of the four points marked on the lattice in Figure 14-7, the first member (x) is less than 3 and the second member (y) is greater than 8?

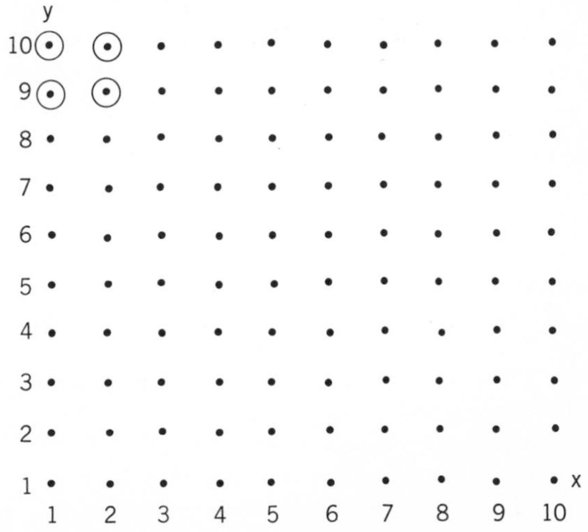

Fig. 14-7

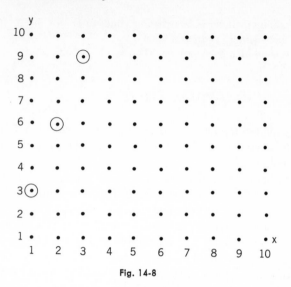

Fig. 14-8

Example 2 $3x = y$; all ordered pairs meeting the given conditions are (1,3), (2,6), (3,9). Do you see that, for each ordered pair in Figure 14-8, the second member (y) is three times the first member (x)?

Fig. 14-9

Notice that each point in a lattice has an ordered pair of numbers corresponding to it. These numbers are called **coordinates of points.** Point A in the lattice in Figure 14-9 corresponds to the ordered pair of numbers (3,2). The number 3 is the *first coordinate* of the point A, 2 is the *second coordinate* of point A. The *first* coordinate tells the *column,* and the *second* coordinate tells the *row.* For example, (1,3) refers to the first column and the third row.

Problem Set 2

1. Make a picture of a 10 x 10 lattice of points. On it mark the following points ⊙:

   (a) (1,4)   (d) (5,5)
   (b) (1,10)   (e) (7,4)
   (c) (10,1)   (f) (10,10)

2. For each point (x,y) mark all points ⊙ that meet the given conditions. Use a 10 x 10 lattice. First list all ordered pairs that meet the given conditions.

(a) $x < 4$ and $y < 2$

(b) $x < y$

(c) $x \leq 3$ and $y \leq 1$

(d) $x \geq y$

(e) $x = y$

(f) $x > y$

(g) $2x = y$

(h) $x \leq 2$

(i) $2y = x$

(j) $y < 3$

(k) $x \leq y$

(l) $4x = y$

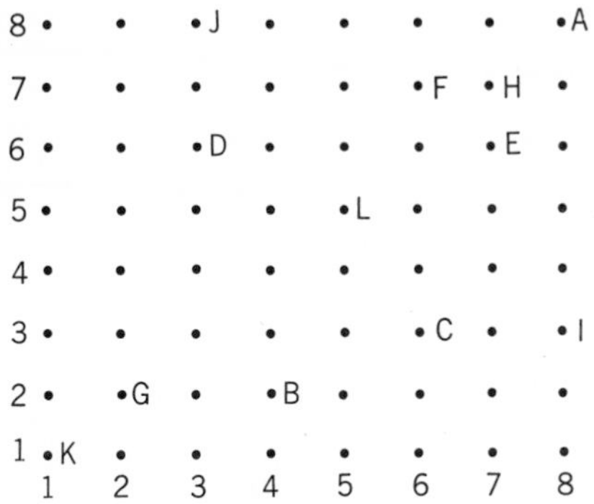

```
8 •    •   •J   •    •    •    •   •A

7 •    •    •   •    •   •F  •H   •

6 •    •   •D   •    •    •   •E   •

5 •    •    •   •   •L   •    •    •

4 •    •    •   •    •    •    •    •

3 •    •    •   •    •   •C   •   •I

2 •   •G   •  •B    •    •    •    •

1 •K   •    •   •    •    •    •    •
   1    2    3   4    5    6    7    8
```

Fig. 14-10

3. (a) For each point named by a letter in the lattice in Figure 14-10, give the ordered number pair corresponding to it. For point A, the answer is $A(8,8)$.
   (b) What is true of the first coordinate of points that are in the same column?
   (c) What is true of the second coordinate of points that are in the same row?
   (d) What is true of the coordinates of points that are in the diagonal from K to A?

4. On 10 x 10 lattices mark the following sets of points. The first coordinate is x, and y is the second coordinate. If y is not mentioned, then y can be any number. Of course, in this case, it is any number from 1 through 10.

(a) $\{(x,y)|x = y\}$ [read: the set of ordered pairs (x,y) such that x is equal to y.]
(b) $\{(x,y)|x \leq y\}$
(c) $\{(x,y)|x \geq y\}$
(d) $\{(x,y)|x < y\}$
(e) $\{(x,y)|x > y\}$
(f) $\{(x,y)|x = 2\}$
(g) $\{(x,y)|y = 10\}$
(h) $\{(x,y)|1 \leq x \leq 3$ and $1 \leq y \leq 3\}$
(i) $\{(x,y)|x \leq 5$ and $y \leq 5\}$
(j) $\{(x,y)|1 < x < 3$ and $y > 6\}$

3. GRAPHS OF SETS

The set of points corresponding to a given sentence is called a **graph** of this sentence. A graph of an ordered pair of numbers is a point. For example, the graph of $(3,2)$ on a 3 x 3 lattice is point A in Figure 14-11.

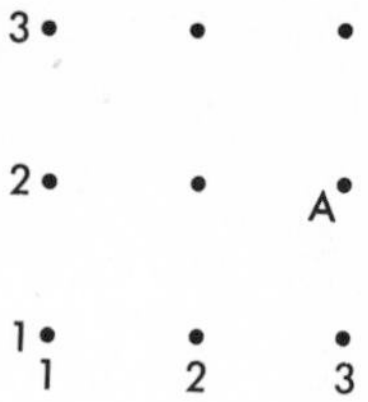

```
3 •       •       •

2 •       •      A•

Fig. 14-11

1•       •       •
 1        2        3
```

The graph of $\{(x,y)|3x = y\}$ on a 10 x 10 lattice is the set of three points marked in Figure 14-12.

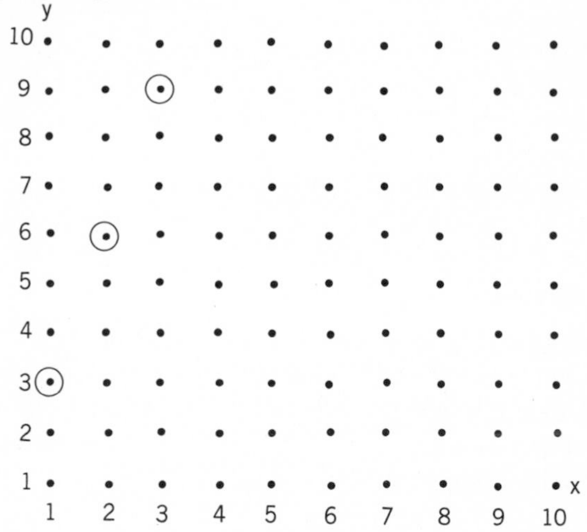

```
 y
10 •   •   •   •   •   •   •   •   •   •

 9 •   •  (•)  •   •   •   •   •   •   •

 8 •   •   •   •   •   •   •   •   •   •

 7 •   •   •   •   •   •   •   •   •   •

 6 •  (•)  •   •   •   •   •   •   •   •

 5 •   •   •   •   •   •   •   •   •   •

 4 •   •   •   •   •   •   •   •   •   •

 3(•)  •   •   •   •   •   •   •   •   •

 2 •   •   •   •   •   •   •   •   •   •

 1 •   •   •   •   •   •   •   •   •   • x
   1   2   3   4   5   6   7   8   9   10
```

Fig. 14-12

By now you probably noticed that, in any lattice, exactly one point corresponds to each ordered pair of numbers chosen from the given universal set. Also to each point there corresponds exactly one ordered pair of numbers.

Definition   There is a one-to-one correspondence between ordered pairs of numbers (x,y) and the points on the x x y lattice.

To learn how to make somewhat more complicated graphs, study the following examples.

Example 1 Graph $\{(x,y)|1 \leq x \leq 3 \text{ and } 7 \leq y \leq 10\}$ on a 10 x 10 lattice.

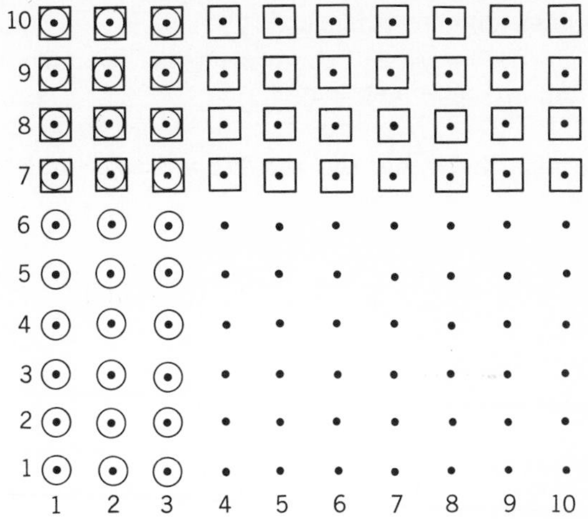

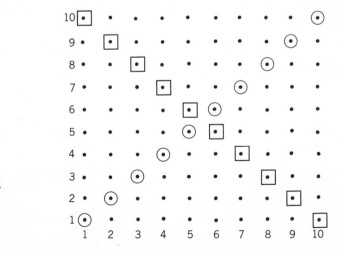

Fig. 14-13

In locating the points in the set $\{(x,y)|\ 1 \le x \le 3$ and $7 \le y \le 10\}$, we first locate the set $\{(x,y)|1 \le x \le 3\}$. The points of this set are marked ⊙ on the lattice (see Figure 14-13). Then we locate the set $\{(x,y)|7 \le y \le 10\}$. The points of this set are marked ▣.

Since we want the set $\{(x,y)|1 \le x \le 3$ *and* $7 \le y \le 10\}$, we are after the points that are in *both* sets. That is, we want the **intersection** of the two sets. This is the set of points marked ◎. How many points are there in the set $\{(x,y)|1 \le x \le 3$ and $7 \le y \le 10\}$?

Example 2 On a 10 x 10 lattice, make a graph of the set $\{(x,y)|x = y$ and $x + y = 11\}$.

First, we graph the set $\{(x,y)|x = y\}$. The points belonging to this set are marked ⊙ (see Figure 14-14). Then we graph the set $\{(x,y)|x + y = 11\}$. These points are marked ▣. We want the intersection of the two

Fig. 14-14

sets. Since no point is marked $\boxdot$, there are no points that belong to both sets. The intersection of the two sets is the empty set. Therefore, $\{(x,y)|x = y$ and $x + y = 11\} = \emptyset$.

Example 3 Graph the set $\{(x,y)|x = 2$ and $y = 10\}$ on a 10×10 lattice.

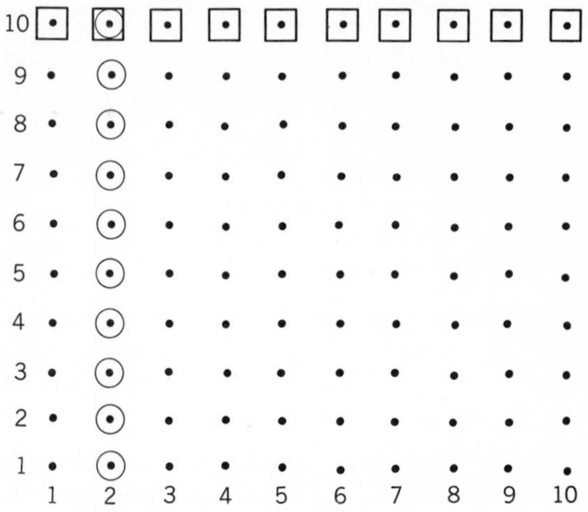

Fig. 14-15

The points belonging to the set $\{(x,y)|x = 2\}$ are marked $\odot$ (see Figure 14-15). Note that, since no restriction is made on y in this set, y may assume all values, 1 through 10. The points that belong to the set $\{(x,y)|y = 10\}$ are marked $\boxdot$. We see that $x = 2$ *and* $y = 10$ means the intersection of the two sets. There is one point that belongs to both sets, namely, the point corresponding to (2,10). Therefore,

$$\{(x,y)|x = y \text{ and } x + y = 11\} = \{(2,10)\}.$$

To graph sets described by inequalities, it is helpful to list ordered number pairs that belong to the set. This is shown in the next example.

Example 4 Graph on a 10×10 lattice $\{(x,y)|x + y \le 7\}$.

We are looking for ordered number pairs in which the sum of both coordinates is at most 7. Let us list these pairs: (1,6), (1,5), (1,4), (1,3), (1,2), (1,1), (2,5), (2,4), (2,3), (2,2), (2,1), (3,4), (3,3), (3,2), (3,1), (4,3), (4,2), (4,1), (5,2), (5,1), (6,1). Points that belong to the set $\{(x,y)|x + y \le 7\}$ are marked $\odot$ on the lattice (see Figure 14-6).

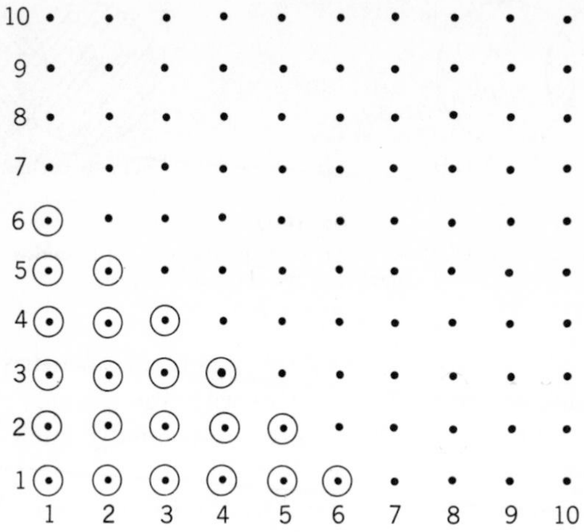

Fig. 14-16

Problem Set 3

On 10 x 10 lattices, mark the two sets separately, then locate the intersection of the two sets. Then list the number pairs that belong to the intersection.

1. $\{(x,y)|9 \leq x \leq 10 \text{ and } 1 \leq y \leq 2\}$
2. $\{(x,y)|4 < x < 5 \text{ and } 4 < y < 5\}$
3. $\{(x,y)|1 < x \leq 2 \text{ and } 1 \leq y < 5\}$
4. $\{(x,y)|1 \leq x \leq 5 \text{ and } 2 < y < 3\}$
5. $\{(x,y)|1 \leq x \leq 10 \text{ and } 1 \leq y \leq 10\}$
6. $\{(x,y)|x = y \text{ and } y = 3\}$
7. $\{(x,y)|x = y \text{ and } x = 10\}$
8. $\{(x,y)|x + y = 11 \text{ and } x = 1\}$
9. $\{(x,y)|x + y = 11 \text{ and } y = 3\}$
10. $\{(x,y)|x + y = 4 \text{ and } x = y\}$
11. $\{(x,y)|x + y = 12 \text{ and } x = y\}$
12. $\{(x,y)|x + y = 7 \text{ and } x = y\}$
13. $\{(x,y)|x = 5 \text{ and } y = 5\}$
14. $\{(x,y)|x - y = 6 \text{ and } x + y = 6\}$
15. $\{(x,y)|x - y = 8 \text{ and } x + y = 2\}$

4. INTERSECTION AND UNION OF SETS

To illustrate graphically the idea of the two binary operations on sets, that is, intersection and union, we present Figure 14-17. Such diagrams are called **Venn diagrams** in recognition of the contributions to set theory

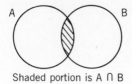

Shaded portion is A ∩ B

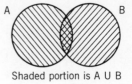

Shaded portion is A ∪ B

Fig. 14-17

Set A consists of the points in the interior of the circle on the left. Set B consists of the points in the interior of the circle B

of John Venn, a British logician of the nineteenth century. The first to introduce the idea of using circles in this way was the eighteenth-century Swiss mathematician Euler. Therefore, occasionally such diagrams are also called Euler circles.

In Example 4 of Section 3 we graphed the solution set of $\{(x,y)|x + y \leq 7\}$. This graph is reproduced in Figure 14-18. On the same lattice we mark the points belonging to the graph of $\{(x,y)|x \leq 3\}$ as $\boxed{\cdot}$.

Fig. 14-18

Some points belong to both graphs. These are marked $\boxed{\odot}$ and are members of the two sets. They belong to the graph of $\{(x,y)|x + y \leq 7$ *and* $x \leq 3\}$ which is the same as $\{(x,y)|x + y \leq 7\} \cap \{(x,y)|x \leq 3\}$.

The coordinates of points belonging to the intersection of the two sets meet both conditions:

1. The sum of the two coordinates is at most 7, that is, $x + y \leq 7$.
2. The first coordinate is at most 3, that is, $x \leq 3$.

What is the union of the two sets, or

$$\{(x,y)|x + y \leq 7\} \cup \{(x,y)|x \leq 3\};$$

which is the same as

$$\{(x,y)|x + y \leq 7 \text{ or } x \leq 3\}?$$

The graph of the union consists of all marked points—⊙, ▣, and ◎. The coordinates of each marked point satisfy at least one of the two conditions.

Problem Set 4

1. In each problem, two sets are given. Do the following:

   (i) Make a 10 x 10 lattice for each problem.
   (ii) Mark the points that belong to each set.
   (iii) Tell which points belong to the intersection of the two sets.
   (iv) Tell which points belong to the union of the two sets.

   (a) $\{(x,y)|x + y \leq 5\}; \{(x,y)|x < 3\}$
   (b) $\{(x,y)|x + y > 7\}; \{(x,y)|y > 4\}$
   (c) $\{(x,y)|2x > 7\}; \{(x,y)|x \leq 2y\}$
   (d) $\{(x,y)|x - y > 4\}; \{(x,y)|x + y \leq 4\}$
   (e) $\{(x,y)|x + 3 > y\}; \{(x,y)|2y \leq 5\}$
   (f) $\{(x,y)|2x \geq 3y\}; \{(x,y)|x \leq y\}$
   (g) $\{(x,y)|x \leq 4\}; \{(x,y)|y \geq 7\}$
   (h) $\{(x,y)|x \geq 10\}; \{(x,y)|y \geq 10\}$
   (i) $\{(x,y)|x + y \leq 2\}; \{(x,y)|x + y \leq 3\}$
   (j) $\{(x,y)|x + y \leq 20\}; \{(x,y)|x + y > 20\}$

2. Each of the following sets of ordered pairs of numbers is described by conditions imposed on the members of the pairs. First describe each set, as in Problem 1. Then graph the sets on 10 x 10 lattices.

   (a) The first member is twice the second member.
   (b) The first member is equal to the second member.
   (c) The second member is five times the first member.
   (d) The second member is one-half the first member.
   (e) The second member is six more than the first member.
   (f) The first member is four less than the second member.
   (g) Three subtracted from the first member equals the second member.
   (h) Three multiplied by the second member equals twice the first member.
   (i) The first member is greater than three times the second member.
   (j) Five added to the first member equals six added to the second member.

5. NEGATIVE AND POSITIVE COORDINATES OF POINTS, QUADRANTS, AND AXES

We shall make a different lattice of points now. Note how the rows and columns are numbered in the lattice in Figure 14-19. We locate points

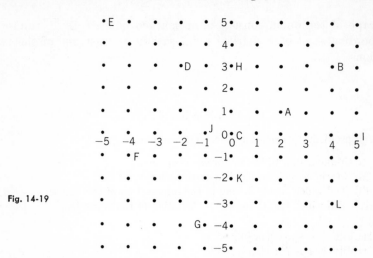

Fig. 14-19

in this lattice the same way as we did on the 10 x 10 lattice before. Check the points listed below to see whether you agree that their coordinates are given correctly in Figure 14-19. Coordinates for one point are stated incorrectly. Find it!

$A(2,1)$, $B(4,3)$, $C(0,0)$, $D(-2,3)$, $E(-5,5)$, $F(-4,-1)$, $G(-1,-4)$,
$H(0,3)$, $I(5,0)$, $J(-1,0)$, $K(0,-2)$, $L(-3,4)$.

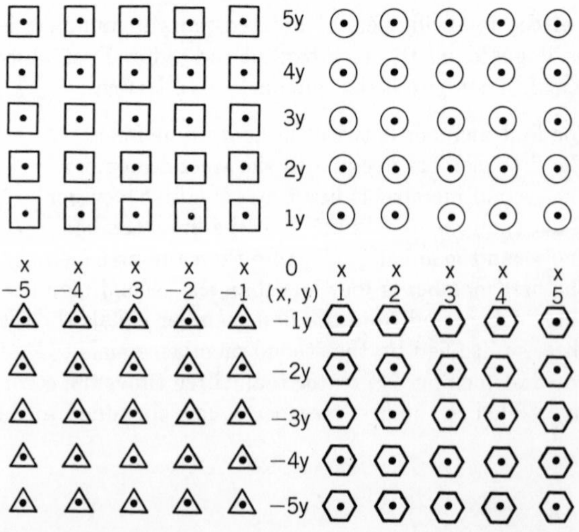

Fig. 14-20

There are six clearly distinguishable subsets of the lattice shown in Figure 14-19. To indicate these subsets in an easily identifiable way, we mark the points in each subset in a different way (see Figure 14-20).

To understand fully which points belong to each of the six subsets, study Figure 14-20 as you answer each of the following questions.

1. Each point in the *first quadrant* is marked $\odot$. If "Q_1" means "first quadrant," then for (x,y), which belongs to Q_1, which of the following is true?

(a) $x > 0$ and $y > 0$ (b) $x > 0$ and $y < 0$
(c) $x < 0$ and $y > 0$ (d) $x = 0$ and $y \neq 0$
(e) $x < 0$ and $y < 0$ (f) $x \neq 0$ and $y = 0$

2. Each point in the *second quadrant* is marked $\boxed{\cdot}$. If "Q_2" means "second quadrant," then for each (x,y), which belongs to Q_2, which of the following is true?

(a) $x > 0$ and $y > 0$ (b) $x > 0$ and $y < 0$
(c) $x < 0$ and $y > 0$ (d) $x = 0$ and $y \neq 0$
(e) $x < 0$ and $y < 0$ (f) $x \neq 0$ and $y = 0$

3. Each point in the *third quadrant* is marked $\triangle$. If "Q_3" means "third quadrant," then for each (x,y), which belongs to Q_3, which of the following is true?

(a) $x > 0$ and $y > 0$ (b) $x < 0$ and $y > 0$
(c) $x < 0$ and $y < 0$ (d) $x = 0$ and $y \neq 0$
(e) $x > 0$ and $y < 0$ (f) $x \neq 0$ and $y = 0$

4. Each point in the *fourth quadrant* is marked $\langle \cdot \rangle$. If "Q_4" means "fourth quadrant," then for each (x,y), which belongs to Q_4, which of the following is true?

(a) $x > 0$ and $y > 0$ (b) $x > 0$ and $y < 0$
(c) $x < 0$ and $y > 0$ (d) $x = 0$ and $y \neq 0$
(e) $x < 0$ and $y < 0$ (f) $x \neq 0$ and $y = 0$

5. Each point that belongs to the *x axis* is marked x. For each (x,y), which belongs to the x axis, which of the following is true?

(a) $x > 0$ and $y > 0$ (b) $x > 0$ and $y < 0$
(c) $x < 0$ and $y > 0$ (d) $x = 0$
(e) $x < 0$ and $y < 0$ (f) $y = 0$

6. Each point that belongs to the *y axis* is marked y. For each (x,y), which belongs to the y axis, which of the following is true?

(a) $x > 0$ and $y > 0$ (b) $x > 0$ and $y > 0$
(c) $x < 0$ and $y > 0$ (d) $x = 0$
(e) $x < 0$ and $y < 0$ (f) $y = 0$

Thus we have identified six subsets of the lattice shown in Figure 14-20. They are the first quadrant, second quadrant, third quadrant, fourth quadrant, x axis and y axis.

Problem Set 5

1. Tell why the intersection of any pair of the six subsets we identified except one is the empty set. Identify the pair of subsets for which the intersection is not the empty set.
2. On your paper, make a lattice like in Figure 14-19. Locate the following points on it. Label the points using the suggested capital letters.

   (a) $A(1,3)$, $B(4,1)$, $C(5,5)$, $D(2,5)$
   (b) $E(-1,5)$, $F(-4,1)$, $G(-5,2)$, $H(-1,1)$
   (c) $I(-2,-5)$, $J(-1,-2)$, $K(-4,-4)$, $L(-5,-2)$
   (d) $M(4,-5)$, $N(5,-3)$, $O(1,-1)$, $P(3,-3)$
   (e) $Q(0,4)$, $P(0,-4)$, $R(0,1)$, $S(0,-1)$
   (f) $T(4,0)$, $U(-2,0)$, $V(5,0)$, $W(0,0)$

3. Imagine that our lattice of points extends indefinitely in all directions. Tell where the point for each pair of coordinates is found: first quadrant, second quadrant, third quadrant, fourth quadrant, x axis, or y axis.

(a) $(-25,-78)$	(b) $(298,0)$	(c) $(0,507)$
(d) $(126,-306)$	(e) $(-1005,-1)$	(f) $(-11,0)$
(g) $(-1125,3)$	(h) $(-99,256)$	(i) $(258,-1139)$
(j) $(0,-368)$	(k) $(706,-365)$	(l) $(2005,3678)$

6. INFINITE LATTICES

In the lattice of points in Figure 14-21 it is indicated that the number of points is unlimited; that is, the points continue on and on. The points in the graph of the set $\{(x,y)|-3 \leq x \leq 2\}$ are marked $\odot$. Remember, however, that it is impossible to mark all the points in this set. Infinitely many points above and below also belong to the graph.

The points in the graph of the set $\{(x,y)|y \leq -3\}$ are marked $\boxed{\cdot}$. Also in this case, infinitely more points to the right, left, and below belong to this set.

The points marked $\boxed{\odot}$ belong to the intersection of the two sets:

$$\{(x,y)|-3 \leq x \leq 2\} \cap \{(x,y)|y \leq -3\},$$

which is the same as

$$\{(x,y)|-3 \leq x \leq 2 \text{ and } y \leq -3\}.$$

Note that infinitely many more points below those marked $\boxed{\odot}$ belong to the intersection of the two sets. But no points above, to the right, and to the left of those marked $\boxed{\odot}$ belong to the intersection.

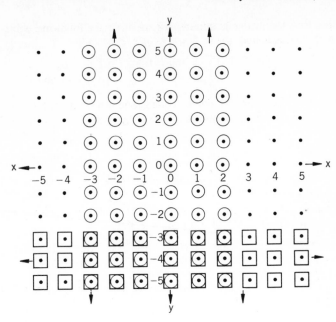

Fig. 14-21

Problem Set 6

1. For this problem use the graph in Figure 14-21.
   (a) Tell which of the following points belong and which do not belong to the graph of $\{(x,y)|-3 \leq x \leq 2\}$.

   (i) $(1,27)$ (ii) $(3,1)$ (iii) $(-4,-2)$
   (iv) $(-2,160)$ (v) $(-3,-298)$ (vi) $(-4,2)$

   (b) Tell which of the following points belong and which do not belong to the graph of $\{(x,y)|y \leq -3\}$.

   (i) $(-3,-17)$ (ii) $(-1,3)$ (iii) $(-100,-200)$
   (iv) $(167,-255)$ (v) $(5,-15)$ (vi) $(-5,-3)$

   (c) Tell which of the following points belong and which do not belong to the graph of $\{(x,y)|-3 \leq x \leq 2\} \cap \{(x,y)|y \leq -3\}$.

   (i) $(0,-215)$ (ii) $(3,-198)$ (iii) $(2,56)$
   (iv) $(-4,-200)$ (v) $(-3,-1000)$ (vi) $(-3,-3)$

2. Graph the sets $A = \{(x,y)|x \geq 3\}$ and $B = \{(x,y)|y < 0\}$ on an infinite lattice like that in Figure 14-19.
3. Assuming that the lattice of Problem 2 is infinite, tell which of the following points belong and which do not belong to the set $A = \{(x,y)|x \geq 3\}$.

   (a) $(1,25)$ (b) $(4,-250)$ (c) $(-3,-250)$
   (d) $(3,25)$ (e) $(3,178)$ (f) $(3,3)$

4. Assuming that the lattice is infinite, tell which of the following points belong and which do not belong to set $B = \{(x,y)|y < 0\}$.

(a) $(37,-2)$ (b) $(-189,-189)$ (c) $(0,0)$
(d) $(37,0)$ (e) $(0,-1)$ (f) $(-200,200)$

5. Tell which of the following points belong and which do not belong to the intersection of A and B, $\{(x,y)|x \geq 3\} \cap \{(x,y)|y < 0\}$.

(a) $(3,0)$ (b) $(157,-105)$ (c) $(0,0)$
(d) $(3,-1)$ (e) $(2,-1)$ (f) $(2.99,-1)$

6. On an infinite lattice, graph the sets $C = \{(x,y)|-5 < x \leq 1\}$ and $D = \{(x,y)|-2 < y \leq 0\}$.

7. Assuming an infinite lattice, tell which of the following points belong and which do not belong to $C = \{(x,y)|-5 < x \leq 1\}$.

(a) $(-4,265)$ (b) $(1,38)$ (c) $(-12,-13)$
(d) $(2,-3)$ (e) $(0,0)$ (f) $(-5,-5)$

8. Tell which of the following points belong and which do not belong to $D = \{(x,y)|-2 < y \leq 0\}$.

(a) $(12,0)$ (b) $(-6,-1)$ (c) $(-1265,-1)$
(d) $(-2,-2)$ (e) $(376,1)$ (f) $(-5,15)$

9. Tell which of the following points belong and which do not belong to $C \cap D = \{(x,y)|-5 < x \leq 1\} \cap \{(x,y)|-2 < y \leq 0\}$.

(a) $(1,0)$ (b) $(0,0)$ (c) $(-2,0)$
(d) $(-5,-1)$ (e) $(-12,-12)$ (f) $(1,-2)$

7. THE RECTANGULAR COORDINATE SYSTEM AND FOUR QUADRANTS

In making graphs on the lattices in Section 6, we considered only those points whose coordinates were integers, that is, positive and negative whole numbers and 0. We now consider pairs of points of real numbers and their graphs in the plane.

The grid like that in Figure 14-22 is called **rectangular coordinate system** or **Cartesian coordinate system**. "Cartesian" comes from the name of a French mathematician, Rene Descartes, the inventor of coordinate or analytic geometry.

There are ten points marked in Figure 14-22. Their names and coordinates are listed below. Identify each point in the figure.

$A(-2,-4\frac{1}{2})$, $B(\sqrt{2},5\frac{1}{3})$, $C(6.8,-8.9)$, $D(-8,3)$, $E(8.1,0)$,
     $F(0,-6\frac{1}{2})$, $G(-7.5,-7.5)$, $H(\sqrt{18},7.2)$, $I(9.5,0)$, $J(0,-\sqrt{17})$.

The rectangular coordinate system can be shown as in Figure 14-23. It consists of two lines perpendicular to each other. These lines divide

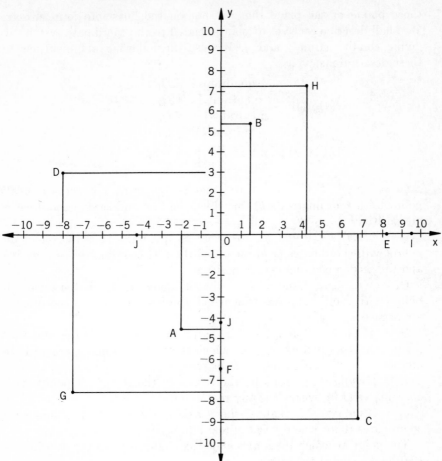

Fig. 14-22

Fig. 14-23

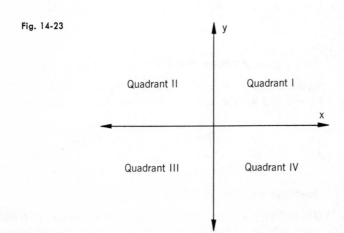

those points of the plane that are not on the lines into four subsets. We shall describe each set of points related to the coordinate system by giving conditions on x and y. We use the following abbreviations in these descriptions:

$$\text{quadrant I} = Q_1$$
$$\text{quadrant II} = Q_2$$
$$\text{quadrant III} = Q_3$$
$$\text{quadrant IV} = Q_4$$
$$x \text{ axis} = x_a$$
$$y \text{ axis} = y_a$$

$Q_1 = \{(x,y) | x > 0 \text{ and } y > 0\}$; that is, quadrant I is the set of all points with coordinates (x,y) for which the first and second coordinates are positive.

$Q_2 = \{(x,y) | x < 0 \text{ and } y > 0\}$; that is, quadrant II is the set of all points with coordinates (x,y) for which the first coordinates are negative and the second coordinates are positive.

$Q_3 = \{(x,y) | x < 0 \text{ and } y < 0\}$; that is, quadrant III is the set of all points with coordinates (x,y) for which the first and second coordinates are negative.

$Q_4 = \{(x,y) | x > 0 \text{ and } y < 0\}$; that is, quadrant IV is the set of all points with coordinates (x,y) for which the first coordinates are positive and the second coordinates are negative.

$x_a = \{(x,y) | y = 0\}$; that is, the x axis is the set of all points with coordinates $(x,0)$, where x is any real number.

$y_a = \{(x,y) | x = 0\}$; that is, the y axis is the set of all points with coordinates $(0,y)$, where y is any real number.

The point at which the x axis and y axis intersect has the coordinates $(0,0)$ and is called the **origin.**

You may have observed that every point of the plane is either in one of the four quadrants or on one of the two axes; the origin belongs to both axes.

Problem Set 7

1. On your paper, make a coordinate-system grid like the one in Figure 14-22. Plot points corresponding to the following ordered number pairs of real numbers.

(a) $A(-1,3)$ (d) $D(\sqrt{5}, -3.4)$ (g) $G(3\frac{1}{4}, 0)$
(b) $B(-.3, -8.4)$ (e) $E(8.5, 2.5)$ (h) $H(-1.6, -8.5)$
(c) $C(\frac{1}{2}, 9\frac{1}{2})$ (f) $F(0, -5\frac{1}{3})$ (i) $I(-\sqrt{26}, \sqrt{30})$

2. For each of the following give a simpler name.

Example $Q_1 \cap Q_2$; $Q_1 \cap Q_2 = \emptyset$, since the intersection of quadrant I and quadrant II is the empty set. Recall that the axes do not belong to any quadrants.

(a) $Q_2 \cap Q_3$

(b) $Q_3 \cap Q_4$

(c) $Q_1 \cap Q_4$

(d) $(Q_1 \cup Q_2) \cap (Q_3 \cup Q_4)$

(e) $(Q_1 \cup Q_4) \cap (Q_2 \cup Q_3)$

(f) $x_a \cap y_a$

(g) $x_a \cap (Q_1 \cup Q_2)$

(h) $y_a \cap (Q_1 \cup Q_4)$

(i) $x_a \cap (Q_1 \cup Q_4)$

(j) $y_a \cap (Q_1 \cup Q_2)$

3. Plot each pair of points given by the following coordinates on a coordinate system. Connect each pair of points with a line segment. (Save your picture for the study of symmetry, Section 8.)

(a) $(2,5)$; $(2,-5)$

(b) $(-4,3)$; $(-4,-3)$

(c) $(0,4\frac{1}{2})$; $(0,-4\frac{1}{2})$

(d) $(1,6\frac{1}{3})$; $(1,-6\frac{1}{3})$

(e) $(-7,1)$; $(-7,-1)$

(f) $(3,4)$; $(-3,4)$

(g) $(1,7)$; $(-1,7)$

(h) $(5,0)$; $(-5,0)$

(i) $(-2,-6\frac{1}{2})$; $(2,-6\frac{1}{2})$

(j) $(-1,-5)$; $(1,-5)$

8. SYMMETRY

The two objects pictured in Figure 14-24 are symmetric with respect to line k. Now examine your picture for Problem 3 in Problem Set 7.

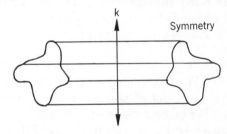

Fig. 14-24

Does the following statement describe correctly the positions of pairs of points in Problem 3, (a), (b), (c), (d), (e)? Each pair of points is symmetric with respect to the x axis.

To simplify writing, let us abbreviate the phrase "the point with coordinates (x,y)" to "the point (x,y)."

We can state that, $\forall_x \forall_y$ point (x,y) and point $(x,-y)$ are symmetric with respect to the x axis.

Is the following a correct statement concerning the pairs of points in Problem 3, (f), (g), (h), (i), (j)? Each pair of points is symmetric with respect to the y axis.

We can state that, $\forall_x \forall_y$ point (x,y) and point $(-x,y)$ are symmetric with respect to the y axis. Stated differently, $\forall_x \forall_y$ point $(-x,y)$ is a mirror reflection of point (x,y) through the y axis.

Now plot on a coordinate system each of the following pairs of points. Connect each pair with a segment.

(a) $(2,5)$; $(-2,-5)$

(b) $(-3,-6)$; $(3,6)$

(c) $(-4,5)$; $(4,-5)$

(d) $(2,-4)$; $(-2,4)$

(e) $(0,3)$; $(0,-3)$

(f) $(4,0)$; $(-4,0)$

Is each pair of the points shown symmetric with respect to the origin? Is the following a correct statement? $\forall_x \forall_y$ point (x,y) and point $(-x,-y)$ are symmetric with respect to the origin.

9. POINTS THAT MAKE UP LINES

We shall take a slightly different approach to the study of the topic of lines. You will be asked to make some pictures, answer questions, and draw your own conclusions. It is important that you follow each step.

1. (a) On a coordinate system, plot the following points:

   (i) $(-2,-7)$
   (ii) $(-2,3\frac{1}{2})$
   (iii) $(-2,0)$
   (iv) $(-2,-4\frac{1}{2})$
   (v) $(-2,8.3)$

(b) Draw a line through the points you plotted.

(c) Did you find that all these points are contained in the same line? Would this line contain all points whose first coordinate is -2, no matter what the second coordinate is?

(d) Did you find this line to be perpendicular to the x axis and parallel to the y axis? This line is a set of points described by $\{(x,y)|x = -2\}$.

(e) Would every set of points for which the first coordinate is some one real number be on a line perpendicular to the x axis?

2. (a) On a coordinate system plot the following points:

   (i) $(-4,3\frac{1}{2})$
   (ii) $(8,3\frac{1}{2})$
   (iii) $(0,3\frac{1}{2})$
   (iv) $(1,3\frac{1}{2})$
   (v) $(-1,3\frac{1}{2})$

(b) Draw a line through the points you plotted.

(c) Did you find this line to be perpendicular to the y axis and parallel to the x axis?

(d) Using braces, describe the set of points making up this line.

(e) Would every set of points for which the second coordinate is some one real number be on a line perpendicular to the y axis?

3. (a) On a coordinate system plot the following points:

   (i) $(2,2)$
   (ii) $(-3,-3)$
   (iii) $(7\frac{1}{2},7\frac{1}{2})$
   (iv) $(0,0)$
   (v) $(-4.6,-4.6)$

(b) Draw a line through the points you plotted.

(c) Does every point that belongs to this line have the same x and y coordinate?

(d) Is $\{(x,y)|x = y\}$ a correct description for this set of points?

4. (a) On a coordinate system plot the following points:

   (i) $(-3,0)$
   (ii) $(-1,0)$
   (iii) $(0,0)$
   (iv) $(5,0)$
   (v) $(6,0)$

(b) Is each of these points contained in the x axis?

(c) Is $\{(x,y)|y = 0\}$ a correct description of this set of points?

5. (a) On a coordinate system plot the following points:

   (i) $(0,4)$
   (ii) $(0,2\frac{1}{2})$
   (iii) $(0,0)$
   (iv) $(0,-1)$
   (v) $(0,-4)$

(b) Is each of these points contained in the y axis?

(c) Is $\{(x,y)|x = 0\}$ a correct description of this set of points?

6. (a) On a coordinate system, plot the following points:

   (i) $(2,1)$
   (ii) $(6,3)$
   (iii) $(-4,-2)$
   (iv) $(-7,-3\frac{1}{2})$
   (v) $(1,\frac{1}{2})$

(b) Will a line fit the points in Problem 6 (a)? Try to draw a line through all these points.

(c) Do you see that, for each of the points in (a), the x coordinate is twice the second coordinate? Using braces, describe the set of points that makes up this line.

7. (a) On a coordinate system plot the following points:

   (i) $(1,3)$
   (ii) $(2,6)$
   (iii) $(-1,-3)$
   (iv) $(\frac{1}{2},1\frac{1}{2})$
   (v) $(-1\frac{1}{2},-4\frac{1}{2})$

(b) Will one line fit these points? Try to draw one.

(c) What is the relation between the x and y coordinates of these points?

(d) Using braces, describe the set of points that makes up this line.

Problem Set 8

1. For each point below give the coordinates of three points: a point symmetric to the given point with respect to the x axis, y axis, and origin.

Example (2,3); x axis (2,−3)
$\quad\quad\quad\quad\quad\quad\;\; y$ axis (−2,3)
$\quad\quad\quad\quad\quad\quad\;\;$ origin (−2,−3)

(a) (1,4)   (b) $(-1\frac{1}{2}, -3\frac{1}{3})$ (c) (0,5)   (d) (0,−6)
(e) (−3,5)   (f) (4,−2.6)   (g) (−1,0)   (h) (0,0)

2. For each point in Problem 1, plot that point and the three related points on a coordinate system. Connect the given point with each of the three related points.

Example (2,3) (Figure 14-25.)

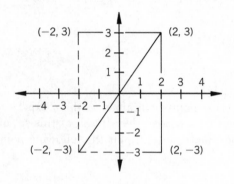

Fig. 14-25

3. In the upper rows in the following tables are listed the first coordinates of points, in the lower rows the second coordinates. In each case, discover the pattern and describe the set. An example is worked out for you.

Example

x	−4	−3	−2	−1	0	1	2	3	4
y	−7	−5	−3	−1	1	3	5	7	9

Pattern: The y coordinate is twice the x coordinate plus 1.
Set: $\{(x,y)|y = 2x + 1\}$.

(a)

x	−4	−3	−2	−1	0	1	2	3	4
y	−8	−6	−4	−2	0	2	4	6	8

(b)

x	-4	-3	-2	-1	0	1	2	3	4
y	-5	-4	-3	-2	-1	0	1	2	3

(c)

x	-4	-3	-2	-1	0	1	2	3	4
y	-3	-2	-1	0	1	2	3	4	5

(d)

x	-4	-3	-2	-1	0	1	2	3	4
y	-12	-9	-6	-3	0	3	6	9	12

(e)

x	-4	-3	-2	-1	0	1	2	3	4
y	-9	-7	-5	-3	-1	1	3	5	7

(f)

x	-4	-3	-2	-1	0	1	2	3	4
y	-5	-3	-1	1	3	5	7	9	11

(g)

x	-4	-3	-2	-1	0	1	2	3	4
y	-1	$-\frac{1}{2}$	0	$\frac{1}{2}$	1	$1\frac{1}{2}$	2	$2\frac{1}{2}$	3

(h)

x	-4	-3	-2	-1	0	1	2	3	4
y	$-\frac{1}{2}$	0	$\frac{1}{2}$	1	$1\frac{1}{2}$	2	$2\frac{1}{2}$	3	$3\frac{1}{2}$

4. In the example for Problem 3, we considered the set $\{(x,y)|y = 2x + 1\}$. The following points were listed in the table: $(-4,-7)$, $(-3,-5)$, $(-2,-3)$, $(-1,-1)$, $(0,1)$, $(1,3)$, $(2,5)$, $(3,7)$, and $(4,9)$. On the coordinate system of Figure 14-26, these points are plotted and a line containing the points is drawn.

For each part of Problem 3, (a) through (h), plot the points listed in the tables and draw lines containing these points. Use a separate coordinate system for each problem.

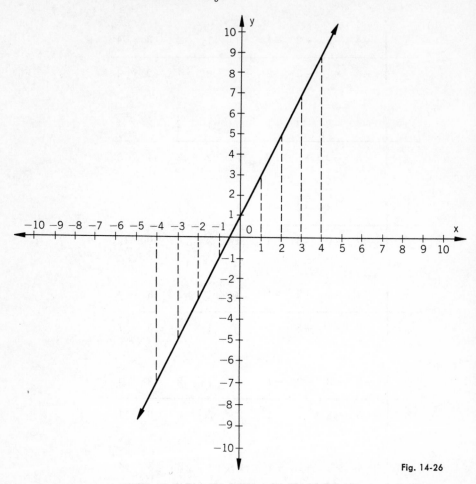

Fig. 14-26

5. Examine the descriptions of sets you gave in Problem 3. Are they of the form $y = ax + b$, that is, of the form y equals some number multiplied by x plus some number? Is the following statement true? Sets of points $\{(x,y)|y = ax + b\}$ are straight lines.

6. For each set below, plot two points on a coordinate system, and draw a picture of a line containing these points.

(a) $\{(x,y)|y = x + 5\}$

(b) $\{(x,y)|y = 2x - 3\}$

(c) $\{(x,y)|y = 3x - 4\}$

(d) $\{(x,y)|y = -x + 4\}$

(e) $\{(x,y)|y = -2x + 1\}$

(f) $\{(x,y)|y = -3x - 2\}$

10. PARABOLAS

Let us consider the following table, in which the first (x) and the second (y) coordinates of 9 points are listed.

x	-4	-3	-2	-1	0	1	2	3	4
y	32	18	8	2	0	2	8	18	32

After some search you may have discovered that there exists a pattern relating the second and the first coordinates: The y coordinate is equal to 2 multiplied by the square of the x coordinate. That is, the set of points suggested by this table is $\{(x,y) | y = 2x^2\}$. Figure 14-27 shows a partial graph of $\{(x,y) | y = 2x^2\}$. It is impossible to show the entire graph because it does not end. Since we agreed to use the set of real numbers as

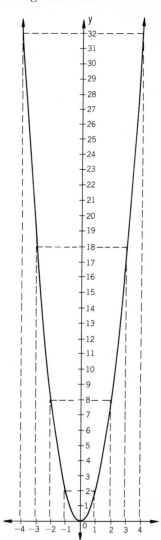

Fig. 14-27

our universal set, the graph of $\{(x,y)|y = 2x^2\}$ is an infinite set of points. A curve like the one shown in Figure 14-27 is called a **parabola**.

Problem Set 9

1. In the upper rows in the following tables are listed the first coordinates of points, in the lower rows the second coordinates. In each case, discover the pattern and describe the set using the brace notation.

(a)

x	-4	-3	-2	-1	0	1	2	3	4
y	16	9	4	1	0	1	4	9	16

(b)

x	-4	-3	-2	-1	0	1	2	3	4
y	8	4.5	2	0.5	0	0.5	2	4.5	8

(c)

x	-4	-3	-2	-1	0	1	2	3	4
y	4	$2\frac{1}{4}$	1	$\frac{1}{4}$	0	$\frac{1}{4}$	1	$2\frac{1}{4}$	4

(d)

x	-4	-3	-2	-1	0	1	2	3	4
y	48	27	12	3	0	3	12	27	48

(e)

x	-4	-3	-2	-1	0	1	2	3	4
y	-16	-9	-4	-1	0	-1	-4	-9	-16

(f)

x	-4	-3	-2	-1	0	1	2	3	4
y	-32	-18	-8	-2	0	-2	-8	-18	-32

(g)

x	-4	-3	-2	-1	0	1	2	3	4
y	-48	-27	-12	-3	0	-3	-12	-27	-48

(h)

x	-4	-3	-2	-1	0	1	2	3	4
y	-8	$-4\frac{1}{2}$	-2	$-\frac{1}{2}$	0	$-\frac{1}{2}$	-2	$-4\frac{1}{2}$	-8

2. Compute the y coordinate of $\{(x,y)|y = 2x^2\}$ for each of the following x coordinates:

(a) $\frac{1}{2}$ (c) $2\frac{1}{2}$ (e) $4\frac{1}{2}$ (g) $-1\frac{1}{2}$ (i) $-3\frac{1}{2}$
(b) $1\frac{1}{2}$ (d) $3\frac{1}{2}$ (f) $-\frac{1}{2}$ (h) $-2\frac{1}{2}$ (j) $-4\frac{1}{2}$

3. Now look at Figure 14-27. Examine each point in Problem 2 to see whether it would fall on the graph of $\{(x,y)|y = 2x^2\}$.
4. For each part of Problem 1, plot the points on a coordinate system. Connect the points to obtain pictures of smooth curves. Are all the curves parabolas?
5. Compare the graphs of $\{(x,y)|y = x^2\}$, $\{(x,y)|y = 2x^2\}$, and $\{(x,y)|y = 3x^2\}$. From the shapes of the three graphs, predict the shape of the graphs of $\{(x,y)|y = 4x^2\}$ and $\{(x,y)|y = 100x^2\}$.
6. Compare the graphs of $\{(x,y)|y = x^2\}$, $\{(x,y)|y = \frac{1}{2}x^2\}$, and $\{(x,y)|y = \frac{1}{4}x^2\}$. From the shapes of these three graphs, predict the shapes of the graphs of $\{(x,y)|y = \frac{1}{10}x^2\}$ and $\{(x,y)|y = \frac{1}{100}x^2\}$.

11. PARABOLAS: THEIR INTERIORS AND EXTERIORS

In problem 1(a) of Problem Set 9, you graphed the parabola $\{(x,y)|y = x^2\}$. In Problem 1(e), you graphed the parabola $\{(x,y)|y = -x^2\}$. Examine these graphs and tell in what way they are similar and in what way they are different. Do graphs of $\{(x,y)|y = 2x^2\}$ (see Figure 14-27) and $\{(x,y)|y = -2x^2\}$ [see your graph for Problem 1(f)] compare in a similar way? How about graphs of $\{(x,y)|y = 3x^2\}$ [see your graph for Problem 1(d)] and $\{(x,y)|y = -3x^2\}$ [see your graph for Problem 1(g)]?

Figure 14-28 shows a graph of the parabola $\{(x,y)|y = x^2\}$. Look at the portion of the plane inside the parabola. It is shaded //// . The following points belong to the interior of the parabola: $(1,9)$, $(-1,1\frac{1}{2})$, $(2,4.001)$, and many others. Note that, for each point in the interior, the following relation between its first and second coordinates is true: $y > x^2$. We can then write a description of the *interior* of this parabola: $\{(x,y)|y > x^2\}$. Thus, the interior of this parabola is the set of points for which the second coordinate is greater than the square of the first coordinate.

The set of points on the outside of the parabola is called the *exterior* of the parabola. Is $\{(x,y)|y < x^2\}$ a correct description of the exterior of the parabola pictured in Figure 14-28?

The set of points $\{(x,y)|y \geq x^2\}$ is equal to $\{(x,y)|y > x^2\} \cup \{(x,y)|y = x^2\}$. Its graph would consist of points that are in the interior of the

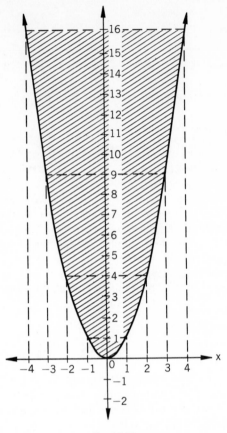

Fig. 14-28

parabola and the points that are on the parabola shown in Figure 14-28. Describe similarly the set of points $\{(x,y)|y \leq x^2\}$.

Let us now consider another set of pairs of numbers listed in the following table.

x	16	9	4	1	0	1	4	9	16
y	-4	-3	-2	-1	0	1	2	3	4

A moment's observation reveals that the pattern suggested by these pairs is that the x coordinate is the square of the y coordinate.

The ordered pairs listed in the table are $(16,-4)$, $(9,-3)$, $(4,-2)$, $(1,-1)$, $(0,0)$, $(1,1)$, $(4,2)$, $(9,3)$, and $(16,4)$. In Figure 14-29 these points are plotted. Do you see that a line would not "fit" these points? A picture of a smooth curve is drawn through the points.

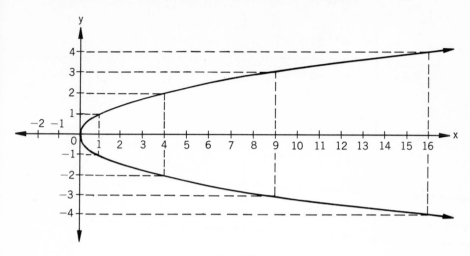

Fig. 14-29

Figure 14-29 shows a part of the graph of $\{(x,y)\,|\,y^2 = x\}$. It would not be possible to show the entire parabola. Explain. How does this parabola differ from the parabolas you studied before?

Problem Set 10

1. In the upper rows of the following tables the first coordinates of points are listed, in the lower rows the second coordinates. In each case, discover the pattern and describe the set using brace notation.

(a)

x	32	18	8	2	0	2	8	18	32
y	-4	-3	-2	-1	0	1	2	3	4

(b)

x	48	27	12	3	0	3	12	27	48
y	-4	-3	-2	-1	0	1	2	3	4

(c)

x	8	$4\frac{1}{2}$	2	$\frac{1}{2}$	0	$\frac{1}{2}$	2	$4\frac{1}{2}$	8
y	-4	-3	-2	-1	0	1	2	3	4

(d)

x	4	$2\frac{1}{4}$	1	$\frac{1}{4}$	0	$\frac{1}{4}$	1	$2\frac{1}{4}$	4
y	-4	-3	-2	-1	0	1	2	3	4

(e)

x	-16	-9	-4	-1	0	-1	-4	-9	-16
y	-4	-3	-2	-1	0	1	2	3	4

(f)

x	-32	-18	-8	-2	0	-2	-8	-18	-32
y	-4	-3	-2	-1	0	1	2	3	4

(g)

x	-8	$-4\frac{1}{2}$	-2	$-\frac{1}{2}$	0	$-\frac{1}{2}$	-2	$-4\frac{1}{2}$	-8
y	-4	-3	-2	-1	0	1	2	3	4

(h)

x	-4	$-2\frac{1}{4}$	-1	$-\frac{1}{4}$	0	$-\frac{1}{4}$	-1	$-2\frac{1}{4}$	-4
y	-4	-3	-2	-1	0	1	2	3	4

2. For the parabola $\{(x,y)|y^2 = x\}$, compute the values of y to one decimal place for the following values of x. [*Hint:* Note that for one value of x, there are two values of y; for example, $(4,2)$ and $(4,-2)$ are on the parabola because $2^2 = 4$ and $(-2)^2 = 4$.]
   (a) 2   (b) 3   (c) 7   (d) 13   (e) 20   (f) 25

3. For each part of Problem 1, plot the listed points on a coordinate system. Connect the points by making a picture of a smooth curve.

4. Compare the shapes of the parabolas $\{(x,y)|y^2 = x\}$ (Figure 14-29), $\{(x,y)|2y^2 = x\}$ [Problem 1(a)], and $\{(x,y)|3y^2 = x\}$ [Problem 1(b)]. On the basis of your observation, predict the shapes of the parabolas $\{(x,y)|10y^2 = x\}$ and $\{(x,y)|100y^2 = x\}$.

5. Compare the shapes of the parabolas $\{(x,y)|y^2 = x\}$ (Figure 14-29), $\{(x,y)|\frac{1}{2}y^2 = x\}$ [Problem 1(c)], and $\{(x,y)|\frac{1}{4}y^2 = x\}$ [Problem 1(d)]. On the basis of your observation, predict the shapes of the parabolas $\{(x,y)|\frac{1}{10}y^2 = x\}$ and $\{(x,y)|\frac{1}{100}y^2 = x\}$.

6. How is the graph of $\{(x,y)|ay^2 = x\}$ affected as larger and larger positive numbers are used for a?

7. Compare the graphs of $\{(x,y)|y^2 = x\}$ (Figure 14-29) and $\{(x,y)|-y^2 = x\}$ [Problem 1(e)]. In what way are they similar and in what way do they differ?

8. Do the same as in Problem 7 for the graphs of $\{(x,y)|2y^2 = x\}$ [Problem 1(a)] and $\{(x,y)|-2y^2 = x\}$ [Problem 1(f)].

9. Do the same as in Problem 8 for the graphs of $\{(x,y)|\frac{1}{2}y^2 = x\}$ [Problem 1(c)] and $\{(x,y)|-\frac{1}{2}y^2 = x\}$ [Problem 1(g)].

10. Make a statement comparing the graphs of $\{(x,y)|ay^2 = x\}$ and $\{(x,y)|-ay^2 = x\}$, where a is a positive number.

11. (a) Draw the graph of $\{(x,y)|x^2 = y\}$. Shade the interior of the parabola. Locate points $(1.9,4)$ and $(-2.5,9)$. Explain why these points are in the interior of the parabola.

    (b) Do you see, for the point $(x,y) = (1.9,4)$, that $x^2 < y$; that is, $(1.9)^2 < 4$. To what is $(1.9)^2$ equal?

    (c) Also do you see, for $(x,y) = (-2.5,9)$, that $x^2 < y$; that is, $(-2.5)^2 < 9$. To what is $(-2.5)^2$ equal?

12. INEQUALITIES AND SUBSETS OF THE PLANE

You have seen that equations and inequalities can be used to describe various sets of points in a plane. For example, $\{(x,y)|y = ax + b\}$ is a set of points making up a line, when a and b are replaced by numerals for numbers $(a \neq 0)$. The set $\{(x,y)|y = ax^2\}$ is a set of points making up a parabola, when a is replaced by a numeral for a nonzero real number.

Figure 14-30 shows a graph of the set of points $\{(x,y)|y > 3\}$. Remember that the plane extends indefinitely in all directions. The set of points $\{(x,y)|y > 3\}$ is marked //// in this figure. Note that we show the **boundary** of this set with a dashed line, indicating that the boundary of the set does not belong to the set $\{(x,y)|y > 3\}$.

Figure 14-31 is a graph of the set $\{(x,y)|y \geq 3\}$. In this case, the boundary $\{(x,y)|y = 3\}$ belongs to the set. Of course, you need to think of the sets extending indefinitely upward, to the right, and to the left.

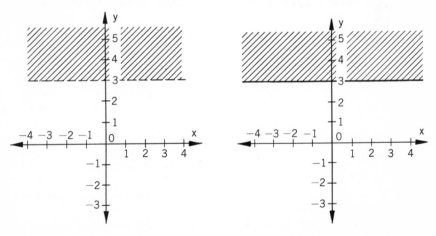

Fig. 14-30   Fig. 14-31

We shall now graph the set $\{(x,y)|x \geq 3$ and $y < -2\}$. We shall graph this set in two parts: $A = \{(x,y)|x \geq 3\}$ and $B = \{(x,y)|y < -2\}$. Set A is marked $////$. Set B is marked $\backslash\backslash\backslash\backslash$. Note that the boundary of set $A = \{(x,y)|x \geq 3\}$ is marked as a solid line because it belongs to the set. The boundary of set $B = \{(x,y)|y < -2\}$ does not belong to the set; therefore it is marked with a dashed line (see Figure 14-32).

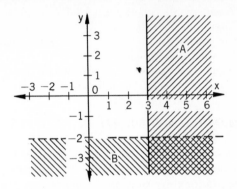

Fig. 14-32

The graph of the set we are seeking is the intersection of the two sets: $A \cap B$. It is that part of the plane which is marked with both shadings. Of course, it extends indefinitely. All points whose first coordinates are greater than or equal to 3 *and* whose second coordinates are less than -2 belong to the set.

Let us change the description of the set above by changing the word *and* to *or:* $\{(x,y)|x \geq 3$ or $y < -2\}$. This set is the same as the set $\{(x,y)|x \geq 3\} \cup \{(x,y)|y < -2\}$. Look at the graph in Figure 14-32. The graph of this set consists of all points in shaded areas. The portions of the plane marked $////$, $\backslash\backslash\backslash\backslash$, and $\mathbf{XXXX}$ are all part of this set.

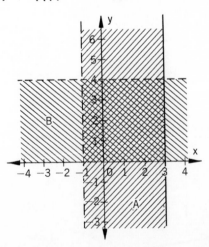

Fig. 14-33

Let us now graph the set $\{(x,y)|-1 < x \leq 3$ and $0 \leq y < 4\}$. As before, we graph the two sets separately: $A = \{(x,y)|-1 < x \leq 3\}$ and $B = \{(x,y)|0 \leq y < 4\}$. Set A is marked //// . Set B is marked \\\\ . Since the descriptions of the sets are linked with the word *and*, we are looking for the intersection of the two sets, $A \cap B$, which is the portion marked **XXXX** . The intersection $A \cap B$ consists of points in the interior of a square, including two sides of the square. Point out in the graph the two sides that belong to $A \cap B$ (see Figure 14-33).

By changing the word *and* to *or* in the descriptions of the set above, we obtain the set $\{(x,y)|-1 < x \leq 3$ or $0 \leq y < 4\}$. This is the set $\{(x,y)|-1 < x \leq 3\} \cup \{(x,y)|0 \leq y < 4\}$. Every point that is in one of the shaded portions in Figure 14-33 belongs to this set.

Problem Set 11

1. On a coordinate system, graph each of the following sets of points:

(a) $\{(x,y)|x > 3\}$ (i) $\{(x,y)|x > 0\}$
(b) $\{(x,y)|x \geq 3\}$ (j) $\{(x,y)|x \geq 0\}$
(c) $\{(x,y)|x < 3\}$ (k) $\{(x,y)|x < 0\}$
(d) $\{(x,y)|x \leq 3\}$ (l) $\{(x,y)|x \leq 0\}$
(e) $\{(x,y)|y > 0\}$ (m) $\{(x,y)|y < -4\}$
(f) $\{(x,y)|y \geq 0\}$ (n) $\{(x,y)|y \leq -4\}$
(g) $\{(x,y)|y < 0\}$ (o) $\{(x,y)|y > -4\}$
(h) $\{(x,y)|y \leq 0\}$ (p) $\{(x,y)|y \geq -4\}$

2. Tell whether each of the following statements is true or false.

Convenient abbreviations: Q_1 = quadrant I
Q_2 = quadrant II
Q_3 = quadrant III
Q_4 = quadrant IV

(a) $\{(x,y)|y > 0\} = Q_1 \cup Q_2$
(b) $\{(x,y)|x \geq 0\} \cup \{(x,y)|x < 0\} = Q_1 \cup Q_2 \cup Q_3 \cup Q_4 \cup x$ axis $\cup$ y axis
(c) $\{(x,y)|x = 0\} \cup \{(x,y)|y = 0\} = x$ axis $\cup$ y axis
(d) $\{(x,y)|x = 0\} \cap \{(x,y)|y = 0\} = \{(0,0)\}$

3. Tell which of the following points belong to the graph of $\{(x,y)|x \geq 3$ and $y < -2\}$ (see Figure 14-32).

(a) $(175, -15\frac{1}{2})$ (b) $(3, -2.0001)$
(c) $(3, -2)$ (d) $(2.99, -6)$

4. Tell which of the following points belong to the graph of $\{(x,y)|x \geq 3\} \cup \{(x,y)|y < -2\}$ (see Figure 14-32).

(a) $(5, -368)$ (b) $(0, -100)$ (c) $(1, -2)$
(d) $(-5, 37)$ (e) $(17, 35)$ (f) $(1, -2.00001)$
(g) $(-189, -189)$ (h) $(17, -35)$ (i) $(3, 9768)$

5. Tell which of the following points belong to the graph of $\{(x,y)|-1 < x \leq 3$ and $0 \leq y < 4\}$ (see Figure 14-33).

 (a) (3,4)   (b) (−0.9999,4)   (c) (0.01,3.99)
 (d) (3,3.9999)   (e) (−0.9999,3.999) (f) (0,0)
 (g) (−1,2)   (h) (2,4)   (i) (0,0.00001)

6. Is the following statement true? (See Figure 14-33.)

$$[\{(x,y)|-1 < x \leq 3\} \cap \{(x,y)|0 \leq y < 4\}]$$
$$\subseteq [\{(x,y)|-1 < x \leq 3\} \cup \{(x,y)|0 \leq y < 4\}].$$

7. Tell which of the following points belong to the graph of $\{(x,y)|-1 < x \leq 3\}$ $\cup \{(x,y)|0 \leq y < 4\}$ (see Figure 14-33).

 (a) (0,1765)   (b) (3,4)   (c) (909,0)
 (d) (−365,0)   (e) (3,1165)   (f) (0,−2064)
 (g) (596,4)   (h) (3,−9071)   (i) (2.1,998365)

8. On a coordinate system, graph each of the following sets. Describe the graphs in terms of the shading used to mark that portion of the plane belonging to the set.

 (a) $A = \{(x,y)|x \leq -2$ and $y \leq -2\}$; $B = \{(x,y)|x \leq -2$ or $y \leq -2\}$
 (b) $A = \{(x,y)|x \geq 0$ and $y < -3\frac{1}{2}\}$; $B = \{(x,y)|x \geq 0$ or $y < -3\frac{1}{2}\}$
 (c) $A = \{(x,y)|x > -1$ and $y > -1\}$; $B = \{(x,y)|x > -1$ or $y > -1\}$
 (d) $A = \{(x,y)|x \geq -1$ and $y \geq -1\}$; $B = \{(x,y)|x \geq -1$ or $y \geq -1\}$
 (e) $A = \{(x,y)|x > 0$ and $y > 0\}$; $B = \{(x,y)|x > 0$ or $y > 0\}$
 (f) $A = \{(x,y)|x < 0$ and $y > 0\}$; $B = \{(x,y)|x < 0$ or $y > 0\}$
 (g) $A = \{(x,y)|x < 0$ and $y < 0\}$; $B = \{(x,y)|x < 0$ or $y < 0\}$
 (h) $A = \{(x,y)|x > 0$ and $y < 0\}$; $B = \{(x,y)|x > 0$ or $y < 0\}$

BIBLIOGRAPHY

Davis, Robert B., *Discovery in Mathematics: A Text for Teachers*. Reading, Mass.: Addison-Wesley Publishing Company, Inc., 1964, pp. 191–200.

Glenn, William H., and Donovan A. Johnson, *Adventures in Graphing*. St. Louis: Webster Publishing Company, 1961.

Markushevich, A. I., *Areas and Logarithms*. Boston: D. C. Heath and Company, 1963.

Nichols, Eugene D., *Pre-Algebra Mathematics*. New York: Holt, Rinehart and Winston, Inc., 1965, Chap. 15.

————, R. Kalin, and H. Garland, *Introduction to Coordinate Geometry* (A Programed Unit). New York: Holt, Rinehart and Winston, Inc., 1963.

Ore, Oystein, *Graphs and Their Uses*. New York: Random House, Inc., 1963.

School Mathematics Study Group, *Mathematics Through Science, Part I: Measurement and Graphing*. Stanford, Calif.: Leland Stanford Junior University, 1963, pp. 73–143.

Shilov, G. E., *How To Construct Graphs*. and I. P. Natanson, *Simplest Maxima and Minima Problems*. Boston: D. C. Heath and Company, 1963.

Vergara, William C., *Mathematics in Everyday Things*. New York: The New American Library, 1962, pp. 61–67.

COMMON UNITS OF MEASURE (U.S.)

$$12 \text{ Inches} = 1 \text{ Foot}$$
$$3 \text{ Feet} = 1 \text{ Yard}$$
$$\left.\begin{array}{l} 1760 \text{ Yards} \\ 5280 \text{ Feet} \end{array}\right\} = 1 \text{ Mile}$$
$$6076 \text{ Feet} \doteq 1 \text{ Nautical mile}$$

1000 Microns	= 1 Millimeter	2.540	Centimeters $\doteq$ 1 Inch
10 Millimeters	= 1 Centimeter	39.37	Inches $\doteq$ 1 Meter
100 Centimeters	= 1 Meter	1.609	Kilometers $\doteq$ 1 Mile
1000 Meters	= 1 Kilometer	.6214	Miles $\doteq$ 1 Kilometer

AREA

43,560 Square feet = 4,840 Square yards = 1 Acre
640 Acres = 1 Section = 1 Square mile
1,076 Square feet $\doteq$ 100 Square meters = 1 Are

VOLUME

Liquid	*Dry*
8 Fluid ounces = 1 Cup	2 Dry pints = 1 Dry quart
2 Cups = 1 Pint	8 Dry quarts = 1 Peck
2 Pints = 1 Quart	4 Pecks = 1 Bushel
4 Quarts = 1 Gallon	(2150 Cubic inches $\doteq$ 1 Bushel)
31½ Gallons = 1 Barrel	
(231 Cubic inches = 1 Gallon)	

1 Fluid ounce = 2 Tablespoons = 8 Fluid drams = 360 Drops = 480 Minims
1.057 Quarts $\doteq$ 1000 Cubic centimeters = 1 Liter
35.31 Cubic feet $\doteq$ 1 Cubic meter = 1 Stere

WEIGHT

60 Grains = 1 Dram   437½ Grains = 1 Ounce

$$\left.\begin{array}{l} 7000 \text{ Grains} \\ 16 \text{ Ounces} \end{array}\right\} = 1 \text{ Pound}$$

2000 Pounds = 1 Ton   1000 Kilograms = 1 Metric ton
480 Grains = 1 Troy ounce   454 Grams $\doteq$ 1 Pound
12 Troy ounces = 1 Troy pound   2,205 Pounds $\doteq$ 1000 Grams = 1 Kilogram

TIME

60 Seconds = 1 Minute	12 Calendar months = 1 Year
60 Minutes = 1 Hour	10 Years = 1 Decade
24 Hours = 1 Day	100 Years = 1 Century
7 Days = 1 Week	1000 Years = 1 Millennium

365.2422 Days $\doteq$ 1 Mean solar year

GLOSSARY

GLOSSARY

This is a list of important terms used in this book. A brief description or an illustration, not necessarily a definition, is given for each term.

Abacus. A counting device which can be adjusted to do arithmetic in any base.

Absolute error. If M is an approximation to T, then $M - T$ is the absolute error of M. For example, if 3.7 is used as an approximation to 4, then $4 - 3.7$, or 0.3, is the absolute error of 3.7.

Absolute value (of a number). The absolute value of a nonnegative number is that number, and the absolute value of a negative number is the opposite of that number.
$$\forall_{x \geq 0} |x| = x \text{ and } \forall_{x < 0} |x| = -x$$

Additive identity. A number n for which it is true that $\forall_x x + n = x$. For real numbers, 0 is the additive identity, since $\forall_x x + 0 = x$.

Additive inverse (of a number). The additive inverse of a number is the number which added to the original number gives the sum 0. If x is the additive inverse of y, then $x + y = 0$.

Adjacent sides (in a polygon). Two sides which share a common vertex.

Altitude (of a parallelogram). A segment connecting two opposite sides or their extensions and perpendicular to each.

Altitude (of a triangle). A segment from a vertex of a triangle perpendicular to the opposite side or its extension.

Amicable numbers. A pair of numbers such that the sum of all proper divisors of each number is equal to the other number.

Angle. The union of two noncollinear rays which have the same endpoint.

Base. (1) In 5^3, 5 is the base.
(2) 326_{seven} is a numeral in base seven.
(3) Any side of a triangle may be considered to be the base.

Basic numeral. In base ten there are ten basic numerals: 0, 1, 2, 3, 4, 5, 6, 7, 8, 9.

Binary numeration system. Numeration system in base two. For example, $11011_{\text{two}} = 27_{\text{ten}}$.

Cardinal number. A number used to tell the number of elements in a set.

Cartesian coordinate system. A reference frame consisting of two perpendicular number lines. Also called "rectangular coordinate system."

Characteristic. The exponent on 10 used when expressing a number in scientific notation.

Circumference. The measure of a circle.

Closure. A set is closed under a given operation if the result of operating on any members of a set also belongs to the set. For example, the set of natural numbers is closed under addition because the sum of any pair of natural numbers is a natural number.

Collinear points. Points which belong to one line.

Complement (of a number). The number obtained by subtracting a given number from the power of ten next greater than the number. For example, the complement of 17 is 83 because 100 is the power of ten next greater than 17, and $100 - 17 = 83$.

Complement (of a set). Set A is a complement of set B if and only if A consists of all elements of the universal set which are not in B. The symbol for the complement of B is $\bar{B}$.

Complementary angles. Two angles for which the sum of the measures is 90°.

Complementary method of subtraction. A method of subtraction based on the use of the complement of a number.

Composite number. A natural number different from 1, which is not a prime number.

Concave curve. A nonconvex curve.

Convex curve. A curve in which the beginning point and the endpoint are the same and a segment connecting any two points in the interior is a subset of the interior.

Coordinate (of a point). A number in an ordered number pair which tells the row or the column in which the point is found.

Coplanar. Belonging to the same plane.

Counting numbers. Natural numbers: 1, 2, 3, 4, 5, 6, ...

Cube root. A cube root of a number is that number which when taken 3 times as a factor gives the number for a product. For example, $\sqrt[3]{8} = 2$ because $2 \times 2 \times 2 = 8$.

Decimal numeral. A numeral in base ten.

Decimal numeration system. Numeration system in base ten.

Dekapart. The number between 1 and 10 used in expressing a number in scientific notation.

Denominator. The number named by the lower numeral in a fractional numeral. For example, the denominator of $\frac{2}{3}$ is 3.

Density. The property of a set of numbers in which there is always a third number between any two given numbers. The set of rational numbers is dense.

Diagonal. A segment connecting two nonadjacent vertices of a polygon.

Diameter (of a circle). A segment connecting two points of a circle and passing through the center.

Difference. The result of subtracting one number from another number or from itself. For example, in $12 - 5 = 7$, 7 is the difference, and in $12 - 12 = 0$, 0 is the difference.

Digit. A basic numeral. In base ten there are ten digits: 0, 1, 2, 3, 4, 5, 6, 7, 8, 9.

Directed real number. A positive or a negative real number.

Disjoint sets. Sets which have no common elements.

Divisor (of a number). 3 is a divisor of 15 because $15 \div 3 = 5$; that is, the quotient is a whole number and the remainder is 0.

Dodecagon. A 12-sided polygon.

Doubling and halving. A method of multiplication of whole numbers which was in use in medieval Europe.

Duodecimal numeration system. Numeration system in base twelve. For example, $111_{\text{twelve}} = 157_{\text{ten}}$.

Element (of a set). A member of a set.

Empty set ($\emptyset$). A set which has no members.

Endpoint (of a segment). The endpoints of $\overline{AB}$ are A and B.

Equal sets. Sets having exactly the same members.

Equiangular triangle. A triangle with each angle measure equal to 60°.

Equilateral triangle. A triangle in which each side has the same measure.

Eratosthenes' Sieve. A method for identifying primes.

Expanded product form. The name for 3^4 in expanded product form is $3 \times 3 \times 3 \times 3$.

Expansion by powers of ten. The expansion by powers of ten of 3457 is $3 \times 10^3 + 4 \times 10^2 + 5 \times 10^1 + 7 \times 10^0$.

Exponent. In 2^3, 3 is the exponent. It tells how many times 2 is used as a factor in a product $(2 \times 2 \times 2)$.

Exponential form. The name for 25 in exponential form is 5^2.

Exterior of an angle. The set of all points which are not in the interior of an angle and not on the angle.

Factor (of a number). A divisor of the number; one of the numbers used in a product. For example, 5 and 7 are factors of 35 because $5 \times 7 = 35$.

Finite set. A set which has a finite number of members.

Fraction. A nondirected number which has a name of the form $\frac{a}{b}$, where a and b are whole numbers $(b \neq 0)$.

Fractional number. The same as fraction.

Fundamental Theorem of Arithmetic. Every composite number can be expressed uniquely as a product of primes.

Grating method. A method of multiplication of whole numbers in which a framework resembling a window grating is used.

Greatest Common Divisor, GCD (of two or more numbers). The greatest number by which each of a given set of numbers is divisible.

Half-line. One of the two subsets into which a point separates a line.

Half-plane. One of the two subsets into which a line separates a plane.

Half-space. One of the two subsets into which a plane separates space.

Hexagon. A 6-sided polygon.

Hypotenuse. The side in a right triangle which is opposite the right angle.

Infinite set. A set which has an infinite number of members.

Integer. A directed whole number or 0.

Interior of an angle. The set of all points "inside" the angle.

Interior of a triangle. The set of all points "inside" the triangle.

Intersection (of two sets). The set which consists of only those elements which belong to both of the two sets.

Inverse (operations). Example: addition and subtraction are inverse operations because $\forall_x \forall_y (x + y) - y = x$ or $\forall_x \forall_y$, if $x + y = z$, then $z - y = x$.

Irrational number. A real number which has no name of the form $\frac{a}{b}$ ($b \neq 0$), with a and b whole numbers. Example: $\sqrt{5}$.

Is greater than ($>$). Example: $5 > 3$.

Is greater than or equal to ($\geq$). Examples: $5 \geq 3; 5 \geq 5$.

Is less than ($<$). Example: $3 < 5$.

Is less than or equal to ($\leq$). Examples: $3 \leq 5; 3 \leq 3$.

Is not equal to ($\neq$). Example: $5 \neq 3$.

Isosceles triangle. A triangle in which two sides have the same measure.

Lattice of points. An array of points arranged in a rectangle or square or an infinite number of points.

Leg (of a right triangle). A side in a right triangle which is adjacent to the right angle.

Lowest Common Multiple, LCM (of two or more numbers). The least number of which each of the two or more given numbers is a factor. For example, LCM of 6 and 14 is 42 because 42 is the least number divisible by both 6 and 14.

Matching sets. Two sets between which there exists a one-to-one correspondence.

Member (of a set). A number or any other thing which belongs to the set.

Midpoint (of a segment). A point which divides a segment into two segments each of the same measure.

Natural numbers. Counting numbers: 1, 2, 3, 4, 5, 6, ...

Negative real number. An opposite of a positive real number. Each negative number is less than 0.

Noncollinear points. Points which are not on the same line.

Noncoplanar points. Points which are not on the same plane.

Nondirected numbers. The numbers of ordinary arithmetic.

Nonrepeating nonterminating decimal. Example: .5151151115 . . . .

Null set. Empty set, that is, a set with no members. The symbol for it is ∅.

Number field. A set of numbers and two operations having the eight properties listed on page 187.

Numeral. A name of a number.

Numeration system. A system of writing names of numbers.

Numerator. The number named by the upper numeral in a fractional numeral. For example, the numerator of $\frac{2}{3}$ is 2.

Octagon. An 8-sided polygon.

One-to-one correspondence. A matching between two sets so that to each element of one set there is assigned exactly one element of the second set and vice versa.

Opposite (of a number). The opposite of a positive number is the negative number with the same absolute value. The opposite of a negative number is the positive number with the same absolute value. The opposite of 0 is 0.

Ordinal number. A number used to identify one of the things in an ordered set of things.

Origin. The point in the coordinate plane assigned to the pair (0, 0).

Parabola. The graph of a set of points given by $y = ax^2 + bx + c$.

Parallelogram. A quadrilateral in which pairs of opposite sides are parallel.

Pentagon. A polygon with five sides.

Percent, %. $1\% = .01 = \frac{1}{100}$.

Perfect number. A number which is equal to the sum of all its proper divisors. For example, 6 is a perfect number because $6 = 1 + 2 + 3$ and 1, 2, and 3 are all proper divisors of 6.

Perimeter (of a polygon). The sum of the measures of all sides of a polygon.

Perpendicular (lines). Two lines intersecting each other so that right angles are formed.

Place value. Place value of 3 in 3001 is three thousand.

Point. The simplest geometric object which has no size.

Positional system. A numeration system in which the value of a basic numeral depends on the position it occupies in the numeral: in 235_{ten}, the value of 2 is two hundreds; in 125_{ten}, the value of 2 is two tens.

Positive real number. A real number which is greater than 0.

Power. A number shown by means of a base and an exponent. For example, 9 is the second power of 3, because $9 = 3^2$.

Prime factor (of a number). A factor which is a prime number.

Prime number. A natural number which has exactly two factors, 1 and the number itself.

Prime-Product Theorem. If a prime divides a product of two natural numbers, then it must divide at least one of them.

Prism. A solid in which each face is a parallelogram.

Product. The result of multiplying a pair of numbers. For example, in $3 \times 4 = 12$, 12 is the product.

Proper divisor of a number. A divisor of a number, excluding the number itself. For example, all proper divisors of 10 are 1, 2, and 5. (See **Divisor.**)

Pythagorean relation. In a right triangle, if a and b are measures of the two legs and c is the measure of the hypotenuse, then $a^2 + b^2 = c^2$, and conversely.

Quadrant. One-fourth of the plane outlined by the coordinate system, not including the points on the axes.

Quadrilateral. A polygon with four sides.

Quinary numeral. A numeral in base five, for example, $321_{\text{five}} = 86_{\text{ten}}$.

Quotient. The result of dividing one number by another number or by itself. For example, in $12 \div 6 = 2$, 2 is the quotient; in $15 \div 15 = 1$, 1 is the quotient.

Radius. A segment connecting any point of a circle with its center.

Ratio. The quotient of a pair of numbers. Example: $\frac{3}{7}$.

Rational number. A real number which has a name of the form $\frac{a}{b}$ ($b \neq 0$), a and b whole numbers. Example: $\frac{5}{7}$.

Rational number of arithmetic. The same as fraction.

Ray. A part of a line having a beginning point and extending indefinitely in one direction.

Real numbers. The set of real numbers is the union of the set of rational numbers and the set of irrational numbers.

Rectangle. A 4-sided polygon with opposite sides parallel and 4 right angles.

Rectangular coordinate system. See **Cartesian coordinate system.**

Rectangular prism. A prism in which each face is a rectangle.

Regular polygon. A polygon with all sides of the same measure and all angles of the same measure.

Relative error. Quotient of absolute error and true value.

Relatively prime (numbers). Two whole numbers with 1 as their only common factor.

Repeating decimal numeral. A decimal numeral in which a block of one or more digits repeats indefinitely. For example, .253253253 . . . , also written as $.\overline{253}$.

Right triangle. A triangle which has one right angle.

Scalene triangle. A triangle in which no two sides have the same measure.

S'choty. A Russian abacus.

Scientific notation. A number is given in scientific notation if it is expressed as the product of a number between 1 and 10 and the correct power of ten. For example, 237 in scientific notation is 2.37×10^2.

Scratch method. A method of performing an operation, used in Europe, in which digits are erased or crossed out as they need to be replaced by other digits.

Segment. A set of points containing two endpoints and all points of the straight line between the two endpoints.

Set. A collection of things.

Signed digit. A digit with "$+$" or "$-$" in front of it. For example, -5 is a signed digit; sometimes it is written as $\overline{5}$.

Simple closed curve. A closed curve which does not intersect itself.

Soroban. A Japanese abacus.

Space. The set of all points.

Square root. A square root of a number is that number which when taken 2 times as a factor gives the number for a product. For example, $\sqrt{36} = 6$ because $6 \times 6 = 36$.

Square root algorithm. A method of finding a square root of a number.

Suan Pan. A Chinese abacus.

Subset (of a set). A is a subset of B ($A \subseteq B$) if and only if every member of A is also a member of B.

Successor (of a number). The whole number immediately following the given whole number. For example, 5 is a successor of 4.

Sum. The result of adding a pair of numbers. For example, in $2 + 7 = 9$, 9 is the sum.

Terminating decimal numeral. A decimal numeral with a finite number of digits. For example, .3702 is a terminating decimal numeral.

Ternary numeration system. Numeration system in base three. For example, $111_{three} = 13_{ten}$.

Tetrahedron. A solid with four triangular faces.

Theorem. A statement which has been proved to be true.

Triangle. A union of three segments, in which each pair of segments has one common point.

Twin primes. A pair of primes which differ by 2. For example, 11 and 13 is a pair of twin primes, because each number is a prime and $13 - 11 = 2$.

Union (of two sets). The set consisting of the members which belong to one or the other of the two given sets (includes members belonging to both sets).

Unit fractional numeral. A fractional numeral with a numerator 1, such as $\frac{1}{2}$, $\frac{1}{3}$, $\frac{1}{12}$, and so on.

Universal quantifier, $\forall_x$. For every x.

Universal set. The set of all things which are chosen for a particular study.

Venn diagram. A pictorial method of showing relations between sets.

Vertex (of an angle). The point of intersection of the two sides of an angle.

Vertex (of a polygon). The point of intersection of two adjacent sides.

Vigesimal. Based on twenty.

Whole numbers. The set of whole numbers is $\{0, 1, 2, 3, 4, 5, 6, \ldots\}$.

Wilson's Theorem. The number N is prime if and only if the number $(N - 1)! + 1$ is divisible by N.

x-axis. The horizontal line in the rectangular coordinate system.

y-axis. The vertical line in the rectangular coordinate system.

Zero. The number of the empty set: $n(\emptyset) = 0$.

INDEX

INDEX